Come Hither

A collection of rhymes and poems for the

young of all ages, made by Walter de la

Mare and embellished

Alec Buckels

Alpha Editions

This edition published in 2020

ISBN : 9789354040573

Design and Setting By
Alpha Editions
www.alphaedis.com
email - alphaedis@gmail.com

COME HITHER

A
COLLECTION
OF RHYMES
AND POEMS
FOR THE
YOUNG OF
ALL AGES

MADE BY
WALTER DE LA MARE

AND EMBELLISHED
BY
ALEC BUCKELS

CONSTABLE & CO
LONDON BOMBAY SYDNEY
MCMXXIII.

TO
LAURA COLTMAN
IN LOVE AND
GRATITUDE

TABLE OF CONTENTS

THE STORY OF THIS BOOK

In my rovings and ramblings as a boy I had often skirted the old stone house in the hollow. But my first clear remembrance of it is of a hot summer's day. I had climbed to the crest of a hill till then unknown to me, and stood there, hot and breathless in the bright slippery grass, looking down on its grey walls and chimneys as if out of a dream. And as if out of a dream already familiar to me.

My real intention in setting out from home that morning had been to get to a place called East Dene. My mother had often spoken to me of East Dene—of its trees and waters and green pastures, and the rare birds and flowers to be found there. Ages ago, she had told me, an ancestor of our family had dwelt in this place. But she smiled a little strangely when I asked her to take me there. " All in good time, my dear," she whispered into my ear, " all in very good time ! Just follow your small nose." What kind of time, I wondered, was *very good time*. And *follow my nose*—how far ? Such reflections indeed only made me the more anxious to be gone.

Early that morning, then, I had started out when the dew was still sparkling, and the night mists had but just lifted. But my young legs soon tired of the steep, boulder-strown hills, the chalky ravines, and burning

sun, and having, as I say, come into view of the house
in the valley, I went no further. Instead, I sat down
on the hot turf—the sweet smell of thyme in the air, a
few harebells nodding around me—and stared, down
and down.

After that first visit, scarcely a week passed but that
I found myself on this hill again. The remembrance
of the house stayed in my mind ; would keep returning
to me, like a bird to its nest. Sometimes even in the
middle of the night I would wake up and lie unable to
sleep again for thinking of it—seeing it in my head ;
solemn, secret, strange.

There is a little flickering lizard called the Chameleon
which, they say, changes its colour according to the place
where it happens to be. So with this house. It was
never the same for two hours together. I have seen it
gathered close up in its hollow in the livid and coppery
gloom of storm ; crouched like a hare in winter under
a mask of snow ; dark and silent beneath the changing
sparkle of the stars ; and like a palace out of an Arabian
tale in the milky radiance of the moon. THRAE was the
name inscribed on its gateway, but in letters so faint
and faded as to be almost illegible.

In a sense I was, I suppose, a trespasser in this Thrae ;
until at least I became acquainted with Miss Taroone,
the lady who lived in it. For I made pretty free with
her valley, paddled and fished in its stream, and now
and then helped myself to a windfall in her green
bird-haunted orchards, where grew a particularly sharp
and bright-rinded apple of which I have never heard the
name. As custom gave me confidence, I ventured
nearer and nearer to the house and would sometimes

take a rest squatting on a manger in the big empty barn, looking out into the sunshine. The wings of the flies shone like glass in its shafts of light, and the robins whistled under its timber roof so shrill as almost to deafen one's ears.

Few strangers passed that way. Now and then I saw in the distance what might have been a beggar. To judge from his bundle he must have done pretty well at the house. Once, as I turned out of a little wood of birches, I met a dreadful-faced man in the lane who lifted up his hand at sight of me, and with white glaring eyes, uttered a horrible imprecation. He was chewing some fruit stolen out of the orchard, and at the very sight of him I ran like Wat himself.

Once, too, as my head looked over the hill-crest, there stood an old carriage and a drowsy horse drawn up beside the porch—with its slender wooden pillars and a kind of tray above, on which rambled winter jasmine, tufts of self-sown weeds and Traveller's Joy. I edged near enough to see there was a crown emblazoned on the panel of the carriage door. Nobody sat inside, and the coachman asleep on the box made me feel more solitary and inquisitive than ever.

Yet in its time the old house must have seen plenty of company. Friends of later years have spoken to me of it. Indeed, not far distant from Thrae as the crow flies, there was a crossing of high roads, so that any traveller from elsewhere not in haste could turn aside and examine the place if he cared for its looks and was in need of a night's lodging. Yet I do not think many such travellers—if they were men merely of the Town— can have *chosen* to lift that knocker or to set ringing that bell. To any one already lost and benighted its looks must have been forbidding.

Well, as I say, again and again, my lessons done, morning or evening would find me either on the grass slopes above Thrae, or actually in its valley If I was tired, I would watch from a good distance off its small dark windows in their stone embrasures, and up above them the round greenish tower or turret over which a winged weather-vane twirled with the wind. I might watch : but the only person that I ever actually observed at the windows was an old maid with flaps to her cap, who would sometimes shake a duster out into the air as if for a signal to someone up in the hills.

Apart from her, I had occasionally seen Miss Taroone herself in the overgrown garden, with her immense shears, or with her trencher of bread-crumbs and other provender, feeding the birds. And I once stole near enough under a hedge to watch this sight. They hopped and pecked in a multitude beneath her hands, tits and robins, starlings and blackbirds, and other much wilder and rarer birds, as if they had no need here for wings, or were under an enchantment more powerful than that of mere crumbs of bread. The meal done, the platter empty, Miss Taroone would clap her hands, and off they would fly with a skirring of wings, with shrill cries and snatches of song to their haunts.

She seemed to mind no weather ; standing bare-headed in heavy rain or scorching sunlight. And I confess the sight of her never failed to alarm me. But I made up my mind always to keep my wits about me and my eyes open ; and never to be *caught* trespassing.

Then one day, as I slid down from the roof of the barn

x

from amid the branches of a chestnut tree, green with its
spiky balls of fruit, I found Miss Taroone standing there
in the entry, looking out on me as if out of a frame, or
like a stone figure in the niche of a church. She made
no stir herself, but her eyes did. Clear cold eyes of the
colour of pebbly water, in which I seemed to be of no
more importance than a boat floating on the sea. I
could neither speak nor run away. I could only gawk
at her, my pockets bulging with the unripe chestnuts
I had pilfered, and a handsome slit in one leg of my
breeches.

She asked me what I did there ; my name ; why I
was not at school ; where I lived ; and did I eat the
chestnuts. It appeared she had more often seen me—
I suppose from her windows—than I had seen her.
She made no movement, never even smiled while I
stammered out answers to her questions, but merely
kept her eyes steadily fixed on me, while her own lips
just opened enough to let the words out of her mouth.
She listened to me with a severe face, and said, " Well,
if you are happy to be here with the rest, so much the
better."

It was a relief when she turned away, bidding me
follow her—and a foolish figure I must have cut as I
clattered after her across the cobbled yard under the
old red-brick arch and so through the porch and into
the house.

When I was sat down in one of the shaded rooms
within the house, she summoned the tall gaunt old maid
with the cap-flaps I had seen at the windows, and bade
her bring me some fruit and a dish of cream. Miss
Taroone watched me while I ate it. And uncommonly

good it was, though I would rather have been enjoying
it alone. From the way she looked at me it might have
been supposed it was a bird or a small animal that was
sitting up at her table. The last spoonful finished, she
asked me yet more questions and appeared to be not
displeased with my rambling answers, for she invited me
to come again and watched me take up my cap and
retire.

This was the first time I was ever in Miss Taroone's
house—within its solid walls I mean; and what a
multitude of rooms, with their coffers and presses and
cabinets, containing I knew not what treasures and
wonders! But Thrae was not Miss Taroone's only
house, for more than once she spoke of another—named
SURE VINE, as if of a family mansion and estate, very
ancient and magnificent. When, thinking of my mother,
I myself ventured a question about East Dene, her
green-grey eyes oddly settled on mine a moment, but
she made no answer. I noticed this particularly.

Soon I was almost as free and familiar in Miss Taroone's
old house as in my own father's. Yet I cannot say that
she was ever anything else than curt with me in her
manner. It was a long time before I became accustomed
to the still, secret way she had of looking at me. I liked
best being in her company when she appeared, as was
usually so, not to be aware that she was not alone. She
had again asked me my name " for a sign " as she said,
" to know you by " ; though she always afterwards
addressed me as Simon. Certainly in those days I was
" simple " enough.

My next friend was the woman whom I had seen
shaking her duster out of the upper windows. She, I

THE STORY OF THIS BOOK

discovered, was called Linnet Sara Queek or Quek or Cuec or Cueque, I don't know how to spell it. She was an exceedingly curious woman and looked as if she had never been any different, though, of course, she must once have been young and have grown up. She was bony, awkward, and angular, and when you spoke to her, she turned on you with a look that was at the same time vacant and piercing. At first she greeted me sourly, but soon became friendlier, and would allow me to sit in her huge kitchen with her parrot, her sleek tabby cat, and perhaps a dainty or two out of her larder.

She was continually muttering—though I could never quite catch what she said ; never idle ; and though slow and awkward in her movements, she did a vast deal of work. With small short-sighted eyes fixed on her mortar she would stand pounding and pounding ; or stewing and seething things in pots—strange-looking roots and fruits and fungi. Her pantry was crammed with pans, jars, bottles, and phials, all labelled in her queer handwriting. An extraordinary place—especially when the sunbeams of evening struck into it from a high window in its white-washed wall.

Linnet she might be called, but her voice was no bird's, unless the crow's ; and you would have guessed at once, at sight of her standing in front of the vast open hearth, stooping a little, her long gaunt arms beside her, that her other name was Sara. But she could tell curious and rambling stories (as true as she could make them) ; and many of them were about the old days in Thrae, older days in Sure Vine, and about Miss Taroone, in whose service she had been since she was a small child.

She told me, too, some specially good tales—as good as Grimm—about some villages she knew of called the Ten Laps; and gave me a custard when I asked for more. I once mentioned East Dene to her, too, and she said there was a short cut to it (though it seemed to me a long way about) through the quarry, by the pits, and that way round. "And then you come to a Wall," she said, staring at me. "And you climb over."

"Did *you*?" said I, laughing; and at that she was huffed.

Boy though I was, it occurred to me that in this immense house there must be a great deal more work than Sara could manage unaided. Something gave me the fancy that other hands must lend their help; but if any maids actually came in to Thrae from East Dene, or from elsewhere, they must have come and gone very late, or early. It seemed bad manners to be too curious. On the other hand, I rarely saw much of the back parts of the house.

I have sometimes wondered if Thrae had not once in fact lain within the borders of East Dene, and that being so, if Miss Taroone, like myself, was unaware of it. It may have been merely pride that closed her lips, for one day, she showed me, with a curious smile, how Thrae's architect, centuries before, had planned its site. She herself led me from room to room; and she talked as she had never talked before.

Its southernmost window looked on a valley, beyond which on clear still days was visible the sea, and perhaps a brig or a schooner on its surface—placid blue as turquoise. Sheer against its easternmost window the sun mounted to his summer solstice from in between a cleft of the hills—like a large topaz between the forks of a catapult. On one side of this cleft valley was a windmill, its sails lanking up into the sky, and sometimes spinning in the wind with an audible faint clatter. Who owned the mill and what he ground I never heard.

Northwards, through a round bull's-eye window you could see, past a maze of coppices and hills, and in the distance, the cock of a cathedral spire. And to the west stood a wood of yew, its pool partially greened over, grey with willows, and the haunt of rare birds. On the one side of this pool spread exceedingly calm meadows; and on the other, in a hollow, the graveyard lay. The stones and bones in it were all apparently of Miss Taroone's kinsfolk. At least Linnet Sara told me so. Nor was she mournful about it. She seemed to have nobody to care for but her mistress; working for love, whatever her wages might be.

It is an odd thing to say, but though I usually tried to avoid meeting Miss Taroone, and was a little afraid of her, there was a most curious happiness at times in being in her company. She never once asked me about my character, never warned me of anything, never said " You must "; and yet I knew well that if in stupidity or carelessness I did anything in her house which she did not approve of, my punishment would come.

She once told me, " Simon, you have, I see, the begin-nings of a bad feverish cold. It is because you were stupid enough yesterday to stand with the sweat on your face talking to me in a draught. It will probably be severe." And so it was.

She never said anything affectionate ; she never lost her temper. I never saw her show any pity or meanness or revenge. "Well, Simon," she would say, "Good morning"; or "Good evening" (as the case might be); "you are always welcome. Have a good look about you. Don't waste your time here. Even when all is said, you will not see too much of me and mine. But don't believe *everything* you may hear in the kitchen. Linnet Sara is a good servant, but still a groper."

Not the least notion of what she meant occurred to me. But I peacocked about for a while as if she had paid me a compliment. An evening or two afterwards, and soon after sunset, I found her sitting in her westward window. Perhaps because rain was coming, the crouching head-stones under the hill looked to be furlongs nearer. "Sleeping, waking; waking, sleeping, Simon;" she said, "sing while you can." Like a little owl I fixed sober eyes on the yew-wood, but again I hadn't any inkling of what she meant.

She would sit patiently listening to me as long as I cared to unbosom myself to her. Her calm, severe, and yet, I think, beautiful face is clear in my memory. It resembles a little the figure in Albrecht Dürer's picture of a woman sitting beneath the wall of a house, with a hound couched beside her, an inclined ladder, the rain-bowed sea in the distance, and a bat—a tablet of magic numbers and a pent-housed bell over her head.

Sometimes I would be questioned at home about my solitary wanderings, but I never mentioned Miss Taroone's name, and spoke of her house a little deceit-fully, since I did not confess how much I loved being in it.

One evening—and it was already growing late—Miss Taroone, after steadily gazing into my eyes for a few moments, asked me if I liked pictures. I professed that

I did, though I had never spent much time in looking at the queer portraits and charts and mementoes that hung thick and closely on her own walls. " Well," she replied, " if you like pictures I must first tell you about Nahum."

I could not at first make head or tail of Mr. Nahum. Even now I am uncertain whether he was Miss Taroone's brother or her nephew or a cousin many times removed ; or whether perhaps she was really and truly Mrs. Taroone and he her only son ; or she still Miss Taroone and he an adopted one. I am not sure even whether or not she had much love for him, though she appeared to speak of him with pride. What I do know is that Miss Taroone had nurtured him from his cradle, and had taught him all the knowledge that was not already his by right of birth.

Before he was come even to be my own age, she told me, Nahum Taroone had loved " exploring." As a boy he had ranged over the countryside for miles around. I never dared ask her if he had sat on Linnet Sara's " Wall " ! He had scrawled plans and charts and maps, marking on them all his wanderings. And not only the roads, paths, chaces, and tracks, the springs and streams, but the rarer birds' nesting-places and the rarer wild flowers, the eatable or poisonous fruits, trees, animal lairs, withies for whips, clay for modelling, elder shoots for pitch pipes, pebbles for his catapult, flint arrows, and everything of that kind. He was a night-boy too ; could guide himself by the stars, was a walking almanac of the moon ; and could decoy owls and nightjars, and find any fox's or badger's earth he was after, even in a dense mist.

THE STORY OF THIS BOOK

I came to know Mr. Nahum pretty well—so far at any rate as one can know anybody from hearsay—before Miss Taroone referred to the pictures again. And I became curious about him, and hoped to see this strange traveller, and frequently hung about Thrae in mere chance of that.

Strangely enough, by the looks on her face and the tones of her voice, Miss Taroone was inclined to mock a little at Mr. Nahum because of his restlessness. She didn't seem to approve of his leaving her so much—though she herself had come from Sure Vine. Her keys would jangle at her chatelaine as if they said, "Ours secrets enough." And she would stand listening, and mute, as if in expectation of voices or a footfall. Then as secretly as I could, I would get away.

All old memories resemble a dream. And so too do these of Miss Taroone and Thrae. When I was most busy and happy and engrossed in it, it seemed to be a house which might at any moment vanish before your eyes, showing itself to be but the outer shell or hiding place of an abode still more enchanting.

This sounds nonsensical. But if you have ever sat and watched a Transformation Scene in a pantomime, did you suppose, just before the harlequin slapped with his wand on what looked like a plain brick-and-mortar wall, that it would instantly after dissolve into a radiant coloured scene of trees and fountains and hidden beings —growing lovelier in their own showing as the splendour spread and their haunts were revealed? Well, so at times I used to feel in *Thrae*.

At last, one late evening in early summer, beckoning me with her finger, Miss Taroone lit a candle in an old brass stick and bade me follow her down a long narrow corridor and up a steep winding stone staircase. " You have heard, Simon, of Mr. Nahum's round room ; now you shall see it."

On the wider step at the top, before a squat oak door, she stayed, lifted her candle, and looked at me. " You will remember," she said, " that what I am about to admit you into is Mr. Nahum's room ; not mine. You may look at the pictures, you may examine anything that interests you, you may compose yourself to the view. But replace what you look at, have a care in your handling, do nothing out of *idle* curiosity, and come away when you are tired. Remember that Mr. Nahum may be returning at any hour. He would be pleased to find you here. But hasten away out of his room the very instant you feel you have no right, lot or pleasure to be in it. Hasten away, I mean, so that you may return to it with a better mind and courage."

She laid two fingers on my shoulder, cast another look into my face under her candle, turned the key in the lock, gently thrust me beyond the door, shut it: and left me to my own devices.

What first I noticed, being for awhile a little alarmed at this strange proceeding, was the evening light that poured in on the room from the encircling windows. Below, by walking some little distance from room to room, corridor to corridor, you could get (as I have said) a single narrow view out north, south, east or west. Here, you could stand in the middle, and turning slowly like a top on your heels, could watch float by one after the other, hill and windmill, ocean, distant city, dark yew-wood.

THE STORY OF THIS BOOK

The crooning of doves was audible on the roof, swallows were coursing in the placid and rosy air, the whole world seemed to be turning softly out of the day's sunshine, stretching long dark shadows across hill and valley as if in delight to be on the verge of rest and slumber again, now that the heats of full summer were so near.

But I believe my first *thought* was—What a boiling hot and glaring place to sit in in the middle of the morning. And then I noticed that heavy curtains hung on either side each rounded window, for shade, conceal- ment and solitude. As soon, however, as my eyes were accustomed to the dazzle, I spent little time upon the great view, but immediately peered about me at what was in this curious chamber.

Never have I seen in any room—and this was none so large—such a hugger-mugger of strange objects—odd- shaped coloured shells, fragments of quartz, thunder- bolts and fossils ; skins of brilliant birds ; outlandish shoes ; heads, faces, masks of stone, wood, glass, wax, and metal; pots, images, glass shapes, and what not ; lanterns and bells ; bits of harness and ornament and weapons. There were, besides, two or three ships of different rigs in glass cases, and one in a green bottle ; peculiar tools, little machines ; silent clocks, instruments of music, skulls and bones of beasts, frowsy bunches of linen or silk queerly marked, and a mummied cat (I think). And partly concealed, as I twisted my head, there, dangling in an alcove, I caught sight of a full- length skeleton, one hollow eye-hole concealed by a curtain looped to the floor from the ceiling.

I just cast my glance round on all these objects without of course seeing them one by one. The air was clear as water in the evening light, a little dust had fallen ; all was in order, though at that first hasty glance there seemed none. Last, but not least, there was row on row of painted pictures. Wherever there was space on the walls free of books, this round tower room was hung with them as close as their frames and nails allowed. There I stood, hearing faintly the birds, conscious of the pouring sunlight, the only live creature amidst this departed traveller's treasures and possessions.

I was so much taken aback by it all, so mystified by Miss Taroone's ways, so cold at sight of the harmless bones above me, and felt so suddenly out of my familiars, that without a moment's hesitation I turned about, flung open the door and went helter skelter clattering down the stairs—out of the glare into the gloom.

There was no sign of Miss Taroone as I crossed through the house and sneaked off hastily through the garden. And not until the barn had shut me out from the lower windows behind me did I look back at the upper ones of Mr. Nahum's tower. Until that moment I did not know how frightened I had been. Yet why, or at what, I cannot even now decide.

But I soon overcame this folly. Miss Taroone made no inquiry how I had fared on this first visit to Mr. Nahum's fortress. As I have said, she seldom asked questions—except with her eyes, expressions, and hands. But some time afterwards, and after two or three spells of exploration, I myself began to talk to her of the strange things up there.

" I have looked at a good many, Miss Taroone. But the pictures ! Some of them are of places I *believe* I know. I wish I could be a traveller and see what the others are of. Did Mr. Nahum paint them all himself?"

Miss Taroone was sitting bolt upright in a high-backed chair, her eyes and face very intent, as always happened when Mr. Nahum's name was mentioned.

" I know very little about them, Simon. When Nahum was younger he used to make pictures of Thrae, and of the woods and valleys hereabouts. There are boxfulls put away. Others are pictures brought back from foreign parts, but many of them, as I believe," she turned her face and looked into a shadowy corner of the room, " are pictures of nothing on earth. He has his two worlds. Take your time. Some day you too, I dare say, will go off on your travels. Remember that, like Nahum, you are as old as the hills which neither spend nor waste time, but dwell in it for ages, as if it were light or sunshine. Some day perhaps Nahum will shake himself free of Thrae altogether. I don't *know*, myself, Simon. This house is enough for me, and what I remember of Sure Vine, compared with which Thrae is but the smallest of bubbles in a large glass."

I do not profess to have understood one half of what Miss Taroone meant in these remarks. It was in English and yet in a hidden tongue.

But by this time I had grown to be bolder in her company, and pounced on this :—" What, please Miss Taroone, do you mean by the ' two worlds ' ? Or shall I ask downstairs?" I added the latter question because now and then in the past Miss Taroone had bidden me go down to Linnet Sara for my answers. She now appeared at first not to have heard it.

" Now I must say to you, Simon," she replied at last, folding her hands on her knee, " wherever you may be in that body of yours, you feel you look out of it, do you not ? "

I nodded. " Yes, Miss Taroone."

" Now think, then, of Mr. Nahum's round room ; where is that ? "

" Up there," said I, pointing up a rambling finger.

" Ah ! " cried Miss Taroone, " so it may be. But even if to-morrow you are thousands of miles distant from here on the other side of this great Ball, or in its bowels, or flying free—you will still carry a picture of it, will you not ? And that will be within you ? "

" Yes, in my mind, Miss Taroone ? " I answered rather sheepishly.

" In your mind," she echoed me, but not as if she were particularly pleased at the fact. " Well, many of the pictures I take it in Mr. Nahum's round tower are of *that* world. His MIND. I have never examined them. My duties are elsewhere. Your duty is to keep your senses, heart and courage and to go where you are called. And in black strange places you will at times lose yourself and find yourself, Simon. Now Mr. Nahum is calling. Don't think of me too much. I have great faith in him. Sit up there with him then. Share your eyes with his pictures. And having seen them, compare them if you will. Say, This is this, and that is that. And make of all that he has exactly what use you can."

With this counsel in my head I once more groped my way up the corkscrew stone staircase, and once more passed on from picture to picture ; in my engrossment actually knocking my head against the dangling foot-bones of Mr. Nahum's treasured and now unalarming skeleton.

The pictures were of all kinds and sizes—in water colour, in chalks, and in oil. Some I liked for their vivid colours and deep shadows, and some I did not like at all. Nor could I always be sure even what they were intended to represent. Many of them completely perplexed me. A few of them seemed to me to be absurd; some made me stupidly ashamed; and one or two of them terrified me. But I went on examining them when I felt inclined, and a week or so after, as I was lifting out one of them into the sunshine, by chance it twisted on its cord and disclosed its wooden back.

And there, pasted on to it, was a scrap of yellowing paper with the letters BLAKE, followed by a number—CXLVII, in Roman figures. As with this one, so with the others. Each had its name and a number.

And even as I stood pondering what this might mean, my eyes rested on a lower shelf of one of Mr. Nahum's cases of books—book-cases which I have forgotten to say stood all round the lower part of the room. I had already discovered that many of these books were the writings of travellers in every part of the globe. One whole book-case consisted of what Mr. Nahum appeared to call Kitchen Work. But the one on a lower shelf which had now taken my attention was new to me—an enormous, thick, home-made-looking volume covered in a greenish shagreen or shark-skin.

Scrawled in ungainly capitals on the strip of vellum pasted to the back of this book was its title: THEOTHER-WORLDE. Would you believe it?—at first I was stupid enough to suppose this title was one word, a word in a strange tongue, which I pronounced to myself as best I could, THEEOTHAWORLDIE—saying the TH as in *thimble*. And that is what, merely for old sake's sake, I have continued to call the book in my mind to this day!

I glanced out of the window. The upper boughs of the yew-wood and the stones this side of it among the bright green grasses were impurpled by the reflected sunlight. Nothing there but motionless shadows. I stood looking vacantly out for a moment or two ; then stooped and lugged out the ponderous fusty old volume on to the floor and raised its clumsy cover.

To my surprise and pleasure, I found, that attached within was the drawing of a boy of about my own age, but dressed like a traveller, whose face faintly resembled a portrait I had noticed on the walls downstairs, though this child had wings painted to his shoulders and there was a half circle of stars around his head. Beneath this portrait in the book, in small letters, was scrawled in a faded handwriting, NAHUM TARUNE. This, then, was Mr. Nahum when he was a boy. It pleased me to find that he was no better a speller than myself. He had not even got his own name right ! I liked his face. He looked out from under his stars at me, full in the eyes.

Next—after I had searched his looks and clothes and what he carried pretty closely—I turned over a few of the stiff leaves and found more of his writing with a big VII scrawled on the top. On page one of this book you will find the writing. I should have been a stupider boy even than I was if I had not at once turned over the pictures till I came to that with VII on the label on the back of it. This picture was of a

Maze outlined in gaudy colours which faded towards the middle—a sort of oasis in which grew a tree. Fabulous-looking animals and creatures with wings sprawled around its margins. After repeated attempts I found to my disappointment that your only way out of the oasis and the maze was, after long groping, by the way you went in. Underneath it was written "*This is the key.*" And above it in green letters stood this: Behold upon the mountains the feet of him that bringeth good tidings, that publisheth peace!

It was unfortunate that so little more of daylight was now left dying in the sky that evening; for as yet I had not the confidence to kindle the wax candles that stood in their brass sticks in the round tower. It was high time for me to be getting home. In my haste to be off I nearly collided with Miss Taroone, who happened to be standing in the dusklight looking out from under her porch. Too much excited even to beg her pardon, I blurted out: "Miss Taroone, I have found out what the pictures are of. It's a Book. *Theeothaworldie*. Mr. Nahum's portrait's in it, but they've put wings to him; and it's all in his writing—rhymes."

She looked down at me, though I could not quite see her face.

"Then, good-night to you, Simon; and happy dreams," she said, in her unfriendly voice.

"I like the round room better and better," I replied as heartily as I could. "That picture of Mr. Nahum—and there are lots more, I think—is a *little* bit like an uncle of mine who died in Russia; my Uncle John."

"John's as good a name, I suppose, as any other, Simon," said Miss Taroone. She stood looking out on the dusky country scene. "There's a heavy dew to-night, and the owls are busy."

They were indeed. Their screechings sounded on all sides of me as I ran off homewards, chanting over to myself the words that had somehow stuck in my memory.

Well, at last I began to read in Mr. Nahum's book—I won't say page by page, but as the fancy took me. It consisted chiefly of rhymes and poems, and some of them had pictured capitals and were decorated in clear bright colours like the pages of the old books illuminated by monks centuries ago. Apart from the poems were here and there pieces of prose. These, I found, always had some bearing on the poems, and, like them, many of them were queerly spelt. Occasionally Mr. Nahum had jotted down his own thoughts in the margin. But the pictures were my first concern.

Sometimes I went off to them from the book in order to find the particular one I wanted. And sometimes the other way round : I would have a good long stare at a picture, then single out the proper rhyme in the book. Often, either in one way or the other, I failed. For there were far fewer pictures than there were pages in the book, and for scores of pages I found no picture at all. It seemed Mr. Nahum had made paintings only of those he liked best.

The book itself, I found, was the first of three, the other two being similar to itself but much thicker and heavier. Into these I dipped occasionally, but found that the rhymes in them interested me less or were less easily understandable. Even some of those in the first book were a little beyond my wits at the time. But experience seems to be like the shining of a bright lantern. It suddenly makes clear in the mind what was already there perhaps, but dim. And often though I immediately liked what I read, long years were to go by before I really understood it, made it my own. There would come a moment, something would happen; and I would say to myself :— " Oh, that, then, is what *that* meant !"

Before going any further I must confess that I was exceedingly slow over Mr. Nahum's writings. Even over Volume I. When first I opened its pages I had had a poor liking for poetry because of a sort of contempt for it. " Poetry !" I would scoff to myself, and would shut up the covers of any such book with a kind of yawn inside me. Some of it had come my way in lesson books. This I could gabble off like a parrot, and with as much understanding ; and I had just begun to grind out a little Latin verse for my father.

But I had never troubled to think about it ; to share my Self with it ; to examine it in order to see whether or not it was true ; or to ask why it was written in this one way and in no other way. But apart from this, there were many old rhymes in Mr. Nahum's book—nursery things— which I had known since I knew anything. And I still have an old childish love for rhymes and jingles like them.

But what about the others ? I began to ponder. After being so many hours alone in Mr. Nahum's room, among his secret belongings, I almost felt his presence there. When your mind is sunk in study, it is as if you were in a dream. But you cannot tell where, or in whose company, you may wake out of a dream. I remember one sultry afternoon being startled out of my wits by a sudden clap of thunder. I looked up, to find the whole room black, zigzag, and strange, and for a moment I fancied Mr. Nahum was actually there behind me ; and not a friendly Mr. Nahum.

That is mere fancy ; though in other ways he became so real to me at last that I would do things as if he had asked me to do them. For this reason, I think, I persevered with his book, swallowing some of the poems as if they were physic, simply because he had written them there. But the more I read, the more I came to enjoy them for their own sakes. Not all of them, of course. But I did see this, that like a carpenter who makes a table, a man who has written a poem has written it like that *on purpose*.

With this thought in my head I tried one day to alter the words of one or two of the simple and easy poems ; or to put the words in a different order. And I found by so doing that you not only altered the sound of the poem, but that even the slightest alteration in the sound a little changed the sense. Either you lost something of the tune and runningness ; or the words did not clash right ; or you blurred the picture the words gave you ; or some half-hidden meaning vanished away. I don't mean that every poem is perfect ; but only that when I changed them it was almost always very much for the worse. I was very slow in all this ; but, still, I went on. No. III, I remember, was the old nursery jingle, " Old King Cole " :—

> Old King Cole was a merry old soul,
> And a merry old soul was he ;
> He called for his pipe,
> And he called for his bowl,
> And he called for his fiddlers three. . . .

xxix

THE STORY OF THIS BOOK

Now, suppose, instead of these four lines of the rhyme you put :—

> Old King Cole was a jolly old man,
> The jolliest old man alive ;
> He called for his cup, and he called for a pipe
> And he called for his fiddlers five.

By so doing you have actually added two extra fiddlers ; and yet somehow you have taken away some of the old three's music. Or you may put :—

'Cole the First was now a monarch advanced in age, and of a convivial temperament. On any festive occasion he would bid his retainers bring him his goblet and smoking materials, and would command his musicians to entertain him on their violins : which they did.'

Well, all the *facts* are there and many more words, but scarcely a trace of *my* old King Cole, and not a single tweedle-eedle of the fiddling. Would anyone trouble to learn that by heart ?

Now underneath this rhyme Mr. Nahum had written a sort of historical account of King Cole, a good deal of it in German and other languages. All I could make out of it was this : if ever a King Cole inhabited the world, he probably had another name ; that he lived too far back in history for anyone to make sure when he had lived or that he had lived at all ; and that his " pipe " and " bowl " probably stand for objects much more mysterious and far less common.

Having the rhyme quite free to myself, I didn't mind reading this ; but if ever I have to give up either, I shall keep the rhyme.

THE STORY OF THIS BOOK

Having discovered, then, that every poem must have been written as it was written, on purpose, I took a little more pains with those I cared for least. In some even then I could not quite piece out the meaning; in others I could not easily catch the beat and rhythm and tune. But I learned to read them very slowly, so as fully and quietly to fill up the time allowed for each line and to listen to its music, and to see and hear all that the words were saying.

Then, too, what Miss Taroone had said came back to my mind. Even when Mr. Nahum's poems were about real things and places and people, they were still only of places and people the words made for me in my *mind*. I must, that is, myself imagine all they told. And I found that the mention in a poem even of quite common and familiar things—such as a star, or a buttercup, or a beetle—did not bring into the mind quite the same kind of images of them as the things and creatures themselves do in the naked eye.

> Now the day is over,
> Night is drawing nigh;
> Shadows of the evening
> Steal across the sky....

This was one of the earliest poems in Mr. Nahum's book. I had often, of course, seen the shadows of evening—every grass-blade or pebble casts its own; but these words not only called them vividly into my mind, but set shadows there (shadows across the sky) that I had never really seen at all—with my own eyes I mean. I discovered afterwards, also, that shadows are only the absence of light, though light is needed to

xxxi

make them visible. Just the same, again, with the sailors in the same poem :

> Guard the sailors tossing
> On the deep blue sea. . . .

They are plain and common words, but their *order* here is the poem's only, and the effect they had on me, and still have, is different from the effect of any other words on the same subject. Though, too, like Mr. Nahum, I have now seen something of the world (have been seasick and nearly drowned) I have never forgotten those imaginary sailors, or that imaginary sea ; can still hear the waves lapping against that (unmentioned) ship's thin wooden walls, as if I myself were sleeping there, down below.

So what I then read has remained a clear and single remembrance, as if I myself had seen it in a world made different, or in a kind of vision or dream. And I think Mr. Nahum had chosen such poems in Volume I. as carried away the imagination like that ; either into the past, or into another mind, or into the all-but-forgotten ; at times as if into another world. And this kind has been my choice in this book.

Not that his picture to a particular poem was always the picture I should have made of it. Take for example another nursery jingle in his book :

> ' How many miles to Babylon ? '
> ' Three score and ten.'
> ' Can I get there by candle-light ? '
> ' Ay, and back again.'

Mr. Nahum's corresponding picture was not of Babylon or of a candle, or of a traveller at all, but of a stone tomb.

THE STORY OF THIS BOOK

On its thick upper slab he had drawn-in an old earthen lamp, with a serpent for handle—its wick alight, and shining up on a small owl perched in the lower branches of the thick tree above.

That is one of the pleasures of reading—you may make any picture out of the words you can and will; and a poem may have as many different meanings as there are different minds.

There I would sit, then, and Mr. Nahum's book made of " one little room an everywhere." And though I was naturally rather stupid and dense, I did in time realise that " rare poems ask rare friends," and that even the simplest ones may have secrets which will need a pretty close searching out.

Of course I could not copy out all of the poems even in THEEOTHAWORLDIE, Volume I., and I took very few from Volumes II. and III. I chose what I liked best—those that, when I read them, never failed to carry me away, as if on a Magic Carpet, or in Seven League Boots, into a region of their own. When the nightingale sings, other birds, it is said, will sit and listen to him : and I remember very well hearing a nightingale so singing on a spray in a dewy hedge, and there were many small birds perched mute and quiet near. The cock crows at midnight; and for miles around his kinsmen answer. The fowler whistles his decoy for the wild duck to come. So certain rhymes and poems affected my mind when I was young, and continue to do so now that I am old.

To these (and the few bits of prose) which I chose from Mr. Nahum, I added others afterwards, and they are in this book too. All of them are in English ; a few

from over the ocean: but how very few they all are by
comparison with the multitudes even of their own kind.
And there are the whole world's languages besides!
Even of my own favourites not all have found a place.
There was not room enough. I have left out others also
that may be found easily elsewhere. I am afraid, too,
there may be many mistakes in my copying, though
I have tried to be careful.

Miss Taroone knew that I was making use of Mr.
Nahum's book ; though she never questioned me about
it. I came and went in her house at last like a rabbit
in a warren, a mouse in a mousery. The hours I spent
in those far-gone days in Mr. Nahum's round room!
At times I wearied of it, and hated his books, and
even wished I had never so much as set eyes on Thrae
at all.

But after such sour moments, a gossip and an apple
with Linnet Sara in her kitchen, or a scamper home, or a
bathe under the hazels in the stream whose source, I
believe, is in the hills beyond East Dene, would set me
to rights again. For sheer joy of return I could scarcely
breathe for a while after remounting the stone staircase,
re-entering Mr. Nahum's room, and closing the door
behind me.

From above his broad scrawled pages I would lift my
eyes to his windows and stare as if out of one dream into
another. How strange from across the sky was the
gentle scented breeze blowing in on my cheek, softly
stirring the dried kingfisher skin that hung from its
beam ; how near understanding then the tongues of the
wild birds ; how close the painted scene—as though I
were but a picture too, and this my frame.

THE STORY OF THIS BOOK

But there came a day that was to remove me out of the neighbourhood of Miss Taroone's Thrae into a different kind of living altogether. I was to be sent to school. After a hot debate with myself, and why I scarcely know, I asked my father's permission to spend the night at Miss Taroone's. He gave me a steady look and said, Yes.

I found Miss Taroone seated on the steps of her porch, and now that I look back at her then, she curiously reminds me—though she was ages older—of a picture you will find in the second stanza of poem No. 233 in this book. Standing before her—it was already getting towards dark—I said I was come to bid her goodbye ; and might I spend the night in Mr. Nahum's round room. She raised her eyes on me, luminous and mysterious as the sky itself, even though in the dusk.

" You may *say*, goodbye, Simon," she replied ; " but unless I myself am much mistaken in you, your feet will not carry you out of all thought of me ; and some day they will return to me whether you will or not."

Inside I was already in a flutter at thought of the hours to come, and I was accustomed to her strange speeches, though this struck on my mind more coldly than usual. I made a little jerk forwards ; " I must thank you, please Miss Taroone, for having been so kind to me," I gulped in an awkward voice. " And I hope," I added, as she made no answer, " I hope I haven't been much of a bother—coming like this, I mean ? "

"None, Simon ; " was her sole reply. The hand that I had begun to hold out, went back into my pocket, and feeling extremely uncomfortable I half turned away.

" Why, who knows ?—" said the solemn voice, " Mr.

Nahum may at this very moment be riding home. Have
a candle alight."

"Thank you, Miss Taroone. Thank you very much
indeed."

With that I turned about and hastened across the
darkening garden into the house. My candlestick and
matches stood ready on the old oak bench at the foot of
the tower. I lit up, and began to climb the cold steps.
My heart in my mouth, I hesitated at the hob-nailed
door ; but managed at last to turn the key in the lock.

With two taller candles kindled, and its curtains
drawn over the western window, I at once began to copy
out the last few things I wanted for mine in Volume I.
But there were two minds in me as midnight drew on,
almost two selves, the one busy with pen and ink, the
other stealthily listening to every faintest sound in my
eyrie, a swift glance now and then up at the darkened
glass only setting me more sharply to work. I had
never before sat in so enormous a silence ; the scratching
of my pen its only tongue.

Steadily burned my candles ; no sound of hoofs, no
owl-cry, no knocking disturbed my peace ; the nightingales had long since journeyed South. What I had
hoped for, expected, dreaded in this long vigil, I cannot
recall ; all that I remember of it is that I began to shiver
a little at last, partly because my young nerves were on
the stretch, and partly because the small hours grew
chill. In the very middle of the night there came to my
ear what seemed a distant talking or gabbling. It may
have been fancy ; it may have been Linnet Sara. What
certainly was fancy is the notion that, as I started up
out of an instant's drowse, a stooping shape had swiftly

withdrawn itself from me. But this was merely the shadow of a dream.

I returned at last from the heavy sleep I had fallen into, my forehead resting on the backs of my hands, and they flat on the huge open volume, my whole body stiff with cold, and the first clear grey of daybreak in the East. And suddenly, as my awakened eyes stared dully about them in that thin light—the old windows, the strange outlandish objects, the clustering pictures, the count- less books, my own ugly writing on my paper—an indescribable despair and anxiety—almost terror even —seized upon me at the rushing thought of my own *ignorance*; of how little I knew, of how unimportant I was. And, again and again, my ignorance. Then I thought of Miss Taroone, of Mr. Nahum, of the life before me, and everything yet to do. And a sullen misery swept up in me at these reflections. And once more I wished from the bottom of my heart that I had never come to this house.

But gradually the light broadened. And with it, confidence began to return. The things around me that had seemed strange and hostile became familiar again. I stood up and stretched myself and, I think, muttered a prayer.

To this day I see the marvellous countryside of that morning with its hills and low thick mists and wood- lands stretched like a painted scene beneath the windows —and that finger of light from the risen Sun presently piercing across the dark air, and as if by a miracle causing birds and water to awake and sing and shine.

With a kind of grief that was yet rapture in my mind, I stood looking out over the cold lichen-crusted

shingled roof of Thrae towards the East and towards
those far horizons. Yet again the apprehension (that
was almost a hope) drew over me that at any moment
wall and chimney-shaft might thin softly away, and the
Transformation Scene begin. I was but just awake:
and so too was the world itself, and ever is. And somewhere Wall or no Wall—was my mother's East Dene. . . .

In a while I crept softly downstairs, let myself out, and
ran off into the morning. Having climbed the hill from
which I had first stared down upon Thrae, I stopped for
a moment to recover my breath, and looked back. I
looked back.

The gilding sun-rays beat low upon the house in the
valley. All was still, wondrous, calm. For a moment
my heart misgave me at this farewell. The next, in
sheer excitement—the cold sweet air, the height, the
morning, a few keen beckoning stars—I broke into a
kind of Indian war-dance in the thin dewy grass, and
then, with a last wave of my hand, like Mr. Nahum
himself, I set off at a sharp walk on the journey that
has not yet come to an end.

MORNING AND MAY

THIS IS THE KEY

THIS is the Key of the Kingdom :
In that Kingdom is a city ;
In that city is a town ;
In that town there is a street ;
In that street there winds a lane ;
In that lane there is a yard ;
In that yard there is a house ;
In that house there waits a room ;
In that room an empty bed ;
And on that bed a basket—
A Basket of Sweet Flowers :
Of Flowers, of Flowers ;
A Basket of Sweet Flowers.

Flowers in a Basket ;
Basket on the bed ;
Bed in the chamber ;
Chamber in the house ;
House in the weedy yard ;
Yard in the winding lane ;
Lane in the broad street ;
Street in the high town ;
Town in the city ;
City in the Kingdom—
This is the Key of the Kingdom.
Of the Kingdom this is the Key.

MORNING AND MAY

A NEW YEAR CAROL

HERE we bring new water
 from the well so clear,
For to worship God with,
 this happy New Year.
Sing levy dew, sing levy dew,
 the water and the wine;
The seven bright gold wires
 and the bugles that do shine.

Sing reign of Fair Maid,
 with gold upon her toe,
Open you the West Door,
 and turn the Old Year go.

Sing reign of Fair Maid
 with gold upon her chin,—
Open you the East Door,
 and let the New Year in.
Sing levy dew, sing levy dew,
 the water and the wine;
The seven bright gold wires
 and the bugles they do shine.

3   HEY! NOW THE DAY DAWNS

"Hay, nou the day dauis;
The jolie Cok crauis;
Nou shroudis the shauis,
 Throu Natur anone.
The thissell-cok cryis
On louers wha lyis,
Nou skaillis the skyis;
 The nicht is neir gone.

"The feildis ouerflouis
With gowans that grouis,

Hey! now the day dawns;
The jolly Cock crows;
Thick-leaved the green shaws,
 Through Nature anon.
The thistle-cock cries
On lovers who lies,
All cloudless the skies;
 The night is near gone.

The fields overflow
With daisies a-blow,

4

HEY! NOW THE DAY DAWNS

Quhair lilies lyk lou is,
　Als rid as the rone.
The turtill that true is,
With nots that reneuis,
Hir pairtie perseuis ;
　The nicht is neir gone.

"Nou Hairtis with Hyndis,
Conforme to thair kyndis,
Hie tursis thair tyndis,
　On grund whair they grone.
Nou Hurchonis, with Hairis,
Ay passis in pairis ;
Quhilk deuly declaris
　The nicht is neir gone . . ."

And lilies like fire shine,
　And red is the rowan.
The wood-dove that true is
Her crooling reneweth,
And her sweet mate pur-
　sueth ;
　The night is near gone.

Now Harts with their Hinds
Conform to their kinds,
They vaunt their branched
　antlers,
　They bell and they groan.
Now Urchins [1] and Hares
Keep apassing in pairs ;
Which duly declares
　The night is near gone. . . .

ALEXANDER MONTGOMERIE

4

THE SLUGGARD

'Tis the voice of a sluggard ; I heard him complain—
"You have waked me too soon ; I must slumber again ; "
As the door on its hinges, so he on his bed,
Turns his sides, and his shoulders, and his heavy head.

"A little more sleep, and a little more slumber "—
Thus he wastes half his days, and his hours without number ;
And when he gets up, he sits folding his hands,
Or walks about saunt'ring, or trifling he stands.

I passed by his garden, and saw the wild brier
The thorn and the thistle grow broader and higher ;
The clothes that hang on him are turning to rags ;
And his money still wastes till he starves or he begs.

I made him a visit, still hoping to find
That he took better care for improving his mind ;

[1] Hedgehogs

5

MORNING AND MAY

He told me his dreams, talked of eating and drinking,
But he scarce reads his Bible, and never loves thinking.

Said I then to my heart : " Here's a lesson for me ;
That man's but a picture of what I might be ;
But thanks to my friends for their care in my breeding,
Who taught me betimes to love working and reading."

ISAAC WATTS

5 HARK, HARK, THE LARK

Hearke, hearke, the Larke at Heaven's gate sings,
  And Phoebus 'gins arise,
His Steeds to water at those Springs
  On chaliced Flowres that lyes :
And winking Mary-buds begin
  To ope their Golden eyes :
With every thing that pretty is,
  My Lady sweet, arise :
    Arise, arise !

WILLIAM SHAKESPEARE

6 THE LARK NOW LEAVES HIS WATERY
      NEST

The lark now leaves his watery nest,
  And climbing shakes his dewy wings ;
He takes your window for the East,
  And to implore your light, he sings :
Awake, awake ! the morn will never rise
Till she can dress her beauty at your eyes.

The merchant bows unto the seaman's star,
  The ploughman from the sun his season takes ;
But still the lover wonders what they are
  Who look for day before his mistress wakes :
Awake, awake ! break through your veils of lawn ;
Then draw your curtains, and begin the dawn !

SIR WILLIAM DAVENANT

EARLY MORN

7

WHEN I did wake this morn from sleep,
  It seemed I heard birds in a dream ;
Then I arose to take the air—
  The lovely air that made birds scream ;
Just as a green hill launched the ship
Of gold, to take its first clear dip.

And it began its journey then,
  As I came forth to take the air ;
The timid Stars had vanished quite,
  The Moon was dying with a stare ;
Horses, and kine, and sheep were seen
As still as pictures, in fields green.

It seemed as though I had surprised
  And trespassed in a golden world
That should have passed while men still slept !
  The joyful birds, the ship of gold,
The horses, kine and sheep did seem
As they would vanish for a dream.
                                    WILLIAM H. DAVIES

GOOD-MORROW

8

PACK, clouds, away, and welcome day !
  With night we banish sorrow.
Sweet air, blow soft, mount, lark, aloft
  To give my Love good morrow.
Wings from the wind to please her mind,
  Notes from the lark I'll borrow :
Bird, prune thy wing, nightingale, sing,
  To give my Love good morrow !
    To give my Love good morrow
    Notes from them all I'll borrow.

Wake from thy nest, robin redbreast !
  Sing, birds, in every furrow,

MORNING AND MAY

And from each hill let music shrill
Give my fair Love good morrow !
Blackbird and thrush in every bush,
Stare,[1] linnet, and cock-sparrow,
You pretty elves, amongst yourselves
Sing my fair Love good morrow !
To give my Love good morrow
Sing, birds, in every furrow !

THOMAS HEYWOOD

THE QUESTION

I DREAMED that, as I wandered by the way,
  Bare Winter suddenly was changed to Spring,
And gentle odours led my steps astray,
  Mixed with a sound of waters murmuring
Along a shelving bank of turf, which lay
  Under a copse, and hardly dared to fling
Its green arms round the bosom of the stream,
But kissed it and then fled, as thou mightest in dream.

There grew pied wind-flowers and violets,
  Daisies, those pearled Arcturi of the earth,
The constellated flower that never sets ;
  Faint oxlips ; tender blue-bells, at whose birth
The sod scarce heaved ; and that tall flower that wets—
  Like a child, half in tenderness and mirth—
Its mother's face with heaven's collected tears,
When the low wind, its playmate's voice, it hears.

And in the warm hedge grew lush eglantine,
  Green cowbind and the moonlight-coloured May
And cherry-blossoms, and white cups, whose wine
  Was the bright dew, yet drained not by the day ;
And wild roses, and ivy serpentine
  With its dark buds and leaves, wandering astray :
And flowers azure, black, and streaked with gold,
Fairer than any wakened eyes behold.

[1] Starling

8

THE QUESTION

And nearer to the river's trembling edge
    There grew broad flag-flowers, purple prankt with
        white,
And starry river-buds among the sedge,
    And floating water-lilies, broad and bright,
Which lit the oak that overhung the hedge
    With moonlight beams of their own watery light ;
And bulrushes, and reeds of such deep green
As soothed the dazzled eye with sober sheen.

Methought that of these visionary flowers
    I made a nosegay, bound in such a way
That the same hues, which in their natural bowers
    Were mingled or opposed, the like array
Kept these imprisoned children of the Hours
    Within my hand,—and then, elate and gay,
I hastened to the spot whence I had come,
That I might there present it—oh ! to Whom ?
PERCY BYSSHE SHELLEY

10   THE FRESH AIR

THE fresh air moves like water round a boat.
    The white clouds wander. Let us wander too.
The whining, wavering plover flap and float.
    That crow is flying after that cuckoo.
Look ! Look ! . . . They're gone. What are the great trees
    calling ?
Just come a little farther, by that edge
Of green, to where the stormy ploughland, falling
    Wave upon wave, is lapping to the hedge.
Oh, what a lovely bank ! Give me your hand.
    Lie down and press your heart against the ground.
Let us both listen till we understand,
    Each through the other, every natural sound . . .
        I can't hear anything to-day, can you,
        But, far and near : " Cuckoo ! Cuckoo ! Cuckoo ! " ?
HAROLD MONRO

11 WEATHERS

This is the weather the cuckoo likes,
  And so do I ;
When showers betumble the chestnut spikes,
  And nestlings fly :
And the little brown nightingale bills his best,
And they sit outside at " The Travellers' Rest,"
And maids come forth sprig-muslin drest,
And citizens dream of the south and west,
  And so do I.

This is the weather the shepherd shuns,
  And so do I ;
When beeches drip in browns and duns,
  And thresh, and ply ;
And hill-hid tides throb, throe on throe,
And meadow rivulets overflow,
And drops on gate-bars hang in a row,
And rooks in families homeward go,
  And so do I.

                              THOMAS HARDY

12 GREEN RAIN

INTO the scented woods we'll go,
And see the blackthorn swim in snow.
High above, in the budding leaves,
A brooding dove awakes and grieves ;
The glades with mingled music stir,
And wildly laughs the woodpecker.
When blackthorn petals pearl the breeze,
There are the twisted hawthorn trees
Thick-set with buds, as clear and pale
As golden water or green hail—
As if a storm of rain had stood
Enchanted in the thorny wood,
And, hearing fairy voices call,
Hung poised, forgetting how to fall.   MARY WEBB

13 SONG ON MAY MORNING

Now the bright morning Star, Dayes harbinger,
Comes dancing from the East, and leads with her
The Flowry *May*, who from her green lap throws
The yellow Cowslip and the pale Primrose.
    Hail, bounteous *May*, that dost inspire
    Mirth and youth and young desire,
    Woods and Groves, are of thy dressing,
    Hill and Dale doth boast thy blessing.
Thus we salute thee with our early Song,
    And welcome thee, and wish thee long.

                      JOHN MILTON

14 SISTER, AWAKE!

SISTER, awake! close not your eyes.
    The day her light discloses,
And the bright morning doth arise
    Out of her bed of roses.

See the clear sun, the world's bright eye,
    In at our window peeping:
Lo, how he blusheth to espy
    Us idle wenches sleeping!

Therefore awake! make haste, I say,
    And let us, without staying,
All in our gowns of green so gay
    Into the park a-maying.

15 HERE WE COME A-PIPING

HERE we come a-piping,
    In Springtime and in May;
Green fruit a-ripening,
    And Winter fled away.

11

MORNING AND MAY

The Queen she sits upon the strand,
Fair as lily, white as wand;
Seven billows on the sea,
Horses riding fast and free,
And bells beyond the sand.

10   AS WE DANCE ROUND

As we dance round a-ring-a-ring,
A maiden goes a-maying;
And here a flower, and there a flower,
Through mead and meadow straying:
O gentle one, why dost thou weep?—
Silver to spend with; gold to keep;
Till spin the green round World asleep,
And Heaven its dews be staying.

17   OLD MAY SONG

ALL in this pleasant evening, together come are we,
  For the summer springs so fresh, green, and gay;
We tell you of a blossoming and buds on every tree,
  Drawing near unto the merry month of May.

Rise up, the master of this house, put on your charm of gold,
  For the summer springs so fresh, green, and gay;
Be not in pride offended with your name we make so bold,
  Drawing near unto the merry month of May.

Rise up, the mistress of this house, with gold along your
    breast;
  For the summer springs so fresh, green and gay;
And if your body be asleep, we hope your soul's at rest,
  Drawing near unto the merry month of May.

Rise up, the children of this house, all in your rich attire,
  For the summer springs so fresh, green, and gay;
And every hair upon your heads shines like the silver wire:
  Drawing near unto the merry month of May.

12

OLD MAY SONG

God bless this house and arbour, your riches and your store,
   For the summer springs so fresh, green, and gay ;
We hope the Lord will prosper you, both now and evermore,
   Drawing near unto the merry month of May.

And now comes we must leave you, in peace and plenty here,
   For the summer springs so fresh, green, and gay ;
We shall not sing you May again until another year,
   To draw you these cold winters away.

18   SONG OF THE MAYERS

   Remember us poor Mayers all,
     And thus do we begin,
   To lead our lives in righteousness,
     Or else we die in sin.

   We have been rambling all the night,
     And almost all the day,
   And now returning back again,
     We have brought you a bunch of May.

   A bunch of May we have brought you,
     And at your door it stands,
   It is but a sprout, but it's well budded out
     By the work of our Lord's hands.

   The hedges and trees they are so green,
     As green as any leek,
   Our Heavenly Father, He watered them
     With his heavenly dew so sweet.

   The heavenly gates are open wide,
     Our paths are beaten plain,
   And if a man be not too far gone,
     He may return again.

   The life of man is but a span,
     It flourishes like a flower ;
   We are here to-day, and gone to-morrow,
     And are dead in an hour.

13

MORNING AND MAY

The moon shines bright, and the stars give a light,
  A little before it is day,
God bless you all, both great and small,
  And send you a joyful May.

AND AS FOR ME

  . . . And as for me, thogh that I can but lyte,[1]
On bokès for to rede I me delyte,
And to hem yeve [2] I feyth and ful credènce,
And in myn herte have hem in reverence
So hertèly, that there is gamè noon
That fro my bokès maketh me to goon,
But hit be seldom on the holyday,
Save, certeynly, whan that the month of May
Is comen, and that I here the foulès [3] singe
And that the flourès ginnen for to springe,—
Farewel my boke, and my devocioun !
  Now have I than swich [4] a condicioun,
That, of alle the flourès in the mede,
Than love I most these flourès whyte and rede.
Swiche as men callen daysies in our toun.
To hem have I so greet affeccioun,
As I seyde erst, whan comen is the May,
That in my bed ther daweth me no day,
That I nam up, and walking in the mede,
To seen this flour agein the sonnè sprede,
When hit uprysith erly by the morwe ;
That blisful sightè softneth all my sorwè.[5] . . .
  And whan that hit is eve, I rennè blyve,[6]
As soon as evere the sonnè ginneth weste,
To seen this flour, how it wol go to reste,
For fere of nyght, so hateth she derknesse ! . . .
GEOFFREY CHAUCER

---

[1] Know but little   [2] Give   [3] Birds
[4] Such [5] Sorrow [6] Run quickly, hasten away

THE SPRING

THE SPRING

20

WHAT bird so sings, yet so does wail ?
O, 'tis the ravished nightingale !
" *Jug, jug, jug, jug, tereu,*" she cries,
And still her woes at midnight rise.
Brave prick-song ! who is't now we hear ?
None but the lark so shrill and clear ;
Now at heaven's gates she claps her wings,
The morn not waking till she sings.
Hark, hark, with what a pretty throat
Poor robin-redbreast tunes his note ;
Hark, how the jolly cuckoos sing
Cuckoo—to welcome in the spring !
Cuckoo—to welcome in the spring !

JOHN LYLY

21

SPRING, THE SWEET SPRING

SPRING, the sweet Spring, is the year's pleasant king ;
Then blooms each thing, then maids dance in a ring,
Cold doth not sting, the pretty birds do sing :
Cuckoo, jug, jug, pu we, to witta woo !

The Palm and May make country houses gay,
Lambs frisk and play, the shepherds pipe all day,
And we hear aye birds tune this merry lay :
Cuckoo, jug, jug, pu we, to witta woo !

The fields breathe sweet, the daisies kiss our feet,
Young lovers meet, old wives a-sunning sit,
In every street these tunes our ears do greet :
Cuckoo, jug, jug, pu we, to witta woo !
Spring, the sweet Spring !

THOMAS NASH

15

22   A MAY DAY

. . . AND now all nature seemed in love ;
The lusty sap began to move ;
New juice did stir the embracing vines,
And birds had drawn their valentines.
The jealous trout that now did lie,
Rose at a well-dissembled fly :
There stood my friend with patient skill,
Attending of his trembling quill.[1]
Already were the eaves possessed
With the swift pilgrim's daubèd nest :
The groves already did rejoice
In Philomel's triumphing voice.
The showers were short, the weather mild,
The morning fresh, the evening smiled.
Joan takes her neat-rubbed pail and now
She trips to milk the sand-red cow ;
Where, for some sturdy football swain,
Joan strokes[2] a sillabub or twain.
The field and gardens were beset
With tulip, crocus, violet ;
And now, though late, the modest rose
Did more than half a blush disclose.
Thus all looked gay, all full of cheer,
To welcome the new-liveried year.

                                    SIR HENRY WOTTON

23   EASTER

I GOT me flowers to straw thy way,
I got me boughs off many a tree :
But thou wast up by break of day,
And brought'st thy sweets along with thee.

The Sun arising in the East,
Though he give light, and the East perfume,[3]

[1] Float   [2] Whips, mills, or beats   [3] Refresh ; make sweet

16

EASTER

If they should offer to contest
With thy arising, they presume.

Can there be any day but this,
Though many sunnes to shine endeavour ?
We count three hundred, but we misse :
There is but one, and that one ever.

GEORGE HERBERT

24

PLEASURE IT IS

PLEASURE it is
    To hear, iwis,[1]
    The birdës sing.
The deer in the dale,
The sheep in the vale,
    The corn springing ;
God's purveyance
For sustenance
    It is for man.
Then we always
To Him give praise,
    And thank Him than,
    And thank Him than.

WILLIAM CORNISH

[1] Truly, in sooth

MOTHER, HOME ⊗
AND SWEETHEART

I SING OF A MAIDEN

I sing of a maiden
· That is makeless,[1]
King of all Kings
To her son she ches.[2]

He came all so still
  Where his mother was,
As dew in April
  That falleth on the grass.

He came all so still
  To his mother's bower,
As dew in April
  That falleth on the flower.

He came all so still
  Where his mother lay,
As dew in April
  That falleth on the spray.

Mother and maiden
  Was never none but she ;
Well may such a lady
  God's mother be.

[1] Mateless and matchless   [2] Chose

26 LULLABY

Upon my lap my sovereign sits
And sucks upon my breast ;
Meantime his love maintains my life
And gives my sense her rest.
　　Sing lullaby, my little boy,
　　Sing lullaby, mine only joy !

When thou hast taken thy repast,
Repose, my babe, on me ;
So may thy mother and thy nurse
Thy cradle also be.
　　Sing lullaby, my little boy,
　　Sing lullaby, mine only joy !

I grieve that duty doth not work
All that my wishing would,
Because I would not be to thee
But in the best I should.
　　Sing lullaby, my little boy,
　　Sing lullaby, mine only joy !

Yet as I am, and as I may,
I must and will be thine,
Though all too little for thy self
Vouchsafing to be mine.
　　Sing lullaby, my little boy,
　　Sing lullaby, mine only joy !

　　　　　　　　　　　RICHARD ROWLANDS

27 THE LITTLE BLACK BOY

My mother bore me in the southern wild,
And I am black, but O ! my soul is white ;
White as an angel is the English child,
But I am black, as if bereaved of light.

My mother taught me underneath a tree,
And, sitting down before the heat of day,

22

THE LITTLE BLACK BOY

She took me on her lap and kissèd me,
And, pointing to the east, began to say :

" Look on the rising sun ; there God does live,
And gives his light, and gives his heat away ;
And flowers and trees and beasts and men receive
Comfort in morning, joy in the noonday.

" And we are put on earth a little space,
That we may learn to bear the beams of love ;
And these black bodies and this sunburnt face
Is but a cloud, and like a shady grove.

" For when our souls have learned the heat to bear,
The cloud will vanish ; we shall hear his voice,
Saying : ' Come out from the grove, my love and care,
And round my golden tent like lambs rejoice.' "

Thus did my mother say, and kissèd me ;
And thus I say to little English boy.
When I from black and he from white cloud free,
And round the tent of God like lambs we joy,

I'll shade him from the heat, till he can bear
To lean in joy upon our Father's knee ;
And then I'll stand and stroke his silver hair,
And be like him, and he will then love me.

WILLIAM BLAKE

THE ECHOING GREEN

THE Sun does arise,
And make happy the skies ;
The merry bells ring
To welcome the Spring ;
The skylark and thrush,
The birds of the bush,
Sing louder around
To the bells' cheerful sound,

23

While our sports shall be seen
On the Echoing Green.

Old John, with white hair,
Does laugh away care,
Sitting under the oak,
Among the old folk,
They laugh at our play,
And soon they all say :
" Such, such were the joys
When we all, girls and boys,
In our youth time were seen
On the Echoing Green."

Till the little ones, weary,
No more can be merry ;
The sun does descend,
And our sports have an end.
Round the laps of their mothers
Many sisters and brothers,
Like birds in their nest,
Are ready for rest,
And sport no more seen
On the darkening Green.

WILLIAM BLAKE

29   IF I HAD BUT TWO LITTLE WINGS

IF I had but two little wings
And were a little feathery bird,
    To you I'd fly, my dear !
But thoughts like these are idle things,
    And I stay here.

But in my sleep to you I fly :
I'm always with you in my sleep !
    The world is all one's own.
But then one wakes, and where am I ?
    All, all alone.

24

IF I HAD BUT TWO LITTLE WINGS

Sleep stays not, though a monarch bids :
So I love to wake ere break of day :
For though my sleep be gone,
Yet while 'tis dark, one shuts one's lids,
And still dreams on.

SAMUEL TAYLOR COLERIDGE

I REMEMBER

I REMEMBER, I remember,
The house where I was born,
The little window where the sun
Came peeping in at morn ;
He never came a wink too soon,
Nor brought too long a day ;
But now, I often wish the night
Had borne my breath away.

I remember, I remember,
The roses, red and white,
The violets, and the lily-cups !—
Those flowers made of light !
The lilacs where the robin built,
And where my brother set
The laburnum on his birth-day,—
The tree is living yet !

I remember, I remember,
Where I was used to swing,
And thought the air must rush as fresh
To swallows on the wing ;
My spirit flew in feathers then,
That is so heavy now,
And summer pools could hardly cool
The fever on my brow !

I remember, I remember,
The fir trees dark and high ;
I used to think their slender tops
Were close against the sky :

MOTHER, HOME AND SWEETHEART

It was a childish ignorance,
But now 'tis little joy
To know I'm farther off from Heaven
Than when I was a boy.

THOMAS HOOD

31 MIDNIGHT ON THE GREAT WESTERN

In the third-class seat sat the journeying boy,
  And the roof-lamp's oily flame
Played down on his listless form and face,
Bewrapt past knowing to what he was going,
  Or whence he came.

In the band of his hat the journeying boy
  Had a ticket stuck ; and a string
Around his neck bore the key of his box,
That twinkled gleams of the lamp's sad beams
  Like a living thing.

What past can be yours, O journeying boy
  Towards a world unknown,
Who calmly, as if incurious quite
On all at stake, can undertake
  This plunge alone ?

Knows your soul a sphere, O journeying boy,
  Our rude realms far above,
Whence with spacious vision you mark and mete
This region of sin that you find you in,
  But are not of ?

THOMAS HARDY

32 THE RUNAWAY

Once when the sun of the year was beginning to fall
We stopped by a mountain pasture to say, " Whose colt ?
A little Morgan had one forefoot on the wall,
The other curled at his heart. He dipped his head
And snorted to us ; and then he had to bolt.

26

THE RUNAWAY

We heard the muffled thunder when he fled
And we saw him or thought we saw him dim and grey
Like a shadow against the curtain of falling flakes.
We said, " The little fellow's afraid of the snow.
He isn't winter broken." " It isn't play
With the little fellow at all. He's running away.
I doubt if even his mother could tell him, ' Sakes,
It's only weather.' He'd think she didn't know.
Where is his mother ? He can't be out alone."
And now he comes again with a clatter of stone
And mounts the wall again with whited eyes
And all his tail that isn't hair up straight.
He shudders his coat as if to throw off flies.
Whoever it is that leaves him out so late
When everything else has gone to stall and bin
Ought to be told to go and bring him in.

ROBERT FROST

33   ON EASTNOR KNOLL

SILENT are the woods, and the dim green boughs are
Hushed in the twilight : yonder, in the path through
The apple orchard, is a tired plough-boy
Calling the cows home.

A bright white star blinks, the pale moon rounds, but
Still the red, lurid wreckage of the sunset
Smoulders in smoky fire, and burns on
The misty hill-tops.

Ghostly it grows, and darker, the burning
Fades into smoke, and now the gusty oaks are
A silent army of phantoms thronging
A land of shadows.

JOHN MASEFIELD

27

54   " HOME NO MORE HOME TO ME "

Home no more home to me, whither must I wander ?
    Hunger my driver, I go where I must.
Cold blows the winter wind over hill and heather ;
    Thick drives the rain, and my roof is in the dust.
Loved of wise men was the shade of my roof-tree.
    The true word of welcome was spoken in the door—
Dear days of old, with the faces in the firelight,
    Kind folks of old, you come again no more.

Home was home then, my dear, full of kindly faces,
    Home was home then, my dear, happy for the child,
Fire and the windows bright glittered on the moorland ;
    Song, tuneful song, built a palace in the wild.
Now, when day dawns on the brow of the moorland,
    Lone stands the house, and the chimney-stone is cold.
Lone let it stand, now the friends are all departed,
    The kind hearts, the true hearts, that loved the place
        of old.

Spring shall come, come again, calling up the moor-fowl,
    Spring shall bring the sun and rain, bring the bees and
        flowers ;
Red shall the heather bloom over hill and valley,
    Soft flow the stream through the even-flowing hours ;
Fair the day shine as it shone on my childhood—
    Fair shine the day on the house with open door ;
Birds come and cry there and twitter in the chimney—
    But I go for ever and come again no more.
                                ROBERT LOUIS STEVENSON

55   DALYAUNCE

Mundus. Welcome, fayre chylde, what is thy name ?

Infans.   I wote not, syr, withouten blame.
        But ofte tyme my moder in her game
        Callèd me dalyaunce.

                    28

DALYAUNCE

Mundus. Dalyaunce, my swetè chylde,
It is a name that is ryght wylde,
For whan thou waxest olde.
It is a name of no substaunce
But, my fayre chylde, what woldest thou have ?

Infans. Syr of some comforte I you crave—
Mete and clothe my lyfe to save :
And I your true servaunt shall be.

Mundus. Fayre chylde, I graunte thee thyne askynge.
I wyll thee fynde [1] whyle thou art yinge [2]
So thou wylte be obedyent to my byddynge.
These garments gaye I gyve to thee.
And also I gyve to thee a name,
And clepe [3] thee Wanton, in every game ;
Tyll XIII yere be come and gone,
And than come agayne to me.

[Infans is now called Wanton.]

Wanton. Gramercy, Worlde, for myne araye,
For now I purpose me to playe.

Mundus. Fare well, fayre chylde, and have good daye.
All rychelesnesse [4] is kynde [5] for thee.

[Mundus goes out leaving Wanton alone.]

Wanton. Aha, Wanton is my name !
I can many a quayntè game.
Lo, my toppe I dryve in same,
Se, it torneth rounde !
I can with my scorgè-stycke
My felowe upon the heed hytte,
And wyghtly [6] from hym make a skyppe
And blere [7] on hym my tonge.
If brother or syster do me chyde
I wyll scratche and also byte.
I can crye, and also kyke,
And mocke them all berewe.

[1] Keep   [2] Young   [3] Call   [4] Heedlessness   [5] Natural
[6] Nimbly   [7] Stick out

MOTHER, HOME AND SWEETHEART

If fader or mother wyll me smyte,
I wyll wryngé [1] with my lyppe ;
And lyghtly from hym make a skyppe ;
And call my damé shrewe.
Aha, a newe game have I founde :
So this gynne [2] it renneth rounde ;
And here another have I founde,
And yet mo [3] can I fynde.
I can mowé [4] on a man ;
And make a lesynge [5] well I can,
And mayntayne it ryght well than.
This connynge [6] came me of kynde.
Ye, syrs, [7] I can well gelde a snayle ;
And catche a cowe by the tayle ;
This is a fayre connynge !
I can daunce, and also skyppe ;
I can playe at the chery pytte ;
And I can wystell you a fytte, [8]
Syres, in a whylowe ryne. [9]
Ye, syrs, and every daye
Whan I to scole shall take the waye
Some good mannes gardyn I wyll assaye,
Perys [10] and plommes to plucke.
I can spye a sparowes nest.
I wyll not go to scole but whan me lest,
For there begynneth a sory fest [11]
Whan the mayster sholde lyfte my docke. [12]
But, syrs, whan I was seven yere of age,
I was sent to the Worlde to také wage.
And this seven yere I have ben his page
And kept his commaundément . . .

[1] Squiggle   [2] Toy or trap   [3] More   [4] Make grimaces
[5] Falsehood   [6] Learning   [7] Yea, sirs   [8] Air, tune, stave
[9] Willow rind   [10] Pears   [11] Feast or fast   [12] Gown or coat-tail

36

CHRISTMAS AT SEA

THE sheets were frozen hard, and they cut the naked hand ;
The decks were like a slide, where a seaman scarce could
stand ;
The wind was a nor'wester, blowing squally off the sea ;
And cliffs and spouting breakers were the only things a-lee.

They heard the surf a-roaring before the break of day ;
But 'twas only with the peep of light we saw how ill we lay.
We tumbled every hand on deck instanter, with a shout,
And we gave her the maintops'l, and stood by to go about.

All day we tacked and tacked between the South Head and
the North ;
All day we hauled the frozen sheets, and got no further forth ;
All day as cold as charity, in bitter pain and dread,
For very life and nature we tacked from head to head.

We gave the South a wider berth, for there the tide-race
roared ;
But every tack we made we brought the North Head close
aboard :
So's we saw the cliffs and houses, and the breakers running
high,
And the coastguard in his garden, with his glass against
his eye.

The frost was on the village roofs as white as ocean foam ;
The good red fires were burning bright in every 'longshore
home ;
The windows sparkled clear, and the chimneys volleyed out ;
And I vow we sniffed the victuals as the vessel went about.

The bells upon the church were rung with a mighty jovial
cheer
For it's just that I should tell you how (of all days in the year)
This day of our adversity was blessèd Christmas morn,
And the house above the coastguard's was the house where
I was born.

MOTHER, HOME AND SWEETHEART

O well I saw the pleasant room, the pleasant faces there,
My mother's silver spectacles, my father's silver hair ;
And well I saw the firelight, like a flight of homely elves,
Go dancing round the china-plates that stand upon the
    shelves.

And well I knew the talk they had, the talk that was of me,
Of the shadow on the household and the son that went
    to sea ;
And O the wicked fool I seemed, in every kind of way,
To be here and hauling frozen ropes on blessèd Christmas
    Day.

They lit the high sea-light, and the dark began to fall.
" All hands to loose topgallant sails," I heard the captain call,
" By the Lord, she'll never stand it," our first mate, Jackson,
    cried.
. . . " It's the one way or the other, Mr. Jackson," he replied.

She staggered to her bearings, but the sails were new and
    good.
And the ship smelt up to windward just as though she
    understood.
As the winter's day was ending, in the entry of the night,
We cleared the weary headland, and passed below the light.

And they heaved a mighty breath, every soul on board but
    me,
As they saw her nose again pointing handsome out to sea ;
But all that I could think of, in the darkness and the cold,
Was just that I was leaving home and my folks were growing
    old.

ROBERT LOUIS STEVENSON

37   TWILIGHT

THE twilight is sad and cloudy,
    The wind blows wild and free,
And like the wings of sea-birds
    Flash the white caps of the sea.

TWILIGHT

But in the fisherman's cottage
    There shines a ruddier light,
And a little face at the window
    Peers out into the night.

Close, close it is pressed to the window,
    As if those childish eyes
Were looking into the darkness,
    To see some form arise.

And a woman's waving shadow
    Is passing to and fro,
Now rising to the ceiling,
    Now bowing and bending low.

What tale do the roaring ocean,
    And the night-wind, bleak and wild,
As they beat at the crazy casement,
    Tell to that little child ?

And why do the roaring ocean,
    And the night-wind, wild and bleak,
As they beat at the heart of the mother,
    Drive the colour from her cheek ?
              HENRY WADSWORTH LONGFELLOW

38   "HOW'S MY BOY ?"

" Ho, sailor of the sea !
How's my boy—my boy ?"
" What's your boy's name, good wife,
And in what good ship sailed he ?"
" My boy John—
He that went to sea—
What care I for the ship, sailor ?
My boy's my boy to me.

· You come back from sea
And not know my John !

                           C

MOTHER, HOME AND SWEETHEART

I might as well have asked some landsman
Yonder down in the town.
There's not an ass in all the parish
But he knows my John.

" How's my boy—my boy ?
And unless you let me know,
I'll swear you are no sailor,
Blue jacket or no,
Brass button or no, sailor,
Anchor and crown or no !
Sure his ship was the Jolly Briton."—
" Speak low, woman, speak low ! "

" And why should I speak low, sailor,
About my own boy John ?
If I was loud as I am proud
I'd sing him o'er the town !
Why should I speak low, sailor ?"
" That good ship went down."

" How's my boy—my boy ?
What care I for the ship, sailor,
I never was aboard her.
Be she afloat, or be she aground,
Sinking or swimming, I'll be bound,
Her owners can afford her !
I say, how's my John ?"
" Every man on board went down,
Every man aboard her."

" How's my boy—my boy ?
What care I for the men, sailor ?
I'm not their mother—
How's my boy—my boy ?
Tell me of him and no other !
How's my boy—my boy ?"

SYDNEY DOBELL

34

39   CAM' YE BY ?

Cam' ye by the salmon fishers ?
Cam' ye by the roperee ?
Saw ye a sailor laddie
Waiting on the coast for me ?

I ken fahr [1] I'm gyain,[2]
I ken fahs [3] gyain wi' me ;
I ha'e a lad o' my ain,
Ye daurna tack 'im fae [4] me.

Stockings of blue silk,
Shoes of patent leather,
Kid to tie them up,
And gold rings on his finger.

Oh for six o'clock !
Oh for seven I weary !
Oh for eight o'clock !
And then I'll see my dearie.

40   MY BOY TAMMY

" WHAR hae ye been a' day, my boy Tammy ?
  Whar hae ye been a' day, my boy Tammy ? "
  " I've been by burn and flow'ry brae,
  Meadow green and mountain grey,
Courtin' o' this young thing just come frae her Mammy."

" And whar gat ye that young thing, my boy Tammy ? "
  " I gat her down in yonder howe,[5]
  Smiling on a broomy knowe,[6]
Herding ae wee Lamb and Ewe for her poor Mammy."

---

[1] Where   [2] Going   [3] Who's   [4] From
[5] Dale or hollow   [6] Knoll or hillock

"What said ye to the bonny bairn, my boy Tammy?"
  "I hae a house, it cost me dear,
  I've walth o' plenishen and gear,[1]
Yese get it a', war't ten times mair, gin [2] ye will leave your
    Mammy.

"The smile gaed aff her bonny face—'I mauna leave my
    Mammy!
  She's gi'en me meat, she's gi'en me claes,[3]
  She's been my comfort a' my days,
My Father's death brought mony waes—I canna leave my
    Mammy.'"

"We'll tak her hame and mak her fain, my ain kind-hearted
    Lammy,
  We'll gie her meat, we'll gi'e her claes,
  We'll be her comfort a' her days:"
The wee thing gi'es her hand, and says, "There, gang and
    ask my Mammy."

"Has she been to kirk wi' thee, my boy Tammy?"
  "She has been to kirk wi' me,
  And the tear was in her ee,
But Oh! she's but a young thing just come frae her Mammy."

HECTOR MACNEILL

41   ROSY APPLE, LEMON, OR PEAR

Rosy apple, lemon, or pear,
Bunch of roses she shall wear;
Gold and silver by her side,
I know who will be the bride.
Take her by her lily-white hand,
    Lead her to the altar;
Give her kisses,—one, two, three,—
    Mother's runaway daughter.

---

[1] Goods and chattels   [2] If   [3] Clothes

42   IN PRAISE OF ISABEL PENNELL

By Saint Mary, my lady,
Your mammy and your daddy
Brought forth a goodly baby !

My maiden Isabell,—
Reflaring [1] rosabell,
The flagrant camamell,

The ruddy rosary,
The sovereign rosemary,
The pretty strawberry,

The columbine, the nepte,[2]
The ieloffer [3] well set,
The proper violet,

Ennewèd, your colour
Is like the daisy flower
After the April shower !

Star of the morrow gray,
The blossom on the spray,
The freshest flower of May ;

Maidenly demure,
Of womanhood the lure,
Wherefore I make you sure :

It were an heavenly health,
It were an endless wealth,
A life for God himself,

To hear this nightingale,
Among the birdès smale,
Warbling in the vale :—

Dug, dug,
Iug. iug,
Good year and good luck,
With chuk, chuk, chuk, chuk !

JOHN SKELTON

[1] Sweet-smelling   [2] Cat-mint   [3] Gillyflower

37

43   MY SWEET SWEETING

She is so proper and so pure,
Full stedfast, stabill and demure,
There is none such, ye may be sure,
          As my swete sweting.

In all thys world, as thynketh me,
Is none so plesaunt to my e'e,
That I am glad soo ofte to see,
          As my swete swetyng.

When I behold my swetyng swete,
Her face, her hands, her minion fete,
They seme to me there is none so mete,
          As my swete swetyng.

Above all other prayse must I,
And love my pretty pygsnye,
For none I fynd so womanly
          As my swete swetyng.

44   SWEET STAY-AT-HOME

Sweet Stay-at-Home, sweet Well-content,
Thou knowest of no strange continent :
Thou hast not felt thy bosom keep
A gentle motion with the deep ;
Thou hast not sailed in Indian seas,
Where scent comes forth in every breeze.
Thou hast not seen the rich grape grow
For miles, as far as eyes can go ;
Thou hast not seen a summer's night
When maids could sew by a worm's light ;
Nor the North Sea in spring send out
Bright hues that like birds flit about
In solid cages of white ice—
Sweet Stay-at-Home, sweet Love-one-place.
Thou hast not seen black fingers pick
White cotton when the bloom is thick,

38

SWEET STAY-AT-HOME

Nor heard black throats in harmony ;
Nor hast thou sat on stones that lie
Flat on the earth, that once did rise
To hide proud kings from common eyes.
Thou hast not seen plains full of bloom
Where green things had such little room
They pleased the eye like fairer flowers—
Sweet Stay-at-Home, all these long hours.
Sweet Well-content, sweet Love-one-place,
Sweet, simple maid, bless thy dear face ;
For thou hast made more homely stuff
Nurture thy gentle self enough ;
I love thee for a heart that's kind—
Not for the knowledge in thy mind.

WILLIAM H. DAVIES

WAITING

45

RICH in the waning light she sat
While the fierce rain on the window spat.
The yellow lamp-glow lit her face,
Shadows cloaked the narrow place
She sat adream in. Then she'd look
Idly upon an idle book ;
Anon would rise and musing peer
Out at the misty street and drear ;
Or with her loosened dark hair play,
Hiding her fingers' snow away ;
And, singing softly, would sing on
When the desire of song had gone.
" O lingering day ! " her bosom sighed,
" O laggard Time ! " each motion cried.
Last she took the lamp and stood
Rich in its flood,
And looked and looked again at what
Her longing fingers' zeal had wrought ;
And turning then did nothing say,
Hiding her thoughts away.

JOHN FREEMAN

46   THE SICK CHILD

Child.   O MOTHER, lay your hand on my brow !
          O mother, mother, where am I now ?
          Why is the room so gaunt and great ?
          Why am I lying awake so late ?

Mother.   Fear not at all : the night is still.
          Nothing is here that means you ill—
          Nothing but lamps the whole town through,
          And never a child awake but you.

Child.   Mother, mother, speak low in my ear,
          Some of the things are so great and near,
          Some are so small and far away,
          I have a fear that I cannot say.
          What have I done, and what do I fear,
          And why are you crying, mother dear ?

Mother.   Out in the city, sounds begin.
          Thank the kind God, the carts come in !
          An hour or two more, and God is so kind,
          The day shall be blue in the window blind,
          Then shall my child go sweetly asleep,
          And dream of the birds and the hills of sheep.
                              ROBERT LOUIS STEVENSON

47   STILLNESS

WHEN the words rustle no more,
   And the last work's done,
When the bolt lies deep in the door,
   And Fire, our Sun,
Falls on the dark-laned meadows of the floor ;

When from the clock's last chime to the next chime
   Silence beats his drum,
And Space with gaunt grey eyes and her brother Time
   Wheeling and whispering come,
She with the mould of form and he with the loom of rhyme :

40

STILLNESS

Then twittering out in the night my thought-birds flee,
  I am emptied of all my dreams :
I only hear Earth turning, only see
  Ether's long bankless streams,
And only know I should drown if you laid not your hand
    on me.

JAMES ELROY FLECKER

48   LINES ON RECEIVING HIS MOTHER'S
PICTURE

O THAT those lips had language ! Life has passed
With me but roughly since I heard thee last.
Those lips are thine—thy own sweet smiles I see,
The same that oft in childhood solaced me ;
Voice only fails, else how distinct they say,
" Grieve not, my child—chase all thy fears away !" . . .
  My Mother ! when I learnt that thou wast dead,
Say, wast thou conscious of the tears I shed ?
Hovered thy spirit o'er thy sorrowing son,
Wretch even then, life's journey just begun ?
Perhaps thou gav'st me, though unseen, a kiss,
Perhaps a tear, if souls can weep in bliss—
Ah, that maternal smile ! it answers—Yes.
I heard the bell tolled on thy burial day,
I saw the hearse that bore thee slow away,
And, turning from my nursery window, drew
A long, long sigh, and wept a last adieu !
But was it such ?—It was. Where thou art gone
Adieus and farewells are a sound unknown.
May I but meet thee on that peaceful shore,
The parting word shall pass my lips no more !
Thy maidens, grieved themselves at my concern,
Oft gave me promise of thy quick return.
What ardently I wished, I long believed,
And, disappointed still, was still deceived,
By expectation every day beguiled,
Dupe of *to-morrow* even from a child.

MOTHER, HOME AND SWEETHEART

Thus many a sad to-morrow came and went,
Till, all my stock of infant sorrow spent,
I learnt at last submission to my lot.
But, though I less deplored thee, ne'er forgot.
   Where once we dwelt our name is heard no more,
Children not thine have trod my nursery floor ;
And where the gardener Robin, day by day,
Drew me to school along the public way,
Delighted with my bauble coach, and wrapped
In scarlet mantle warm, and velvet-capped,
'Tis now become a history little known,
That once we called the pastoral house our own.
Short-lived possession ! but the record fair
That memory keeps, of all thy kindness there,
Still outlives many a storm, that has effaced
A thousand other themes less deeply traced.
Thy nightly visits to my chamber made,
That thou mightst know me safe and warmly laid ;
Thy morning bounties ere I left my home,
The biscuit, or confectionery plum ;
The fragrant waters on my cheek bestowed
By thy own hand, till fresh they shone and glowed ;
All this, and more endearing still than all,
Thy constant flow of love, that knew no fall. . . .

WILLIAM COWPER

49   THE CHIMNEY SWEEPER

WHEN my mother died I was very young,
And my father sold me while yet my tongue
Could scarcely cry " 'weep ! 'weep ! 'weep ! 'weep ! "
So your chimneys I sweep, and in soot I sleep.

There's little Tom Dacre, who cried when his head,
That curled like a lamb's back, was shaved : so I said
" Hush, Tom ! never mind it, for when your head's bare
You know that the soot cannot spoil your white hair."

THE CHIMNEY SWEEPER

And so he was quiet, and that very night,
As Tom was a-sleeping, he had such a sight !
That thousands of sweepers, Dick, Joe, Ned, and Jack,
Were all of them locked up in coffins of black.

And by came an Angel who had a bright key,
And he opened the coffins and set them all free ;
Then down a green plain leaping, laughing, they run,
And wash in a river, and shine in the Sun.

Then naked and white, all their bags left behind,
They rise upon clouds and sport in the wind ;
And the Angel told Tom, if he'd be a good boy,
He'd have God for his father, and never want joy.

And so Tom awoke ; and we rose in the dark,
And got with our bags and our brushes to work.
Tho' the morning was cold, Tom was happy and warm ;
So if all do their duty they need not fear harm.

WILLIAM BLAKE

50   BONNIE GEORGE CAMPBELL

Hie upon Hielands,
   and laigh upon Tay,
Bonnie George Campbell
   rode out on a day.

Saddled and briddled
   and booted rade he ;
Toom [1] hame cam' the saddle,
   but never cam' he.

Down cam' his auld mither,
   greetin' [2] fu' sair,
And down cam' his bonny wife,
   wringin' her hair :—

[1] Empty   [2] Weeping

43

" My meadow lies green,
  and my corn is unshorn,
My barn is to build
  and my babe is unborn."

Saddled and briddled
  and booted rade he ;
Toom hame cam' the saddle
  but never cam' he.

THE ORPHAN'S SONG

51

I HAD a little bird,
I took it from the nest ;
I prest it, and blest it,
And nurst it in my breast.

I set it on the ground,
I danced round and round,
And sang about it so cheerly,
With " Hey my little bird, and ho my little bird,
And ho but I love thee dearly ! "

I make a little feast
Of food soft and sweet,
I hold it in my breast,
And coax it to eat ;

I pit, and I pat,
I call it this and that,
And sing about it so cheerly,
With " Hey my little bird, and ho my little bird,
And ho but I love thee dearly ! "

I may kiss, I may sing,
But I can't make it feed,
It taketh no heed
Of any pleasant thing.

44

THE ORPHAN'S SONG

I scolded and I socked,
But it minded not a whit,
Its little mouth was locked,
And I could not open it.

Tho' with pit, and with pat,
And with this, and with that,
I sang about it so cheerly,
With " Hey my little bird, and ho my little bird,
And ho but I love thee dearly ! "

But when the day was done,
And the room was at rest,
And I sat all alone
With my birdie in my breast,

And the light had fled,
And not a sound was heard,
Then my little bird
Lifted up its head,

And the little mouth
Loosed its sullen pride,
And it opened, it opened,
With a yearning strong and wide.

Swifter than I speak
I brought it food once more,
But the poor little beak
Was locked as before.

I sat down again,
And not a creature stirred ;
I laid the little bird
Again where it had laid ;

And again when nothing stirred,
And not a word I said,
Then my little bird
Lifted up its head,

And the little beak
Loosed its stubborn pride,
And it opened, it opened,
With a yearning strong and wide.

It lay in my breast,
It uttered no cry,
'Twas famished, 'twas famished,
And I couldn't tell why.

I couldn't tell why,
But I saw that it would die,
For all that I kept dancing round and round,
And singing about it so cheerly,
With " Hey my little bird, and ho my little bird,
And ho but I love thee dearly ! "

I never look sad,
I hear what people say,
I laugh when they are gay
And they think I am glad.

My tears never start,
I never say a word,
But I think that my heart
Is like that little bird.

Every day I read,
And I sing, and I play,
But thro' the long day
It taketh no heed.

It taketh no heed
Of any pleasant thing,
I know it doth not read,
I know it doth not sing.

With my mouth I read,
With my hands I play,
My shut heart is shut,
Coax it how you may.

THE ORPHAN'S SONG

You may coax it how you may
While the day is broad and bright,
But in the dead night
When the guests are gone away,

And no more the music sweet
Up the house doth pass,
Nor the dancing feet
Shake the nursery glass ;

And I've heard my aunt
Along the corridor,
And my uncle gaunt
Lock his chamber door ;

And upon the stair
All is hushed and still,
And the last wheel
Is silent in the square ;

And the nurses snore,
And the dim sheets rise and fall,
And the lamplight's on the wall,
And the mouse is on the floor ;

And the curtains of my bed
Are like a heavy cloud,
And the clock ticks loud,
And sounds are in my head ;

And little Lizzie sleeps
Softly at my side,
It opens, it opens,
With a yearning strong and wide !

It yearns in my breast,
It utters no cry,
'Tis famished, 'tis famished,
And I feel that I shall die,
I feel that I shall die,
And none will know why.

MOTHER, HOME AND SWEETHEART

Tho' the pleasant life is dancing round and round,
And singing about me so cheerly,
With " Hey my little bird, and ho my little bird,
And ho but I love thee dearly ! "

SYDNEY DOBELL

THE FIRST GRIEF

" Oh ! call my brother back to me,
  I cannot play alone ;
The summer comes with flower and bee—
  Where is my brother gone ?

" The butterfly is glancing bright
  Across the sunbeam's track ;
I care not now to chase its flight—
  Oh ! call my brother back.

" The flowers run wild—the flowers we sowed
  Around our garden tree ;
Our vine is drooping with its load—
  Oh ! call him back to me."

" He would not hear my voice, fair child !
  He may not come to thee ;
The face that once like spring-time smiled
  On earth no more thou'lt see.

" A rose's brief, bright life of joy,
  Such unto him was given ;
Go—thou must play alone, my boy—
  Thy brother is in heaven ! "

" And has he left the birds and flowers,
  And must I call in vain ;
And through the long, long summer hours,
  Will he not come again ?

48

THE FIRST GRIEF

" And by the brook, and in the glade,
   Are all our wanderings o'er ?
Oh ! while my brother with me played,
   Would I had loved him more ! "

FELICIA HEMANS

53   THE POPLAR FIELD

THE poplars are felled ; farewell to the shade
And the whispering sound of the cool colonnade ;
The winds play no longer and sing in the leaves,
Nor Ouse on his bosom their image receives.

Twelve years have elapsed since I first took a view
Of my favourite field, and the bank where they grew ;
And now in the grass behold they are laid,
And the tree is my seat that once lent me a shade.

The blackbird has fled to another retreat
Where the hazels afford him a screen from the heat,
And the scene where his melody charmed me before
Resounds with his sweet-flowing ditty no more.

My fugitive years are all hasting away,
And I must ere long lie as lowly as they
With a turf on my breast, and a stone at my head,
Ere another such grove shall arise in its stead.

'Tis a sight to engage me, if anything can,
To muse on the perishing pleasures of man ;
Though his life be a dream, his enjoyments, I see,
Have a being less durable even than he.

WILLIAM COWPER

54   FAREWELL

Nor soon shall I forget—a sheet
Of golden water, cold and sweet,
The young moon with her head in veils
Of silver, and the nightingales.

MOTHER, HOME AND SWEETHEART

A wain of hay came up the lane—
O fields I shall not walk again,
And trees I shall not see, so still
Against a sky of daffodil!

Fields where my happy heart had rest,
And where my heart was heaviest,
I shall remember them at peace
Drenched in moon-silver like a fleece.

The golden water sweet and cold,
The moon of silver and of gold,
The dew upon the gray grass-spears,
I shall remember them with tears.

KATHARINE TYNAN

55 " YE BANKS AND BRAES O' BONNIE DOON "

Ye banks and braes o' bonnie Doon,
  How can ye bloom sae fair?
How can ye chant, ye little birds,
  And I sae fu' o' care?

Thou'lt break my heart, thou bonnie bird
  That sings upon the bough;
Thou minds me o' the happy days
  When my fause Luve was true.

Thou'll break my heart, thou bonnie bird
  That sings beside thy mate;
For sae I sat, and sae I sang,
  And wist na o' my fate.

Aft hae I roved by bonnie Doon
  To see the woodbine twine,
And ilka[1] bird sang o' its love;
  And sae did I o' mine.

[1] Every.

" YE BANKS AND BRAES O' BONNIE DOON "

Wi' lightsome heart I pu'd a rose,
  Frae aff its thorny tree ;
And my fause luver staw [1] the rose,
  But left the thorn wi' me.

ROBERT BURNS

56   TO A RIVER IN THE SOUTH

CALL me no more, O gentle stream,
To wander through thy sunny dream,
No more to lean at twilight cool
Above thy weir and glimmering pool.

Surely I know thy hoary dawns,
The silver crisp on all thy lawns,
The softly swirling undersong
That rocks thy reeds the winter long.

Surely I know the joys that ring
Through the green deeps of leafy spring ;
I know the elfin cups and domes
That are their small and secret homes.

Yet is the light for ever lost
That daily once thy meadows crossed,
The voice no more by thee is heard
That matched the song of stream and bird.

Call me no more !—thy waters roll
Here, in the world that is my soul,
And here, though Earth be drowned in night,
Old love shall dwell with old delight.

HENRY NEWBOLT

---

[1] Stole

51

57   THE DESERTED HOUSE

There's no smoke in the chimney,
   And the rain beats on the floor ;
There's no glass in the window,
   There's no wood in the door ;
The heather grows behind the house,
   And the sand lies before.

No hand hath trained the ivy,
   The walls are gray and bare ;
The boats upon the sea sail by,
   Nor ever tarry there.
No beast of the field comes nigh,
   Nor any bird of the air.

              MARY COLERIDGE

58   AN OLD WOMAN OF THE ROADS

O, to have a little house !
   To own the hearth and stool and all !
The heaped-up sods upon the fire,
   The pile of turf against the wall !

To have a clock with weights and chains
   And pendulum swinging up and down !
A dresser filled with shining delph,
   Speckled and white and blue and brown !

I could be busy all the day
   Clearing and sweeping hearth and floor,
And fixing on their shelf again
   My white and blue and speckled store !

I could be quiet there at night
   Beside the fire and by myself,
Sure of a bed, and loth to leave
   The ticking clock and the shining delph !

AN OLD WOMAN OF THE ROADS

Och ! but I'm weary of mist and dark,
   And roads where there's never a house or bush,
And tired I am of bog and road
   And the crying wind and the lonesome hush !

And I am praying to God on high,
   And I am praying Him night and day,
For a little house—a house of my own—
   Out of the wind's and the rain's way.

PADRAIC COLUM

59   A DESERTED HOME

HERE where the fields lie lonely and untended,
   Once stood the old house grey among the trees,
Once to the hills rolled the waves of the cornland—
   Long waves and golden, softer than the sea's.

Long, long ago has the ploughshare rusted,
   Long has the barn stood roofless and forlorn ;
But oh ! far away are some who still remember
   The songs of the young girls binding up the corn.

Here where the windows shone across the darkness,
   Here where the stars once watched above the fold,
Still watch the stars, but the sheepfold is empty ;
   Falls now the rain where the hearth glowed of old.

Here where the leagues of melancholy lough-sedge
   Moan in the wind round the grey forsaken shore,
Once waved the corn in the mid-month of autumn,
   Once sped the dance when the corn was on the floor.

SIDNEY ROYSE LYSAGHT

60   UNDER THE WOODS

WHEN these old woods were young
The thrushes' ancestors
As sweetly sung
In the old years.

MOTHER, HOME AND SWEETHEART

There was no garden here,
Apples nor mistletoe ;
No children dear
Ran to and fro.

New then was this thatched cot,
But the keeper was old,
And he had not
Much lead or gold.

Most silent beech and yew :
As he went round about
The woods to view
Seldom he shot.

But now that he is gone
Out of most memories,
Still lingers on,
A stoat of his,

But one, shrivelled and green,
And with no scent at all,
And barely seen
On this shed wall.   EDWARD THOMAS

61   " BLOWS THE WIND TO-DAY "

BLOWS the wind to-day, and the sun and the rain are flying,
    Blows the wind on the moors to-day and now,
Where about the graves of the martyrs the whaups are crying,
    My heart remembers how !

Grey recumbent tombs of the dead in desert places,
    Standing stones on the vacant wine-red moor,
Hills of sheep, and the howes of the silent vanished races,
    And winds, austere and pure :

Be it granted me to behold you again in dying,
    Hills of home ! and to hear again the call ;
Hear about the graves of the martyrs the peewees crying,
    And hear no more at all.   ROBERT LOUIS STEVENSON

THE TWA BROTHERS

THERE were twa brethren in the north,
   They went [1] to the school thegither ;
The one unto the other said,
   " Will you try a warsle [2] afore ? "

They warsled up, they warsled down,
   Till Sir John fell to the ground,
And there was a knife in Sir Willie's pouch,
   Gied him a deadlie wound.

" O brither dear, take me on your back,
   Carry me to yon burn clear,
And wash the blood from off my wound,
   And it will bleed nae mair."

He took him up upon his back,
   Carried him to yon burn clear,
And washd the blood from off his wound,
   And aye it bled the mair.

" O brither dear, take me on your back,
   Carry me to yon kirk-yard,
And dig a grave baith wide and deep,
   And lay my body there."

He's taen him up upon his back,
   Carried him to yon kirk-yard,
And dug a grave baith deep and wide,
   And laid his body there.

" But what will I say to my father dear,
   Gin [3] he chance to say, Willie, whar's John ? "
" Oh say that he's to England gone,
   To buy him a cask of wine."

" And what will I say to my mother dear,
   Gin she chance to say, Willie, whar's John ? '

---

[1] Had been   [2] Wrestle   [3] If

MOTHER, HOME AND SWEETHEART

" Oh say that he's to England gone,
    To buy her a new silk gown."

" And what will I say to my sister dear,
    Gin she chance to say, Willie, whar's John ?"
" Oh say that he's to England gone,
    To buy her a wedding ring."

" But what will I say to her you lo'e dear,
    Gin she cry, Why tarries my John ? "
" Oh tell her I lie in Kirk-land fair,
    And home shall never come."

63   THE DEAD KNIGHT

THE cleanly rush of the mountain air,
And the mumbling, grumbling humble-bees,
Are the only things that wander there,
The pitiful bones are laid at ease,
The grass has grown in his tangled hair,
And a rambling bramble binds his knees.

To shrieve his soul from the pangs of hell,
The only requiem-bells that rang
Were the hare-bell and the heather-bell.
Hushed he is with the holy spell
In the gentle hymn the wind sang,
And he lies quiet, and sleeps well.

He is bleached and blanched with the summer sun ;
The misty rain and the cold dew
Have altered him from the kingly one
(That his lady loved, and his men knew)
And dwindled him to a skeleton.

The vetches have twined about his bones,
The straggling ivy twists and creeps
In his eye-sockets ; the nettle keeps
Vigil about him while he sleeps.

THE DEAD KNIGHT

Over his body the wind moans
With a dreary tune throughout the day,
In a chorus wistful, eerie, thin
As the gull's cry—as the cry in the bay,
The mournful word the seas say
When tides are wandering out or in.

JOHN MASEFIELD

64   SHEATH AND KNIFE

ONE king's daughter said to anither,
  Brume blumes bonnie and grows sae fair,
" We'll gae ride like sister and brither,"
  And we'll neer gae down to the brume nae mair.

" We'll ride doun into yonder valley,
  Brume blumes bonnie and grows sae fair,
Whare the greene green trees are budding sae gaily.
  And we'll neer gae down to the brume nae mair.

" Wi hawke and hounde we will hunt sae rarely,
  Brume blumes bonnie and grows sae fair,
And we'll come back in the morning early."
  And we'll neer gae down to the brume nae mair.

They rade on like sister and brither,
  Brume blumes bonnie and grows sae fair,
And they hunted and hawket in the valley thegether.
  And we'll neer gae down to the brume nae mair.

" Now, lady, hauld my horse and my hawk,
  Brume blumes bonnie and grows sae fair,
For I maun na [1] ride, and I daur na [2] walk,
  And we'll neer gae down to the brume nae mair."

" But set me doun be the rute o' this tree,
  Brume blumes bonnie and grows sae fair,
For there ha'e I dreamt that my bed sall be."
  And we'll neer gae down to the brume nae mair.

[1] Must not   [2] Dare not

57

The ae king's daughter did lift doun the ither,
Brume blumes bonnie and grows sae fair,
She was licht in her armis like ony fether.
And we'll neer gae down to the brume nae mair.

Bonnie Lady Ann sat doun be the tree,
Brume blumes bonnie and grows sae fair,
And a wide grave was houkit [1] whare nane suld be.
And we'll neer gae down to the brume nae mair.

The hawk had nae lure, and the horse had nae master,
Brume blumes bonnie and grows sae fair,
And the faithless hounds thro' the woods ran faster.
And we'll neer gae down to the brume nae mair.

The one king's daughter has ridden awa',
Brume blumes bonnie and grows sae fair,
But bonnie Lady Ann lay in the deed-thraw.[2]
And we'll neer gae down to the brume nae mair.

65   I HAVE A YOUNG SISTER

I have a yong suster
   fer beyondyn the se ;
Many be the drowryis
   that che sente me.

Che sente me the cherye,
   withoutyn ony ston,
And so che dede (the) dowe,
   withoutyn ony bon.

Sche sente me the brere,
   withoutyn ony rynde,
Sche bad me love my lem-
   man
   withoute longgyng.

I have a young sister
   Far beyond the sea ;
Many are the keepsakes
   That she's sent me.

She sent me a cherry—
   It hadn't any stone ;
And so she did a wood dove
   Withouten any bone.

She sent me a briar
   Withouten any rind ;
She bade me love my sweet-
   heart
   Without longing in my
   mind.

[1] Dug. delved   [2] Her death-throes

I HAVE A YOUNG SISTER

How shuld ony cherye
  be withoute ston ?
And how shuld ony dowe
  ben withoute bon ?

How shuld any brere
  ben withoute rynde ?
How shuld I love my lemman
  without longyng ?

Quan the cherye was a flour,
  than hadde it non ston ;
Quan the dowe was an ey,
  than hadde it non bon.

Quan the brere was onbred,
  than hadde it non rynd ;
Quan the mayden hayt that
  che lovit,
che is without longing.

How should any cherry
  Be without a stone ?
And how should any wood
  dove
Be without a bone ?

How should any briar,
  Be without rind ?
And how love a sweetheart
  Without longing in my
  mind ?

When the cherry was a flower
  Then it had no stone ;
When the wood-dove was an
  egg
Then it had no bone.

When the briar was unbred
  Then it had no rind ;
And when a maid hath that
  she loves,
She longs not in her mind.

66   ANNABEL LEE

IT was many and many a year ago,
  In a kingdom by the sea,
That a maiden there lived whom you may know
  By the name of Annabel Lee ;
And this maiden she lived with no other thought
  Than to love and be loved by me.

I was a child and she was a child,
  In this kingdom by the sea ;
But we loved with a love that was more than love—
  I and my Annabel Lee ;
With a love that the winged seraphs of heaven
  Coveted her and me.

MOTHER, HOME AND SWEETHEART

And this was the reason that, long ago,
  In this kingdom by the sea,
A wind blew out of a cloud, chilling
  My beautiful Annabel Lee ;
So that her highborn kinsman came
  And bore her away from me,
To shut her up in a sepulchre
  In this kingdom by the sea.

The angels, not half so happy in heaven,
  Went envying her and me—
Yes !—that was the reason (as all men know,
  In this kingdom by the sea)
That the wind came out of the cloud by night,
  Chilling and killing my Annabel Lee.

But our love it was stronger by far than the love
  Of those who were older than we,
  Of many far wiser than we ;
And neither the angels in heaven above
  Nor the demons down under the sea
Can ever dissever my soul from the soul
  Of the beautiful Annabel Lee.

For the moon never beams without bringing me dreams
  Of the beautiful Annabel Lee ;
And the stars never rise but I feel the bright eyes
  Of the beautiful Annabel Lee ;
And so, all the night-tide, I lie down by the side
Of my darling—my darling—my life and my bride,
  In the sepulchre there by the sea,
In her tomb by the sounding sea.

EDGAR ALLAN POE

67   THE SHELL

THE SHELL

AND then I pressed the shell
  Close to my ear
And listened well,
And straightway like a bell
  Came low and clear
The slow, sad murmur of far distant seas,
Whipped by an icy breeze
  Upon a shore
Wind-swept and desolate.
  It was a sunless strand that never bore
The footprint of a man,
  Nor felt the weight
Since time began
Of any human quality or stir
Save what the dreary winds and waves incur.
And in the hush of waters was the sound
Of pebbles rolling round,
For ever rolling with a hollow sound.
And bubbling sea-weeds as the waters go
Swish to and fro
Their long, cold tentacles of slimy grey.
There was no day,
Nor ever came a night
Setting the stars alight
To wonder at the moon :
Was twilight only and the frightened croon,
Smitten to whimpers, of the dreary wind
. And waves that journeyed blind—
  And then I loosed my ear—oh, it was sweet
To hear a cart go jolting down the street !
                              JAMES STEPHENS

FEASTS : FAIRS : ⊕ ⊕
BEGGARS : GIPSIES :

LONDON BRIDGE is broken down,
Dance o'er my Lady Lee,
London Bridge is broken down,
With a gay lady.

How shall we build it up again ?
Dance o'er my Lady Lee,
How shall we build it up again ?
With a gay lady.

Silver and gold will be stole away,
Dance o'er my Lady Lee,
Silver and gold will be stole away,
With a gay lady.

Build it up with iron and steel,
Dance o'er my Lady Lee,
Build it up with iron and steel,
With a gay lady.

Iron and steel will bend and bow,
Dance o'er my Lady Lee,
Iron and steel will bend and bow,
With a gay lady.

Build it up with wood and clay,
Dance o'er my Lady Lee,
Build it up with wood and clay,
With a gay lady.

FEASTS : FAIRS : BEGGARS : GIPSIES

Wood and clay will wash away,
Dance o'er my Lady Lee,
Wood and clay will wash away,
With a gay lady.

Build it up with stone so strong,
Dance o'er my Lady Lee,
Huzza ! 'twill last for ages long,
With a gay lady.

69   ## HOLY THURSDAY

'Twas on a Holy Thursday, their innocent faces clean,
Came children walking two and two, in red and blue and
green,
Grey-headed beadles walked before, with wands as white
as snow,
Till into the high dome of Paul's they like Thames' waters
flow.

O what a multitude they seemed, these flowers of London
town !
Seated in companies they sit with radiance all their own.
The hum of multitudes was there, but multitudes of lambs,
Thousands of little boys and girls raising their innocent hands.

Now, like a mighty wind they raise to Heaven the voice of
song,
Or like harmonious thunderings the seats of Heaven among.
Beneath them sit the agèd men, wise guardians of the poor ;
Then cherish pity, lest you drive an angel from your door.
WILLIAM BLAKE

70   ## THE MAYORS

This city and this country has brought forth many mayors
To sit in state, and give forth laws out of their old oak chairs,
With face as brown as any nut with drinking of strong ale—
Good English hospitality, O then it did not fail !

THE MAYORS

With scarlet gowns and broad gold lace, would make a yeoman
    sweat ;
With stockings rolled above their knees and shoes as black
    as jet ;
With eating beef and drinking beer, O they were stout and
    hale—
Good English hospitality, O then it did not fail !

Thus sitting at the table wide the Mayor and Aldermen
Were fit to give law to the city ; each ate as much as ten :
The hungry poor entered the hall to eat good beef and
    ale—
Good English hospitality, O then it did not fail !

WILLIAM BLAKE

71   THE FINE OLD ENGLISH GENTLEMAN

I'LL sing you a good old song,
    Made by a good old pate,
Of a fine old English gentleman
    Who had an old estate,
And who kept up his old mansion
    At a bountiful old rate ;
With a good old porter to relieve
    The old poor at his gate,
Like a fine old English gentleman
    All of the olden time.

His hall so old was hung around
    With pikes and guns and bows,
And swords, and good old bucklers,
    That had stood some tough old blows ;
'Twas there *his worship* held his state
    In doublet and trunk hose,
And quaffed his cup of good old sack,
    To warm his good old nose,
Like a fine old English gentleman
    All of the olden time.

FEASTS : FAIRS : BEGGARS : GIPSIES

When winter's cold brought frost and snow,
  He opened house to all ;
And though threescore and ten his years,
  He featly led the ball ;
Nor was the houseless wanderer
  E'er driven from his hall ;
For while he feasted all the great,
  He ne'er forgot the small ;
Like a fine old English gentleman
  All of the olden time.

But time, though old, is strong in flight,
  And years rolled swiftly by ;
And Autumn's falling leaves proclaimed
  This good old man must die !
He laid him down right tranquilly,
  Gave up life's latest sigh ;
And mournful stillness reigned around,
  And tears bedewed each eye,
For this fine old English gentleman
  All of the olden time.

Now surely this is better far
  Than all the new parade
Of theatres and fancy balls,
  " At home " and masquerade :
And much more economical,
  For all his bills were paid.
Then leave your new vagaries quite,
  And take up the old trade
Of a fine old English gentleman,
  All of the olden time.

BRING US IN GOOD ALE

BRING US IN GOOD ALE

Bring us in good ale, and bring us in good ale ;
For our blessed Lady sake bring us in good ale !

BRING us in no browne bred, for that is made of brane,[1]
Nor bring us in no white bred, for therein is no gane,
But bring us in good ale !

Bring us in no befe, for there is many bones,
But bring us in good ale, for that goth downe at ones,
And bring us in good ale !

Bring us in no bacon, for that is passing fat,
But bring us in good ale, and gife us enought of that ;
And bring us in good ale !

Bring us in no mutton, for that is often lene,
Nor bring us in no tripes, for they be seldom clene,
But bring us in good ale !

Bring us in no egges, for there are many schelles,
But bring us in good ale, and gife us nothing elles ;
And bring us in good ale !

Bring us in no butter, for therein are many hores,[2]
Nor bring us in no pigges flesch, for that will make us
bores,
But bring us in good ale !

Bring us in no podinges, for therein is all Godes good,[3]
Nor bring us in no venesen, for that is not for our blod ;
But bring us in good ale !

Bring us in no capons flesch, for that is ofte dere,
Nor bring us in no dokes[4] flesch, for they slober in the
mere,
But bring us in good ale !

[1] Bran   [2] Hairs   [3] Yeast   [4] Duck's

73   THE VISION OF MAC CONGLINNE

A VISION that appeared to me,
An apparition wonderful
      I tell to all :
There was a coracle all of lard
Within a Port of New-Milk Lake
      Upon the world's smooth sea.

We went into that man-of-war,
'Twas warrior-like to take the road
      O'er ocean's heaving waves.
Our oar-strokes then we pulled
Across the level of the main,
Throwing the sea's harvest up
      Like honey, the sea-soil.

The fort we reached was beautiful,
With works of custards thick,
      Beyond the lake.
Fresh butter was the bridge in front,
The rubble dyke was fair white wheat,
      Bacon the palisade.

Stately, pleasantly it sat,
A compact house and strong.
      Then I went in :
The door of it was hung beef,
The threshold was dry bread,
      Cheese-curds the walls. . . .

Behind it was a well of wine,
Beer and bragget in streams,
      Each full pool to the taste.
Malt in smooth wavy sea
Over a lard-spring's brink
      Flowed through the floor. . . .

A row of fragrant apple-trees,
An orchard in its pink-tipped bloom,
      Between it and the hill.

70

THE VISION OF MAC CONGLINNE

A forest tall of real leeks,
Of onions and of carrots, stood
Behind the house.

Within, a household generous,
A welcome of red, firm-fed men,
Around the fire :
Seven bead-strings and necklets seven
Of cheeses and of bits of tripe
Round each man's neck.

The Chief in cloak of beefy fat
Beside his noble wife and fair
I then beheld.
Below the lofty cauldron's spit
Then the Dispenser I beheld,
His fleshfork on his back.

74   ## STOOL-BALL

. . . Now milkmaids' pails are deckt with flowers,
And men begin to drink in bowers,
The mackarels come up in shoals,
To fill the mouths of hungry souls ;
Sweet sillabubs, and lip-loved tansey,
For William is prepared by Nancy.
Much time is wasted now away,
At pigeon-holes, and nine-pin play,
Whilst hob-nail Dick, and simp'ring Frances,
Trip it away in country dances ;
At stool-ball and at barley-break,
Wherewith they harmless pastime make. . . .

75   ## MILKING PAILS

Mary's gone a-milking,
A rea, a ria, a roses,
Mary's gone a-milking,
Gentle sweet mother o' mine.

71

Take your pails and go after her,
A rea, a ria, a roses,
Take your pails and go after her,
Gentle sweet daughter o' mine.

Buy me a pair of new milking pails,
A rea, a ria, a roses,
Buy me a pair of new milking pails,
Gentle sweet mother o' mine.

Where's the money to come from,
A rea, a ria, a roses,
Where's the money to come from,
Gentle sweet daughter o' mine ?

Sell my father's feather bed,
A rea, a ria, a roses,
Sell my father's feather bed,
Gentle sweet mother o' mine.

What's your father to sleep on,
A rea, a ria, a roses,
What's your father to sleep on,
Gentle sweet daughter o' mine ?

Put him in the truckle bed,
A rea, a ria, a roses,
Put him in the truckle bed,
Gentle sweet mother o' mine.

What are the children to sleep on,
A rea, a ria, a roses,
What are the children to sleep on,
Gentle sweet daughter o' mine ?

Put them in the pig-sty,
A rea, a ria, a roses,
Put them in the pig-sty,
Gentle sweet mother o' mine.

What are the pigs to lie in,
A rea, a ria, a roses,

MILKING PAILS

What are the pigs to lie in,
Gentle sweet daughter o' mine?

Put them in the washing-tubs,
A rea, a ria, a roses,
Put them in the washing-tubs,
Gentle sweet mother o' mine.

What am I to wash in,
A rea, a ria, a roses,
What am I to wash in,
Gentle sweet daughter o' mine?

Wash in the thimble,
A rea, a ria, a roses,
Wash in the thimble,
Gentle sweet mother o' mine.

Thimble won't hold your father's shirt,
A rea, a ria, a roses,
Thimble won't hold your father's shirt,
Gentle sweet daughter o' mine.

Wash in the river,
A rea, a ria, a roses,
Wash in the river,
Gentle sweet mother o' mine.

Suppose the clothes should blow away,
A rea, a ria, a roses,
Suppose the clothes should blow away,
Gentle sweet daughter o' mine?

Set a man to watch them,
A rea, a ria, a roses,
Set a man to watch them,
Gentle sweet mother o' mine.

Suppose the man should go to sleep,
A rea, a ria, a roses,
Suppose the man should go to sleep,
Gentle sweet daughter o' mine?

73

Take a boat and go after them,
   A rea, a ria, a roses,
Take a boat and go after them,
   Gentle sweet mother o' mine.

Suppose the boat should be upset,
   A rea, a ria, a roses,
Suppose the boat should be upset,
   Gentle sweet daughter o' mine?

Then that would be an end of you,
   A rea, a ria, a roses,
Then that would be an end of you,
   Gentle sweet mother o' mine!

76   THE PEDLAR'S SONG

Lawne as white as driven Snow,
Cypresse blacke as ere was Crow,
Cloves as sweete as Damaske Roses,
Maskes for faces, and for noses,
Bugle-bracelet, Necke-lace Amber,
Perfume for a Ladies Chamber :
Golden Quoifes, and Stomachers
For my Lads, to give their deers :
Pins, and peaking-stickes of steele :
What Maids lacke from head to heele :
   Come buy of me, come : come buy, come buy,
   Buy Lads, or else your Lasses cry : Come buy.
                              WILLIAM SHAKESPEARE

77   FINE KNACKS FOR LADIES

Fine knacks for ladies ! cheap, choice, brave, and new,
   Good pennyworths—but money cannot move :
I keep a fair but for the Fair to view—
   A beggar may be liberal of love.
Though all my wares be trash, the heart is true,
                        The heart is true.

74

FINE KNACKS FOR LADIES

Great gifts are guiles and look for gifts again ;
  My trifles come as treasures from my mind :
It is a priceless jewel to be plain ;
  Sometimes in shell the orient'st pearls we find :—
Of others take a sheaf, of me a grain !
          Of me a grain ! . . .

OH ! DEAR !

Oh ! dear ! what can the matter be ?
Dear ! dear ! what can the matter be ?
Oh ! dear ! what can the matter be ?
Johnny's so long at the fair.

He promised he'd buy me a fairing should please me,
And then for a kiss, oh ! he vowed he would tease me,
He promised he'd bring me a bunch of blue ribbons
To tie up my bonny brown hair.

And it's oh ! dear ! what can the matter be ?
Dear ! dear ! what can the matter be ?
Oh ! dear ! what can the matter be ?
Johnny's so long at the fair.

He promised he'd bring me a basket of posies,
· A garland of lilies, a garland of roses,
A little straw hat, to set off the blue ribbons
That tie up my bonny brown hair.

And it's oh ! dear ! what can the matter be ?
Dear ! dear ! what can the matter be ?
Oh ! dear ! what can the matter be ?
Johnny's so long at the fair.

SLEDBURN FAIR

I'd oft heard tell of this Sledburn fair,
  And fain I would gan thither,
'Twere in the prime of summer-time,
  In fine and pleasant weather ;

FEASTS : FAIRS : BEGGARS : GIPSIES

My Dad and Mam they did agree
 That Nell and I should gae
See for to view this Sledburn fair,
 And ride on Dobbin, oh . . .

So Nell gat on and I gat on,
 And we both rode off together,
And of everybody we did meet
 Enquired how far 'twas thither?
Until we came to t'other field end,
 'Twas about steeple high,
" See yonder, Nell, see yonder, Nell,
 There's Sledburn town," cried I.

And when we reached this famous town
 We enquirèd for an alehouse,
We lookèd up and saw a sign
 As high as any gallows ;
We called for Harry, the ostler,
 To give our horse some hay,
For we had come to Sledburn Fair
 And meant to stop all day.

The landlord then himself came out
 And led us up an entry ;
He took us in the finest room
 As if we'd been quite gentry.
And puddings and sauce they did so smell,
 Pies and roast beef so rare,
" Oh, Zooks ! " says Nell, " we've acted well
 In coming to Sledburn Fair."

80   WIDDECOMBE FAIR

" Tom Pearse, Tom Pearse, lend me your gray mare,"
 All along, down along, out along, lee.
" For I want for to go to Widdecombe Fair,
 Wi' Bill Brewer, Jan Stewer, Peter Gurney, Peter Davy,
 Dan'l Whiddon, Harry Hawk,

WIDDECOMBE FAIR

Old Uncle Tom Cobley and all."
  Old Uncle Tom Cobley and all.

" And when shall I see again my gray mare?"
  All along, down along, out along, lee.
" By Friday soon, or Saturday noon,
  Wi' Bill Brewer, Jan Stewer, Peter Gurney, Peter Davy,
    Dan'l Whiddon, Harry Hawk,
  Old Uncle Tom Cobley and all."
    Old Uncle Tom Cobley and all.

Then Friday came and Saturday noon,
  All along, down along, out along, lee.
But Tom Pearse's old mare hath not trotted home,
  Wi' Bill Brewer, Jan Stewer, Peter Gurney, Peter Davy,
    Dan'l Whiddon, Harry Hawk,
  Old Uncle Tom Cobley and all.
    Old Uncle Tom Cobley and all.

So Tom Pearse he got up to the top o' the hill,
  All along, down along, out along, lee.
And he seed his old mare down a-making her will,
  Wi' Bill Brewer, Jan Stewer, Peter Gurney, Peter Davy,
    Dan'l Whiddon, Harry Hawk,
  Old Uncle Tom Cobley and all.
    Old Uncle Tom Cobley and all.

So Tom Pearse's old mare her took sick and her died,
  All along, down along, out along, lee.
And Tom he sat down on a stone, and he cried
  Wi' Bill Brewer, Jan Stewer, Peter Gurney, Peter Davy,
    Dan'l Whiddon, Harry Hawk,
  Old Uncle Tom Cobley and all.
    Old Uncle Tom Cobley and all.

But this isn't the end o' this shocking affair,
  All along, down along, out along, lee.
Nor, though they be dead, of the horrid career
  Of Bill Brewer, Jan Stewer, Peter Gurney, Peter Davy,
    Dan'l Whiddon, Harry Hawk,

77

FEASTS : FAIRS : BEGGARS : GIPSIES

Old Uncle Tom Cobley and all.
Old Uncle Tom Cobley and all.

When the wind whistles cold on the moor of a night,
All along, down along, out along, lee.
Tom Pearse's old mare doth appear, gashly white,
Wi' Bill Brewer, Jan Stewer, Peter Gurney, Peter Davy,
Dan'l Whiddon, Harry Hawk,
Old Uncle Tom Cobley and all.
Old Uncle Tom Cobley and all.

And all the long night be heard skirling and groans,
All along, down along, out along, lee.
From Tom Pearse's old mare in her rattling bones,
And from Bill Brewer, Jan Stewer, Peter Gurney, Peter
Davy, Dan'l Whiddon, Harry Hawk,
Old Uncle Tom Cobley and all.
Old Uncle Tom Cobley and all.

81   GIPSIES

 THE snow falls deep ; the forest lies alone ;
 The boy goes hasty for his load of brakes,[1]
 Then thinks upon the fire and hurries back ;
 The gipsy knocks his hands and tucks them up,
 And seeks his squalid camp, half hid in snow,
 Beneath the oak which breaks away the wind,
 And bushes close in snow-like hovel warm ;
 There tainted mutton wastes upon the coals,
 And the half-wasted dog squats close and rubs,
 Then feels the heat too strong, and goes aloof ;
 He watches well, but none a bit can spare,
 And vainly waits the morsel thrown away.
 Tis thus they live—a picture to the place,
 A quiet, pilfering, unprotected race.
         JOHN CLARE

[1] Bracken

82   THE IDLERS

THE gipsies lit their fires by the chalk-pit gate anew,
And the hoppled horses supped in the further dusk and dew;
The gnats flocked round the smoke like idlers as they were
And through the goss and bushes the owls began to churr.

An ell above the woods the last of sunset glowed
With a dusky gold that filled the pond beside the road ;
The cricketers had done, the leas all silent lay,
And the carrier's clattering wheels went past and died away.

The gipsies lolled and gossiped, and ate their stolen swedes,
Made merry with mouth-organs, worked toys with piths of
        reeds :
The old wives puffed their pipes, nigh as black as their hair,
And not one of them all seemed to know the name of care.

                                    EDMUND BLUNDEN

83   THE WRAGGLE TAGGLE GIPSIES

    THERE were three gipsies a-come to my door,
    And down-stairs ran this a-lady, O !
    One sang high, and another sang low,
    And the other sang, Bonny, bonny Biscay, O !

    Then she pulled off her silk-finished gown
    And put on hose of leather, O !
    The ragged, ragged rags about our door—
    She's gone with the wraggle taggle gipsies, O !

    It was late last night, when my lord came home,
    Enquiring for his a-lady, O !
    The servants said, on every hand :
    " She's gone with the wraggle taggle gipsies, O ! "

    " O saddle to me my milk-white steed.
    Go and fetch me my pony, O !
    That I may ride and seek my bride,
    Who is gone with the wraggle taggle gipsies, O ! "

                        79

O he rode high and he rode low,
He rode through woods and copses too,
Until he came to an open field,
And there he espied his a-lady, O !

" What makes you leave your house and land ?
What makes you leave your money, O ?
What makes you leave your new-wedded lord ;
To go with the wraggle taggle gipsies, O ? "

" What care I for my house and my land ?
What care I for my money, O ?
What care I for my new-wedded lord ?
I'm off with the wraggle taggle gipsies, O ! "

" Last night you slept on a goose-feather bed,
With the sheet turned down so bravely, O !
And to-night you'll sleep in a cold open field,
Along with the wraggle taggle gipsies, O ! "

" What care I for a goose-feather bed,
With the sheet turned down so bravely, O ?
For to-night I shall sleep in a cold open field,
Along with the wraggle taggle gipsies, O ! "

84   WHERE DO THE GIPSIES COME FROM ?

WHERE do the gipsies come from ?
The gipsies come from Egypt.
The fiery sun begot them,
    Their dam was the desert dry.
She lay there stripped and basking,
And gave them suck for the asking,
And an Emperor's bone to play with,
    Whenever she heard them cry.

What did the gipsies do there ?
They built a tomb for Pharaoh,
They built a tomb for Pharaoh,
    So tall it touched the sky.

WHERE DO THE GIPSIES COME FROM?

They buried him deep inside it,
Then let what would betide it,
They saddled their lean-ribbed ponies
And left him there to die.

What do the gipsies do now?
They follow the Sun, their father,
They follow the Sun, their father,
    They know not whither nor why.
Whatever they find they take it,
And if it's a law they break it.
So never you talk to a gipsy,
    Or look in a gipsy's eye.

H. H. BASHFORD

85   BEGGARS

WHAT noise of viols is so sweet
    As when our merry clappers ring?
What mirth doth want when beggars meet?
    A beggar's life is for a king.
Eat, drink, and play, sleep when we list,
Go where we will—so stocks be missed.
    Bright shines the sun; play, beggars, play!
    Here's scraps enough to serve to-day.

The world is ours, and ours alone;
    For we alone have world at will.
We purchase not—all is our own;
    Both fields and street we beggars fill.
    Bright shines the sun; play, beggars, play!
    Here's scraps enough to serve to-day.

FRANK DAVIDSON

86   "WEEP, WEEP, YE WOODMEN!"

WEEP, weep, ye woodmen! wail;
    Your hands with sorrow wring!
Your master Robin Hood lies dead,
    Therefore sigh as you sing.

81   F

Here lie his primer and his beads,
　His bent bow and his arrows keen,
His good sword and his holy cross :
　Now cast on flowers fresh and green.

And, as they fall, shed tears and say
　Well, well-a-day ! well, well-a-day !
Thus cast ye flowers fresh, and sing,
　And on to Wakefield take your way.
                              ANTHONY MUNDAY

87　　　MY HANDSOME GILDEROY

GILDEROY was a bonnie boy,
　Had roses tull [1] his shoone,
His stockings were of silken soy,
　Wi' garters hanging doune :
It was, I weene, a comelie sight,
　To see sae trim a boy ;
He was my joy and heart's delight,
　My handsome Gilderoy.

Oh ! sike twe [2] charming een he had,
　A breath as sweet as rose ;
He never ware a Highland plaid,
　But costly silken clothes.
He gained the luve of ladies gay,
　Nane eir tull him was coy,
Ah ! wae is mee ! I mourn the day,
　For my dear Gilderoy.

My Gilderoy and I were born
　Baith in one toun together ;
We scant [3] were seven years beforn
　We gan to luve each other ;

[1] To　　　[2] Such two　　　[3] Scarce

MY HANDSOME GILDEROY

Our daddies and our mammies thay
    Were fill'd wi' mickle joy,
To think upon the bridal day
    'Twixt me and Gilderoy.

For Gilderoy, that luve of mine,
    Gude faith ! I freely bought
A wedding sark of Holland fine
    Wi' silken flowers wrought :
And he gied me a wedding ring,
    Which I received with joy,
Nae lad nor lassie eir could sing
    Like me and Gilderoy.

Wi' mickle joy we spent our prime,
    Till we were baith sixteen,
And aft we past the langsome time
    Among the leaves sae green :
Aft on the banks we'd sit us thair,
    And sweetly kiss and toy ;
Wi' garlands gay wad deck my hair
    My handsome Gilderoy.

Oh ! that he still had been content
    Wi' me to lead his life ;
But, ah ! his manfu' heart was bent
    To stir in feats of strife.
And he in many a venturous deed
    His courage bauld wad try ;
And now this gars [1] mine heart to bleed
    For my dear Gilderoy.

And when of me his leave he tuik,
    The tears they wet mine ee ;
I gave tull him a parting luik,
    " My benison gang wi' thee !
God speed thee weil, mine ain dear heart,
    For gane is all my joy ;

---

[1] Makes

My heart is rent, sith we maun part,
My handsome Gilderoy ! "

My Gilderoy, baith far and near,
Was feared in ev'ry toun,
And bauldly bare away the gear
Of many a lawland loun :
Nane eir durst meet him man to man,
He was sae brave a boy ;
At length wi' numbers he was tane,
My winsome Gilderoy.

Wae worth the loun that made the laws,
To hang a man for gear,
To 'reave of life for ox or ass,
For sheep, or horse, or mare :
Had not their laws been made sae strick,
I neir had lost my joy ;
Wi' sorrow neir had wat my cheek
For my dear Gilderoy.

Giff [1] Gilderoy had done amisse,
He mought hae banisht been,
Ah, what fair cruelty is this,
To hang sike handsome men !
To hang the flower o' Scottish land,
Sae sweet and fair a boy ;
Nae lady had so white a hand
As thee, my Gilderoy.

Of Gilderoy sae fraid they were,
They bound him mickle strong,
Tull Edenburrow they led him thair,
And on a gallows hung :
They hung him high aboon the rest,
He was so trim a boy :
Thair dyed the youth whom I lued best,
My handsome Gilderoy.

[1] If

MY HANDSOME GILDEROY

Thus having yielded up his breath,
  I bare his corpse away ;
Wi' tears, that trickled for his death,
  I washt his comely clay ;
And siker [1] in a grave sae deep
  I laid the dear-lued boy,
And now for evir maun I weep
  My winsome Gilderoy.

[1] Safely

BEASTS OF THE FIELD
FOWLS OF THE AIR.

BINGO

THE miller's mill-dog lay at the mill-door,
And his name was Little Bingo.
B with an I, I with an N, N with a G, G with an O,
And his name was Little Bingo.

The miller he bought a cask of ale,
And he called it right good Stingo.
S with a T, T with an I, I with an N, N with a G, G with an O,
And he called it right good Stingo.

The miller he went to town one day,
And he bought a wedding Ring-o !
R with an I, I with an N, N with a G, G with an O,
And he bought a wedding Ring-o !

89   THE IRISH HARPER AND HIS DOG

On the green banks of Shannon, when Sheelah was nigh,
No blithe Irish lad was so happy as I ;
No harp like my own could so cheerily play,
And wherever I went was my poor dog Tray.

When at last I was forced from my Sheelah to part,
She said—while the sorrow was big at her heart—
" Oh ! remember your Sheelah, when far, far away,
And be kind, my dear Pat, to our poor dog Tray."

Poor dog ! he was faithful and kind, to be sure,
And he constantly loved me, although I was poor ;

BEASTS OF THE FIELD: FOWLS OF THE AIR

When the sour-looking folks sent me heartless away,
I had always a friend in my poor dog Tray.

When the road was so dark, and the night was so cold,
And Pat and his dog were grown weary and old,
How snugly we slept in my old coat of grey,
And he licked me for kindness—my poor dog Tray.

Though my wallet was scant, I remembered his case,
Nor refused my last crust to his pitiful face ;
But he died at my feet on a cold winter day,
And I played a lament for my poor dog Tray.

Where now shall I go, poor, forsaken, and blind ?
Can I find one to guide me, so faithful and kind ?
To my sweet native village, so far, far away,
I can never return with my poor dog Tray.

THOMAS CAMPBELL

90   POOR OLD HORSE

My clothing was once of the linsey woolsey fine,
My tail it grew at length, my coat did likewise shine ;
But now I'm growing old ; my beauty does decay,
My master frowns upon me ; one day I heard him say,
            Poor old horse : poor old horse.

Once I was kept in the stable snug and warm,
To keep my tender limbs from any cold or harm ;
But now, in open fields, I am forced for to go,
In all sorts of weather, let it be hail, rain, freeze, or snow.
            Poor old horse : poor old horse.

Once I was fed on the very best corn and hay
That ever grew in yon fields, or in yon meadows gay ;
But now there's no such doing can I find at all,
I'm glad to pick the green sprouts that grow behind yon wall.
            Poor old horse : poor old horse.

POOR OLD HORSE

" You are old, you are cold, you are deaf, dull, dumb and
    slow,
You are not fit for anything, or in my team to draw.
You have eaten all my hay, you have spoiled all my straw,
So hang him, whip, stick him, to the huntsman let him go."
             Poor old horse : poor old horse.

My hide unto the tanners then I would freely give,
My body to the hound dogs, I would rather die than live,
Likewise my poor old bones that have carried you many
    a mile,
Over hedges, ditches, brooks, bridges, likewise gates and
    stiles.
          Poor old horse : poor old horse.

91   AY ME, ALAS, HEIGH HO !

    Ay me, alas, heigh ho, heigh ho !
    Thus doth Messalina go
    Up and down the house a-crying,
    For her monkey lies a-dying.
    Death, thou art too cruel
    To bereave her of her jewel,
    Or to make a seizure
    Of her only treasure.
    If her monkey die,
    She will sit and cry,
    Fie fie fie fie fie !

92   THE FLY

    ONCE musing as I sat,
    And candle burning by,
    When all were hushed, I might discern
    A simple, sely fly ;
    That flew before mine eyes,
    With free rejoicing heart,
    And here and there with wings did play,
    As void of pain and smart.

Sometime by me she sat
When she had played her fill ;
And ever when she rested had
About she fluttered still.
When I perceived her well
Rejoicing in her place,
" O happy fly ! " (quoth I), and eke
O worm in happy case !
Which of us two is best ?
I that have reason ?   No :
But thou that reason art without,
And therefore void of woe.
I live, and so dost thou :
But I live all in pain,
And subject am to one, alas !
That makes my grief her gain.
Thou livest, but feel'st no grief ;
No love doth thee torment.
A happy thing for me it were
(If God were so content)
That thou with pen were placèd here,
And I sat in thy place :
Then I should joy as thou dost now,
And thou should'st wail thy case.

BARNABE GOOGE

93   BÊTE HUMAINE

RIDING through Ruwu swamp, about sunrise,
I saw the world awake ; and as the ray
Touched the tall grasses where they sleeping lay,
Lo, the bright air alive with dragonflies :
With brittle wings aquiver, and great eyes
Piloting crimson bodies, slender and gay.
I aimed at one, and struck it, and it lay
Broken and lifeless, with fast-fading dyes . . .

BÊTE HUMAINE

Then my soul sickened with a sudden pain
And horror, at my own careless cruelty,
That in an idle moment I had slain
A creature whose sweet life it is to fly :
Like beasts that prey with tooth and claw . . .
    Nay, they
Must slay to live, but what excuse had I ?
                        FRANCIS BRETT YOUNG

94
THE LAMB

Little Lamb, who made thee ?
Dost thou know who made thee ?
Gave thee life, and bid thee feed,
By the stream, and o'er the mead ;
Gave thee clothing of delight,
Softest clothing, woolly, bright ;
Gave thee such a tender voice,
Making all the vales rejoice ?
    Little Lamb, who made thee ?
    Dost thou know who made thee ?

Little Lamb, I'll tell thee,
Little Lamb, I'll tell thee :
He is callèd by thy name,
For He calls Himself a Lamb.
He is meek, and He is mild ;
He became a little child.
I a child, and thou a lamb,
We are callèd by His name.
    Little Lamb, God bless thee !
    Little Lamb, God bless thee !
                 WILLIAM BLAKE

95   THE SALE OF THE PET LAMB

Oh ! poverty is a weary thing, 'tis full of grief and pain ;
It boweth down the heart of man, and dulls his cunning
    brain ;
It maketh even the little child with heavy sighs complain. . . .

A thousand flocks were on the hills, a thousand flocks and
    more,
Feeding in sunshine pleasantly ; they were the rich man's
    store :
There was the while one little lamb beside a cottage door ;

A little lamb that rested with the children 'neath the tree,
That ate, meek creature, from their hands, and nestled to
    their knee ;
That had a place within their hearts, one of the family.

But want, even as an armèd man, came down upon their shed,
The father laboured all day long that his children might
    be fed,
And, one by one, their household things were sold to buy
    them bread.

That father, with a downcast eye, upon his threshold stood,
Gaunt poverty each pleasant thought had in his heart
    subdued.
" What is the creature's life to us ? " said he : " 'twill buy
    us food.

" Ay, though the children weep all day, and with down-
    drooping head
Each does his small task mournfully, the hungry must be fed ;
And that which has a price to bring must go to buy us
    bread."

It went.   Oh ! parting has a pang the hardest heart to wring,
But the tender soul of a little child with fervent love doth
    cling,
With love that hath no feignings false, unto each gentle thing.

THE SALE OF THE PET LAMB

Therefore most sorrowful it was those children small to see,
Most sorrowful to hear them plead for the lamb so piteously :
" Oh ! mother dear, it loveth us ; and what beside have
we ? "

" Let's take him to the broad green hill ! " in his impotent
despair
Said one strong boy : " let's take him off, the hills are wide
and fair ;
I know a little hiding-place, and we will keep him there."

Oh vain ! They took the little lamb, and straightway
tied him down,
With a strong cord they tied him fast ; and o'er the common
brown,
And o'er the hot and flinty roads, they took him to the
town.

The little children through that day, and throughout all the
morrow,
From every thing about the house a mournful thought did
borrow ;
The very bread they had to eat was food unto their sorrow.

Oh ! poverty is a weary thing, 'tis full of grief and pain ;
It keepeth down the soul of man, as with an iron chain ;
It maketh even the little child with heavy sighs complain.

MARY HOWITT

96   A CHILD'S PET

When I sailed out of Baltimore
    With twice a thousand head of sheep,
They would not eat, they would not drink,
    But bleated o'er the deep.

Inside the pens we crawled each day,
    To sort the living from the dead ;
And when we reached the Mersey's mouth,
    Had lost five hundred head.

Yet every night and day one sheep,
That had no fear of man or sea,
Stuck through the bars its pleading face,
And it was stroked by me.

And to the sheep-men standing near,
" You see," I said, " this one tame sheep :
It seems a child has lost her pet,
And cried herself to sleep."

So every time we passed it by,
Sailing to England's slaughter-house,
Eight ragged sheep-men—tramps and thieves—
Would stroke that sheep's black nose.

WILLIAM H. DAVIES

97   THE SNARE

I HEAR a sudden cry of pain !
There is a rabbit in a snare :
Now I hear the cry again,
But I cannot tell from where.

But I cannot tell from where
He is calling out for aid ;
Crying on the frightened air,
Making everything afraid.

Making everything afraid,
Wrinkling up his little face,
As he cries again for aid ;
And I cannot find the place !

And I cannot find the place
Where his paw is in the snare :
Little one ! Oh, little one !
I am searching everywhere.

JAMES STEPHENS

THE MONK AND HIS PET CAT

I AND my white Pangur
Have each his special art :
His mind is set on hunting mice,
Mine is upon my special craft.

I love to rest—better than any fame !—
With close study at my little book ;
White Pangur does not envy me :
He loves his childish play.

When in our house we two are all alone—
A tale without tedium !
We have—sport never-ending !
Something to exercise our wit.

At times by feats of derring-do
A mouse sticks in his net,
While into my net there drops
A difficult problem of hard meaning.

He points his full shining eye
Against the fence of the wall :
I point my clear though feeble eye
Against the keenness of science.

He rejoices with quick leaps
When in his sharp claw sticks a mouse :
I too rejoice when I have grasped
A problem difficult and dearly loved.

Though we are thus at all times,
Neither hinders the other,
Each of us pleased with his own art
Amuses himself alone.

He is a master of the work
Which every day he does :
While I am at my own work
To bring difficulty to clearness.

99   THE TYGER

Tyger! Tyger! burning bright
In the forests of the night,
What immortal hand or eye
Could frame thy fearful symmetry?

In what distant deeps or skies
Burnt the fire of thine eyes?
On what wings dare he aspire?
What the hand dare seize the fire?

And what shoulder, and what art,
Could twist the sinews of thy heart?
And when thy heart began to beat,
What dread hand? and what dread feet?

What the hammer? what the chain?
In what furnace was thy brain?
What the anvil? what dread grasp
Dare its deadly terrors clasp?

When the stars threw down their spears,
And watered heaven with their tears,
Did he smile his work to see?
Did He who made the Lamb make thee?

Tyger! Tyger! burning bright
In the forests of the night,
What immortal hand or eye,
Dare frame thy fearful symmetry?

WILLIAM BLAKE

100   THE NYMPH COMPLAINING FOR THE
            DEATH OF HER FAWN

The wanton Troopers riding by
Have shot my Fawn, and it will dye.
Ungentlemen! they cannot thrive
Who killed thee. Thou ne'er didst alive

DEATH OF A FAWN

Them any Harm : alas ! nor cou'd
Thy Death yet do them any Good . . .
For it was full of sport, and light
Of foot and heart, and did invite
Me to its game ; it seemed to bless
Itself in me ; how could I less
Than love it ?   O, I cannot be
Unkind to a beast that loveth me . . .
  With sweetest Milk, and Sugar, first
I it at mine own Fingers nurst ;
And as it grew, so every Day
It waxed more white and sweet than they.
It had so sweet a Breath ! And oft
I blushed to see its Foot more soft,
And white (shall I say than *my* Hand ?)
Nay, any Ladie's of the Land.
  It is a wond'rous Thing how fleet
'Twas on those little Silver Feet ;
With what a pretty skipping Grace,
It oft would challenge me the Race ;
And when 't had left me far away,
'Twould stay, and run again, and stay ;
For it was nimbler much than Hindes,
And trod as if on the Four Winds.
  I have a Garden of my own,
But so with Roses over-grown,
And Lillies, that you would it guess
To be a little Wilderness ;
And all the Spring Time of the Year
It only lovèd to be there.
Among the Beds of Lillies I
Have sought it oft, where it should lye ;
Yet could not, till it self would rise,
Find it, although before mine Eyes :
For, in the flaxen Lillies' Shade,
It like a Bank of Lillies laid.
Upon the Roses it would feed,
Until its Lips ev'n seemed to bleed ;

And then to me 'twould boldly trip,
And print those Roses on my Lip.
But all its chief Delight was still
On Roses thus itself to fill,
And its pure Virgin Limbs to fold
In whitest sheets of Lillies cold:
Had it lived long, it would have been
Lillies without, Roses within. . . .

ANDREW MARVELL

101   OF ALL THE BIRDS

Of all the birds that I do know,
    Philip my sparrow hath no peer;
For sit she high, or sit she low,
    Be she far off, or be she near,
There is no bird so fair, so fine,
Nor yet so fresh as this of mine;
For when she once hath felt a fit,
Philip will cry still: *Yet, yet, yet.*

Come in a morning merrily
    When Philip hath been lately fed;
Or in an evening soberly
    When Philip list to go to bed;
It is a heaven to hear my Phipp,
How she can chirp with merry lip,
For when she once hath felt a fit,
Philip will cry still: *Yet, yet, yet.*

She never wanders far abroad,
    But is at home when I do call.
If I command she lays on load [1]
    With lips, with teeth, with tongue and all.
She chants, she chirps, she makes such cheer,
That I believe she hath no peer.
For when she once hath felt the fit,
Philip will cry still: *Yet, yet, yet.*

[1] Lustily

100

OF ALL THE BIRDS

And yet besides all this good sport
  My Philip can both sing and dance,
With new found toys of sundry sort
  My Philip can both prick and prance.
And if you say but : Fend cut,[1] Phipp !
Lord, how the peat [2] will turn and skip !
For when she once hath felt the fit,
Philip will cry still : *Yet, yet, yet.*

And to tell truth he were to blame—
  Having so fine a bird as she,
To make him all this goodly game
  Without suspect or jealousy—
He were a churl and knew no good,
Would see her faint for lack of food,
  For when she once hath felt the fit,
Philip will cry still : *Yet, yet, yet.*

THE DEAD SPARROW

TELL me not of joy : there's none,
Now my little Sparrow's gone :
    He, just as you,
    Would try and woo,
He would chirp and flatter me ;
He would hang the wing awhile—
Till at length he saw me smile
Lord, how sullen he would be !

He would catch a crumb, and then
Sporting, let it go agen ;
    He from my lip
    Would moisture sip ;
He would from my trencher feed ;
Then would hop, and then would run,
And cry *Philip* when he'd done.
O ! whose heart can choose but bleed ?

[1] *Cave !*   [2] Pretty dear

O how eager would he fight,
And ne'er hurt, though he did bite.
No morn did pass,
But on my glass
He would sit, and mark and do
What I did —now ruffle all
His feathers o'er, now let 'em fall ;
And then straightway sleek them too.

Whence will Cupid get his darts
Feathered now to pierce our hearts ?
A wound he may
Not, Love, convey,
Now this faithful bird is gone ;
O let mournful turtles join
With loving red-breasts, and combine
To sing dirges o'er his stone !

WILLIAM CARTWRIGHT

103   ON A LITTLE BIRD

HERE lies a little bird.
Once all day long
In Martha's house was heard
His rippling song.

Tread lightly where he lies
Beneath this stone
With nerveless wings, closed eyes,
And sweet voice gone.

MARTIN ARMSTRONG

104   ADLESTROP

YES.   I remember Adlestrop—
The name, because one afternoon
Of heat the express-train drew up there
Unwontedly.   It was late June.

ADLESTROP

The steam hissed.   Someone cleared his throat.
No one left and no one came
On the bare platform.   What I saw
Was Adlestrop—only the name

And willows, willow-herb, and grass,
And meadowsweet, and haycocks dry,
No whit less still and lonely fair
Than the high cloudlets in the sky.

And for that minute a blackbird sang
Close by, and round him, mistier,
Farther and farther, all the birds
Of Oxfordshire and Gloucestershire.

EDWARD THOMAS

105   THE REVERIE OF POOR SUSAN

AT the corner of Wood Street, when daylight appears,
Hangs a Thrush that sings loud, it has sung for three years :
Poor Susan has passed by the spot, and has heard
In the silence of morning the song of the bird.

'Tis a note of enchantment ; what ails her ?   She sees
A mountain ascending, a vision of trees ;
Bright volumes of vapour through Lothbury glide,
And a river flows on through the vale of Cheapside.

Green pastures she views in the midst of the dale
Down which she so often has tripped with her pail ;
And a single small cottage, a nest like a dove's,
The one only dwelling on earth that she loves.

She looks, and her heart is in heaven : but they fade,
The mist and the river, the hill and the shade ;
The stream will not flow, and the hill will not rise,
And the colours have all passed away from her eyes !

WILLIAM WORDSWORTH

106   THE THRUSH'S SONG

Dear, dear, dear,
  Is the rocky glen,
Far away, far away, far away
  The haunts of men.

Here shall we dwell in love
With the lark and the dove,
Cuckoo and cornrail ;
Feast on the banded snail,
  Worm and gilded fly ;
Drink of the crystal rill
Winding adown the hill,
  Never to dry.

With glee, with glee, with glee,
  Cheer up, cheer up, cheer up, here
Nothing to harm us, then sing merrily,
  Sing to the loved ones whose nest is near—
Qui, qui, qui, kweeu quip,
Tiurru, tiurru, chipiwi,
Too-tee, too-tee, chiu choo,
Chirri, chirri, chooee,
Quiu, qui, qui.

                          W. MACGILLIVRAY

107   SWEET SUFFOLK OWL

Sweet Suffolk Owl, so trimly dight
With feathers, like a lady bright,
  Thou sing'st alone, sitting by night,
    Te whit ! Te whoo ! Te whit ! To whit !

Thy note that forth so freely rolls
With shrill command the mouse controls ;
And sings a dirge for dying souls—
    Te whit ! Te whoo ! Te whit ! To whit !
                          THOMAS VAUTOR

104

108   WHO ? WHO ?

" WHO—Who—the bride will be ? "
" The owl she the bride shall be."
        The owl quoth,
        Again to them both,
" I am sure a grim ladye ;
        Not I the bride can be,
        I not the bride can be !"

109   WHEN CATS RUN HOME

WHEN cats run home and light is come,
    And dew is cold upon the ground,
And the far-off stream is dumb,
    And the whirring sail goes round,
    And the whirring sail goes round ;
        Alone and warming his five wits,
        The white owl in the belfry sits.

When merry milkmaids click the latch,
    And rarely smells the new-mown hay,
And the cock hath sung beneath the thatch
    Twice or thrice his roundelay,
    Twice or thrice his roundelay ;
        Alone and warming his five wits,
        The white owl in the belfry sits.
                    ALFRED, LORD TENNYSON

110   ONCE

ONCE I was a monarch's daughter,
    And sat on a lady's knee ;
But am now a nightly rover,
    Banished to the ivy tree.

Crying hoo, hoo, hoo, hoo, hoo, hoo,
    Hoo, hoo, hoo, my feet are cold.
Pity me, for here you see me
    Persecuted, poor, and old.

111   THE WATER-OUSEL

WHERE on the wrinkled stream the willows lean,
And fling a very ecstasy of green
Down the dim crystal ; and the chestnut tree
Admires her large-leaved shadow, swift and free,
A water-ousel came, with such a flight
As archangels might envy. Soft and bright
Upon a water-kissing bough she lit,
And washed and preened her silver breast, though it
Was dazzling fair before. Then twittering
She sang, and made obeisance to the Spring.
And in the wavering amber at her feet
Her silent shadow, with obedience meet,
Made her quick, imitative curtsies, too.
Maybe she dreamed a nest, so safe and dear,
Where the keen spray leaps whitely to the weir ;
And smooth, warm eggs that hold a mystery ;
And stirrings of life and twitterings, that she
Is passionately glad of ; and a breast
As silver-white as hers, which without rest
Or languor, borne by spread wings swift and strong,
Shall fly upon her service all day long.
She hears a presage in the ancient thunder
Of the silken fall, and her small soul in wonder
Makes preparation as she deems most right,
Repurifying what before was white
Against the day when, like a beautiful dream,
Two little ousels shall fly with her down stream,
And even the poor, dumb shadow-bird shall flit
With two small shadows following after it.
                                        MARY WEBB

112   L'OISEAU BLEU

THE lake lay blue below the hill.
    O'er it, as I looked, there flew
Across the waters, cold and still,
    A bird whose wings were palest blue.
                    106

L'OISEAU BLEU

The sky above was blue at last,
  The sky beneath me blue in blue.
A moment, ere the bird had passed,
  It caught his image as he flew.

MARY COLERIDGE

113   I HAD A DOVE

I HAD a dove and the sweet dove died ;
  And I have thought it died of grieving :
O, what could it grieve for ?   Its feet were tied,
  With a silken thread of my own hand's weaving ;
Sweet little red feet ! why should you die—
Why should you leave me, sweet bird ! Why ?
You lived alone in the forest-tree,
Why, pretty thing ! would you not live with me ?
I kissed you oft and gave you white peas ;
Why not live sweetly, as in the green trees ?

JOHN KEATS

114   PHILOMEL

As it fell upon a day
In the merry month of May,
Sitting in a pleasant shade
Which a grove of myrtles made,
Beasts did leap and birds did sing,
Trees did grow and plants did spring ;
Everything did banish moan
Save the Nightingale alone :
She, poor bird, as all forlorn
Leaned her breast up-till a thorn,
And there sung the doleful'st ditty.
That to hear it was great pity.

Fie, fie, fie ! now would she cry ;
Tereu, tereu ! by and by ;
That to hear her so complain
Scarce I could from tears refrain ;

107

For her griefs so lively shown
Made me think upon mine own.
Ah ! thought I, thou mourn'st in vain,
None takes pity on thy pain :
Senseless trees they cannot hear thee,
Ruthless beasts they will not cheer thee :
King Pandion he is dead,
All thy friends are lapped in lead ;
All thy fellow birds do sing
Careless of thy sorrowing :
Even so, poor bird, like thee,
None alive will pity me.

RICHARD BARNFIELD

115   A SPARROW-HAWK

A SPARHAWK proud did hold in wicked jail
Music's sweet chorister, the Nightingale ;
To whom with sighs she said : " O set me free,
And in my song I'll praise no bird but thee."
The Hawk replied : " I will not lose my diet
To let a thousand such enjoy their quiet."

116   THE EAGLE

HE clasps the crag with crooked hands ;
Close to the sun in lonely lands,
Ringed with the azure world, he stands.

The wrinkled sea beneath him crawls ;
He watches from his mountain walls,
And like a thunderbolt he falls.

ALFRED, LORD TENNYSON

117 THE TWA CORBIES

As I was walking all alane,
I heard twa corbies making a mane,
And tane unto the tither say :—
" Where sall we gang and dine to-day ?"

" —In behint yon auld fail dyke,[1]
I wat there lies a new-slain Knight ;
And naebody kens that he lies there
But his hawk, his hound, and lady fair.

" His hound is to the hunting gane,
His hawk to fetch the wild-fowl hame,
His lady's ta'en another mate,
So we may mak our dinner sweet.

" Ye'll sit on his white hause-bane,
And I'll pick out his bonnie blue een.
Wi' ae lock o' his gowden hair
We'll theek[2] our nest when it grows bare.

" Mony a one for him maks mane,
But nane sall ken where he is gane.
O'er his white banes, where they are bare,
The wind sall blaw for evermair."

118 IN THE WILDERNESS

CHRIST of His gentleness
Thirsting and hungering
Walked in the wilderness ;
Soft words of grace He spoke
Unto lost desert-folk
That listened wondering.
He heard the bitterns call
From ruined palace-wall,
Answered them brotherly.

[1] Green-walled ditch   [2] Thatch : mend

He held communion
With the she-pelican
Of lonely piety.
Basilisk, cockatrice,
Flocked to His homilies,
With mail of dread device,
With monstrous barbèd stings,
With eager dragon-eyes ;
Great rats on leather wings
And poor blind broken things,
Foul in their miseries.
And ever with Him went,
Of all His wanderings
Comrade, with ragged coat,
Gaunt ribs—poor innocent—
Bleeding foot, burning throat,
The guileless old scape-goat ;
For forty nights and days
Followed in Jesus' ways,
Sure guard behind Him kept,
Tears like a lover wept.

ROBERT GRAVES

119   STUPIDITY STREET

I saw with open eyes
Singing birds sweet
Sold in the shops
For the people to eat,
Sold in the shops of
Stupidity Street.

I saw in vision
The worm in the wheat,
And in the shops nothing
For people to eat ;
Nothing for sale in
Stupidity Street.

RALPH HODGSON

120

COME WARY ONE

" ' COME wary one, come slender feet,
Come pretty bird and sing to me,
I have a cage of wizard wood
With perch of ebony ;
Come pretty bird, there's dainty food,
There's cherry, plum, and strawberry,
In my red cage, my wizard cage,
The cage I made for thee.'

" The bird flew down, the bird flew in,
The cherries they were dried and dead,
She tied him with a silken skein
To a perch of molten lead ;
And first most dire he did complain,
And next he sulky sad did fall,
Chained to his perch, his burning perch,
He would not sing at all.

" There came an elf, a silent elf,
A silver wand hung by his side,
And when that wand lay on the door,
The door did open wide.
The pretty bird with beak he tore
That silken skein, then out flew he,
From that red cage, that greedy cage,
That cage of wizardry."

RUTH MANNING-SANDERS

121 UPON THE LARK AND THE FOWLER

THOU simple Bird what mak'st thou here to play ?
Look, there's the Fowler, prethee come away.
Dost not behold the Net ? Look there 'tis spread,
Venture a little further thou art dead.
  Is there not room enough in all the Field
For thee to play in, but thou needs must yield

To the deceitful glitt'ring of a Glass,
Placed betwixt Nets to bring thy death to pass ?
  Bird, if thou art so much for dazling light,
Look, there's the Sun above thee, dart upright.
Thy nature is to soar up to the Sky,
Why wilt thou come down to the nets, and dye ?
  Take no heed to the Fowler's tempting Call ;
This whistle he enchanteth Birds withal.
Or if thou seest a live Bird in his net,
Believe she's there 'cause thence she cannot get.
Look how he tempteth thee with his Decoy,
That he may rob thee of thy Life, thy Joy :
Come, prethee Bird, I prethee come away,
Why should this net thee take, when 'scape thou may ?
  Hadst thou not Wings, or were thy feathers pulled,
Or wast thou blind or fast asleep wer't lulled :
The case would somewhat alter, but for thee,
Thy eyes are ope, and thou hast Wings to see.
  Remember that thy Song is in thy Rise,
Not in thy Fall, Earth's not thy Paradise.
Keep up aloft then, let thy circuits be
Above, where Birds from Fowlers nets are free. . . .

                                        JOHN BUNYAN

122   THE BIRDS

He.   WHERE thou dwellest, in what Grove,
        Tell me Fair One, tell me Love ;
        Where thou thy charming nest dost build,
        O thou pride of every field !

She. Yonder stands a lonely tree,
        There I live and mourn for thee ;
        Morning drinks my silent tear,
        And evening winds my sorrow bear.

He.   O thou summer's harmony,
        I have lived and mourned for thee ;
        Each day I mourn along the wood,
        And night hath heard my sorrows loud.

THE BIRDS

She. Dost thou truly long for me ?
And am I thus sweet to thee ?
Sorrow now is at an end,
O my Lover and my Friend !

He. Come, on wings of joy we'll fly
To where my bower hangs on high ;
Come, and make thy calm retreat
Among green leaves and blossoms sweet.

WILLIAM BLAKE

123   TWO PEWITS

UNDER the after-sunset sky
Two pewits sport and cry,
More white than is the moon on high
Riding the dark surge silently ;
More black than earth.   Their cry
Is the one sound under the sky.
They alone move, now low, now high,
And merrily they cry
To the mischievous Spring sky,
Plunging earthward, tossing high,
Over the ghost who wonders why
So merrily they cry and fly,
Nor choose 'twixt earth and sky,
While the moon's quarter silently
Rides, and earth rests as silently.

EDWARD THOMAS

124   TO A WATERFOWL

WHITHER, midst falling dew,
While glow the heavens with the last steps of day
Far, through their rosy depths, dost thou pursue
Thy solitary way ?

Vainly the fowler's eye
Might mark thy distant flight to do thee wrong,

113   H

BEASTS OF THE FIELD: FOWLS OF THE AIR

As, darkly painted on the crimson sky,
    Thy figure floats along.

    Seek'st thou the plashy brink
Of weedy lake, or marge of river wide,
Or where the rocking billows rise and sink
    On the chafed ocean-side ?

    There is a Power whose care
Teaches thy way along that pathless coast,—
The desert and illimitable air,—
    Lone wandering, but not lost.

    All day thy wings have fanned
At that far height, the cold thin atmosphere,
Yet stoop not, weary, to the welcome land,
    Though the dark night is near.

    And soon that toil shall end ;
Soon shalt thou find a summer home, and rest,
And scream among thy fellows ; reeds shall bend,
    Soon, o'er thy sheltered nest.

    Thou'rt gone : the abyss of heaven
Hath swallowed up thy form ; yet, on my heart
Deeply hath sunk the lesson thou hast given,
    And shall not soon depart.

    He who, from zone to zone,
Guides through the boundless sky thy certain flight,
In the long way that I must tread alone,
    Will lead my steps aright.
                            WILLIAM CULLEN BRYANT

125 ## MIDNIGHT

... MIDNIGHT was come, when every vital thing
With sweet sound sleep their weary limbs did rest,
The beasts were still, the little birds that sing
Now sweetly slept, beside their mother's breast,
The old and all were shrouded in their nest :
    The waters calm, the cruel seas did cease,
    The woods, and fields, and all things held their peace.

The golden stars were whirled amid their race,
And on the earth did laugh with twinkling light,
When each thing, nestled in his resting-place,
Forgat day's pain with pleasure of the night :
The hare had not the greedy hounds in sight,
    The fearful deer of death stood not in doubt,
    The partridge dreamed not of the falcon's foot.

The ugly bear now minded not the stake,
Nor how the cruel mastives do him tear ;
The stag lay still unrousèd from the brake ;
The foamy boar feared not the hunter's spear :
All things were still, in desert, bush, and brere : [1]
    With quiet heart, now from their travails ceased,
    Soundly they slept in midst of all their rest.
             THOMAS SACKVILLE, LORD BUCKHURST

---

[1] Briar : wildwood

ELPHIN : OUPH : FAY.

126   COME UNTO THESE YELLOW SANDS

(*Ariel singing*)   COME unto these yellow sands,
                And then take hands :
            Curtsied when you have, and kist,
                The wilde waves whist :
        Foote it featly heere, and there,
        And sweete Sprights the burthen beare.
        Harke, harke, *bowgh wawgh* :
        The watch-dogges barke, *bowgh wawgh*.
            Hark, hark, I heare,
        The straine of strutting Chanticlere
            Cry *Cockadidle-dowe*.
                        WILLIAM SHAKESPEARE

127   THE ELVES' DANCE

            ROUND about, round about
                In a fair ring-a,
            Thus we dance, thus we dance
                And thus we sing-a,
            Trip and go, to and fro
                Over this green-a,
            All about, in and out,
                For our brave Queen-a.

ELPHIN, OUPH AND FAY

128

BY THE MOON

By the Moone we sport and play,
With the night begins our day:
As we daunce the deaw doth fall,
Trip it little urchins all:
Lightly as the little Bee,
Two by two, and three by three:
And about go we, and about go wee.

" I do come about the coppes,
Leaping upon flowers toppes:
Then I get upon a flie,
Shee carries me above the skie:
And trip and goe."

" When a deawe drop falleth downe,
And doth light upon my crowne,
Then I shake my head and skip,
And about I trip.
Two by two, and three by three:
And about go we, and about go wee."

THOMAS RAVENSCROFT

129

FOR A MOCKING VOICE

Who calls? Who calls? Who?
Did you call? Did you?—
I call! I call! I!
Follow where I fly.—
Where? O where? O where?
On Earth or in the Air?—
Where you come, I'm gone!
Where you fly, I've flown!—
Stay! ah, stay! ah, stay,
Pretty Elf, and play!
Tell me where you are—
Ha, ha, ha, ha, ha!

ELEANOR FARJEON

130 WHERE THE BEE SUCKS

WHERE the Bee sucks, there suck I,
In a Cowslip's bell I lie,
There I cowch when Owles do crie ;
On the Batt's back I doe flie
After Sommer merrily.
Merrily, merrily, shall I live now
Under the blossom that hangs on the Bow.

WILLIAM SHAKESPEARE

131 ECHO

How see you Echo ? When she calls I see
Her pale face looking down through some great tree,
Whose world of green is like a moving sea,
That shells re-echo.
I see her with a white face like a mask,
That vanishes to come again ; damask
Her cheek, but deeply pale,
Her eyes are green,
With a silver sheen,
And she mocks the thing you ask.
" O Echo !" (hear the children calling) " are you there ?" . . .
" Where ?" . . .

When the wind blows over the hill,
She hides with a vagrant will,
And call you may loud, and call you may long,
She lays finger on lip when the winds are strong,
And for all your pains she is still.
But when young plants spring, and the chiff-chaffs sing,
And the scarlet capped woodpecker flies through the vale,
She is out all day,
Through the fragrant May,
To babble and tattle her Yea and Nay.
" O Echo !" (still the children call) " Where are you ?
    where ?" . . .
" Air . . ."   VISCOUNTESS GREY

132 THE SPLENDOUR FALLS

THE splendour falls on castle walls
  And snowy summits old in story :
The long light shakes across the lakes,
  And the wild cataract leaps in glory.
Blow, bugle, blow, set the wild echoes flying,
Blow, bugle ; answer, echoes, dying, dying, dying.

O hark, O hear ! how thin and clear,
  And thinner, clearer, farther going !
O sweet and far from cliff and scar
  The horns of Elfland faintly blowing !
Blow, let us hear the purple glens replying :
Blow, bugle ; answer, echoes, dying, dying, dying.

O love, they die in yon rich sky,
  They faint on hill or field or river :
Our echoes roll from soul to soul,
  And grow for ever and for ever.
Blow, bugle, blow, set the wild echoes flying,
And answer, echoes, answer, dying, dying, dying.
                        ALFRED, LORD TENNYSON

133 THE FAIRIES

UP the airy mountain,
    Down the rushy glen,
We daren't go a-hunting
    For fear of little men ;
Wee folk, good folk,
    Trooping all together ;
Green jacket, red cap,
    And white owl's feather !

Down along the rocky shore
    Some make their home,
They live on crispy pancakes
    Of yellow tide-foam ;

122

THE FAIRIES

Some in the reeds
 Of the black mountain-lake,
With frogs for their watch-dogs,
 All night awake.

High on the hill-top
 The old King sits ;
He is now so old and gray
 He's nigh lost his wits.
With a bridge of white mist
 Columbkill he crosses,
On his stately journeys
 From Slieveleague to Rosses ;
Or going up with music
 On cold starry nights,
To sup with the Queen
 Of the gay Northern Lights.

They stole little Bridget
 For seven years long ;
When she came down again
 Her friends were all gone.
They took her lightly back,
 Between the night and morrow,
They thought that she was fast asleep,
 But she was dead with sorrow.
They have kept her ever since
 Deep within the lake,
On a bed of flag-leaves,
 Watching till she wake.

By the craggy hill-side,
 Through the mosses bare,
They have planted thorn-trees
 For pleasure here and there.
Is any man so daring
 As to dig one up in spite,
He shall find the thornies set
 In his bed at night.

ELPHIN, OUPH AND FAY

Up the airy mountain,
  Down the rushy glen,
We daren't go a-hunting
  For fear of little men ;
Wee folk, good folk,
  Trooping all together ;
Green jacket, red cap,
  And white owl's feather !

WILLIAM ALLINGHAM

134   OVERHEARD ON A SALTMARSH

Nymph, nymph, what are your beads ?

Green glass, goblin. Why do you stare at them ?

Give them me.

No.

Give them me.   Give them me.

No.

Then I will howl all night in the reeds,
Lie in the mud and howl for them.

Goblin, why do you love them so ?

They are better than stars or water,
Better than voices of winds that sing,
Better than any man's fair daughter,
Your green glass beads on a silver ring.

Hush, I stole them out of the moon.

Give me your beads, I want them.

No.

I will howl in a deep lagoon
For your green glass beads, I love them so.
Give them me.   Give them.

No.

HAROLD MONRO

THE FAIRY THORN

" Get up, our Anna dear, from the weary spinning wheel ;
   For your father's on the hill, and your mother is asleep :
Come up above the crags, and we'll dance a highland reel
   Around the fairy thorn on the steep."

At Anna Grace's door 'twas thus the maidens cried,
   Three merry maidens fair in kirtles of the green ;
And Anna laid the rock [1] and the weary wheel aside,
   The fairest of the four, I ween.

They're glancing through the glimmer of the quiet eve,
   Away in milky wavings of neck and ankle bare ;
The heavy-sliding stream in its sleep song they leave,
   And the crags in the ghostly air.

And linking hand and hand, and singing as they go,
   The maids along the hill-side have ta'en their fearless way,
Till they come to where the rowan trees in lonely beauty grow
   Beside the Fairy Hawthorn grey.

The hawthorn stands between   the ashes tall and slim,
   Like matron with her twin grand-daughters at her knee ;
The rowan berries cluster o'er her low head grey and dim
   In ruddy kisses sweet to see.

The merry maidens four   have ranged them in a row,
   Between each lovely couple a stately rowan stem,
And away in mazes wavy, like skimming birds they go,
   Oh, never carolled bird like them !

But solemn is the silence of the silvery haze
   That drinks away their voices in echoless repose,
And dreamily the evening has stilled the haunted braes,
   And dreamier the gloaming grows.

And sinking one by one, like lark-notes from the sky
   When the falcon's shadow saileth across the open shaw,

[1] Distaff

ELPHIN, OUPH AND FAY

Are hushed the maidens' voices, as cowering down they lie
   In the flutter of their sudden awe.

For, from the air above, and the grassy ground beneath,
   And from the mountain-ashes and the old Whitethorn
    between,
A power of faint enchantment doth through their beings
   breathe,
    And they sink down together on the green.

They sink together silent, and stealing side to side,
   They fling their lovely arms o'er their drooping necks so
    fair.
Then vainly strive again their naked arms to hide,
   For their shrinking necks again are bare.

Thus clasped and prostrate all, with their heads together
   bowed,
   Soft o'er their bosom's beating—the only human sound—
They hear the silky footsteps of the silent fairy crowd,
    Like a river in the air, gliding round.

Nor scream can any raise, nor prayer can any say,
   But wild, wild, the terror of the speechless three—
For they feel fair Anna Grace drawn silently away,
    By whom they dare not look to see.

They feel their tresses twine with her parting locks of gold,
   And the curls elastic falling, as her head withdraws ;
They feel her sliding arms from their tranced arms unfold,
    But they dare not look to see the cause :

For heavy on their senses the faint enchantment lies
   Through all that night of anguish and perilous amaze ;
And neither fear nor wonder can ope their quivering eyes
    Or their limbs from the cold ground raise,

Till out of Night the Earth has rolled her dewy side,
   With every haunted mountain and streamy vale below ;
When, as the mist dissolves in the yellow morning-tide,
    The maidens' trance dissolveth so.

THE FAIRY THORN

Then fly the ghastly three as swiftly as they may,
  And tell their tale of sorrow to anxious friends in vain—
They pined away and died within the year and day,
  And ne'er was Anna Grace seen again.

SAMUEL FERGUSON

136   THE QUEEN OF ELFLAND

TRUE Thomas lay oer yond grassy bank,
  And he beheld a ladie gay,
A ladie that was brisk and bold,
  Come riding oer the fernie brae.

Her skirt was of the grass-green silk,
  Her mantel of the velvet fine,
At ilka tett of her horse's mane
  Hung fifty silver bells and nine.

True Thomas he took off his hat,
  And bowed him low down till his knee :
" All hail, thou mighty Queen of Heaven !
  For your peer on earth I never did see."

" O no, O no, True Thomas," she says,
  " That name does not belong to me ;
I am but the queen of fair Elfland,
  And I'm come here for to visit thee. . . .

" But ye maun go wi me now, Thomas,
  True Thomas, ye maun go wi me,
For ye maun serve me seven years,
  Thro weel or wae as may chance to be.

" Then harp and carp, Thomas," she said,
  " Then harp and carp alang wi me ;
But it will be seven years and a day
  Till ye win back to yere ain countrie."

She turned about her milk-white steed,
  And took True Thomas up behind,

127

ELPHIN, OUPH AND FAY

And aye wheneer her bridle rang,
   The steed flew swifter than the wind.

For forty days and forty nights
   He wade thro red blude to the knee,
And he saw neither sun nor moon,
   But heard the roaring of the sea.

O they rade on, and further on,
   Until they came to a garden green :
" Light down, light down, ye ladie free,
   Some of that fruit let me pull to thee."

" O no, O no, True Thomas," she says,
   " That fruit maun not be touched by thee,
For a' the plagues that are in hell
   Light on the fruit of this countrie.

" But I have a loaf here in my lap,
   Likewise a bottle of claret wine,
And now ere we go farther on,
   We'll rest a while, and ye may dine."

When he had eaten and drunk his fill :—
   " Lay down your head upon my knee,"
The lady sayd, " ere we climb yon hill
   And I will show you fairlies three.

" O see not ye yon narrow road,
   So thick beset wi thorns and briers ?
That is the path of righteousness,
   Tho after it but few enquires.

" And see not ye that braid braid road,
   That lies across yon lillie leven ?
That is the path of wickedness,
   Tho some call it the road to heaven

" And see not ye that bonny road,
   Which winds about the fernie brae ?
That is the road to fair Elfland,
   Where you and I this night maun gae

THE QUEEN OF ELFLAND

" But Thomas, ye maun hold your tongue,
    Whatever you may hear or see,
For gin ae word you should chance to speak,
    You will neer get back to your ain countrie."

He has gotten a coat of the even cloth,
    And a pair of shoes of velvet green,
And till seven years were past and gone
    True Thomas on earth was never seen.

137   LA BELLE DAME SANS MERCI

O, WHAT can ail thee, knight at arms,
    Alone and palely loitering ;
The sedge has withered from the lake,
    And no birds sing.

O, what can ail thee, knight at arms,
    So haggard and so woe-begone ?
The squirrel's granary is full,
    And the harvest's done.

I see a lilly on thy brow
    With anguish moist and fever-dew,
And on thy cheeks a fading rose
    Fast withereth too.

I met a lady in the meads,
    Full beautiful—a faery's child,
Her hair was long, her foot was light,
    And her eyes were wild.

I made a garland for her head,
    And bracelets too, and fragrant zone ;
She looked at me as she did love,
    And made sweet moan.

I set her on my pacing steed
    And nothing else saw all day long ;
For sideways would she lean, and sing
    A faery's song.

ELPHIN, OUPH AND FAY

She found me roots of relish sweet,
  And honey wild and manna dew;
And sure in language strange she said—
  I love thee true.

She took me to her elfin grot,
  And there she gazed and sighed full sore:
And there I shut her wild wild eyes
  With kisses four.

And there she lullèd me asleep,
  And there I dreamed, ah woe betide,
The latest dream I ever dreamed
  On the cold hill side.

I saw pale kings and princes too,
  Pale warriors, death-pale were they all:
They cry'd—" La belle Dame sans Merci
  Hath thee in thrall!"

I saw their starved lips in the gloam
  With horrid warning gapèd wide,
And I awoke, and found me here
  On the cold hill side.

And this is why I sojourn here
  Alone and palely loitering,
Though the sedge is withered from the lake,
  And no birds sing.

JOHN KEATS

138   SABRINA

" SABRINA fair
  Listen where thou art sitting
Under the glassie, cool, translucent wave,
  In twisted braids of Lillies knitting
The loose train of thy amber-dropping hair,
  Listen for dear honour's sake,
  Goddess of the silver lake,
      Listen and save!...

130

SABRINA

By all the *Nymphs* that nightly dance
Upon thy streams with wily glance,
Rise, rise, and heave thy rosie head
From thy coral-pav'n bed,
And bridle in thy headlong wave,
Till thou our summons answered have.
   Listen and save ! "

" By the rushy-fringèd bank,
Where grows the Willow and the Osier dank,
 My sliding Chariot stayes,
Thick set with Agat, and the azurn sheen
Of Turkis blew, and Emrauld green
 That in the channell strayes,
Whilst from off the waters fleet
Thus I set my printless feet
O're the Cowslips Velvet head,
 That bends not as I tread,
Gentle swain at thy request
  I am here."   JOHN MILTON

139   NOW THE HUNGRY LION ROARS

" Now the hungry Lyon rores,
And the Wolfe behowls the Moone :
Whilst the heavy ploughman snores,
All with weary taske fordone.
Now the wasted brands doe glow,
Whil'st the scritch-owle scritching loud,
Puts the wretch that lies in woe
In remembrance of a shrowd.
Now it is the time of night
That the graves, all gaping wide,
Every one lets forth his spright,
In the Church-way paths to glide.
And we Fairies, that do runne
By the triple *Hecate's* teame,
From the presence of the Sunne,
Following darknesse like a dreame,

ELPHIN, OUPH AND FAY

Now are frollicke ; not a Mouse
Shall disturbe this hallowed house.
I am sent with broome before,
To sweep the dust behinde the doore."

" Through the house give glimmering light,
By the dead and drowsie fier ;
Everie Elfe and Fairie spright
Hop as light as bird from brier ! . . ."

WILLIAM SHAKESPEARE

140   THE FAIRIES FEAST

. . . *Awn.*   Who feasts tonight ?

Some Elves.   Prince Olbin is truth-plight
              To Rosalind, daughter of the Faery Queen.

Other Elves. She's a mannikin changeling ; her name shows it.

Other Elves. We have heard tell ; that she as dream is fair.

Awn.   I've heard old Paigle say, fays gave for her
              To humans, in the cradle, Moonsheen bright.

Other Elves. And Eglantine should wedded be this night,
              To Ivytwine, in the laughing full moon.

Moth.   I was there and saw it : on hoar roots,
              All gnarled and knotty, of an antique oak, . . .
              Crowned, some with plighted frets of violets
                  sweet ;
              Other, with flower-cups many-hewed, had dight
              Their locks of gold ; the gentle faeries sate :
              All in their watchet cloaks : were dainty mats
              Spread under them, of dwarve-wives rushen
                  work :
              And primroses were strewed before their feet.
              They at banquet sate, from dim of after-
              noon . . .   (*Enter more elves running.*)

Howt.   Whence come ye foothot ?

THE FAIRIES FEAST

One of the new-come Elves.   O Awn, O Howt !
        Not past a league from hence, lies close-cropped
           plot,
        Where purple milkworts blow, which conies
           haunt,
        Amidst the windy heath. We saw gnomes
           dance
        There ; that not bigger been than harvest mice.
        Some of their heads were deckt, as seemed to us,
        With moonbeams bright : and those tonight
           hold feast :
        Though in them there none utterance is of
           speech.

Awn.   Be those our mothers' cousins, dainty of grace :
        But seld now, in a moonlight, are they seen.
        They live not longer than do humble been.

Elves.   We saw of living herb, intressed with moss,
        Their small wrought cabins open on the grass.

Awn.   Other, in gossamer bowers, wonne underclod.

Elves.   And each gnome held in hand a looking glass ;
        Wherein he keeked, and kissed oft the Moons
           face.

Awn.   Are they a faery offspring, without sex,
        Of the stars' rays.

Elves.   They'd wings on their flit feet ;
        That seemed, in their oft shining, glancing drops
        Of rain, which beat on bosom of the grass :
        Wherein be some congealed as adamant.
          We stooped to gaze (a neighbour tussock hid
          us,)
        On sight so fair : their beauty being such,
        That seemed us it all living thought did pass.
        Yet were we spied ! for looked down full upon
          us,

ELPHIN, OUPH AND FAY

Disclosing then murk skies, Moons clear still
  face.
In that they shrunk back, and clapped tó
  their doors. . . .

CHARLES M. DOUGHTY

SUMMER : GREENWOOD
SOLITUDE. ☙ ☙ ☙ ☙

THE HUNT IS UP

THE hunt is up, the hunt is up,
   And it is well nigh day ;
And Harry our King is gone hunting
   To bring his deer to bay.

The east is bright with morning light,
   And darkness it is fled ;
And the merry horn wakes up the morn
   To leave his idle bed.

Behold the skies with golden dyes
   Are glowing all around ;
The grass is green, and so are the treen
   All laughing at the sound.

The horses snort to be at sport,
   The dogs are running free,
The woods rejoice at the merry noise
   Of *Hey tantara tee ree !*

The sun is glad to see us clad
   All in our lusty green,
And smiles in the sky as he riseth high
   To see and to be seen.

Awake all men, I say again,
   Be merry as you may ;
For Harry our King is gone hunting,
   To bring his deer to bay.

THE CHEERFUL HORN

THE cheerful arn he blaws in the marn,
And we'll a-'untin' goo ;
The cheerful arn he blaws in the marn,
And we'll a-'untin' goo,
  And we'll a-'untin' goo,
  And we'll a-'untin' goo . . .
    Var all my vancy dwells upon Nancy,
    And I'll zing Tally ho !
    Var all my vancy dwells upon Nancy,
    And I'll zing Tally ho !

The vox jumps awer the 'edge zo 'igh,
  An' the 'ouns all atter un goo ;
    Var all my vancy dwells upon Nancy,
    And I'll zing Tally ho !

Then never despoise the soldjer lod,
  Thof 'is ztaition be boot low ;
    Var all my vancy dwells upon Nancy,
    And I'll zing Tally ho !

Then push about the coop, my bwoys,
  An' we will wumwards goo,
    Var all my vancy dwells upon Nancy,
    And I'll zing Tally ho !

If you áx me the zénze of this zóng vur to téll,
  Or the reäzon vur to zhow ;
Woy, I doän't exacaly knoo,
Woy, I doän't exacaly knoo :
    Var all my vancy dwells upon Nancy,
    And I'll zing Tally ho !
    Var all my vancy dwells upon Nancy,
    And I'll zing Tally ho !

143   JOHN PEEL

D'YE ken John Peel with his coat so gay ?
D'ye ken John Peel at the break of the day ?
D'ye ken John Peel when he's far, far away,
With his hounds and his horn in the morning ?
    'Twas the sound of his horn called me from my bed,
    And the cry of his hounds has me oft-times led,
    For Peel's *View-hollo* would awaken the dead,
    Or a fox from his lair in the morning.

D'ye ken that bitch whose tongue is death ?
D'ye ken her sons of peerless faith ?
D'ye ken that a fox with his last breath
Cursed them all as he died in the morning ?

Yes, I ken John Peel and Ruby too
Ranter and Royal and Bellman as true ;
From the drag to the chase, from the chase to a view,
From a view to the death in the morning.

And I've followed John Peel both often and far
O'er the rasper-fence and the gate and the bar,
From Low Denton Holme up to Scratchmere Scar,
When we vied for the brush in the morning.

Then here's to John Peel with my heart and soul,
Come fill—fill to him another strong bowl :
And we'll follow John Peel through fair and through foul,
While we're waked by his horn in the morning.
    'Twas the sound of his horn called me from my bed,
    And the cry of his hounds has me oft-times led,
    For Peel's *View-hollo* would awaken the dead
    Or a fox from his lair in the morning.
JOHN WOODCOCK GRAVES

144 THE SCHOOLBOY

I LOVE to rise in a summer morn
When the birds sing on every tree ;
The distant huntsman winds his horn,
And the skylark sings with me.
O ! what sweet company.

But to go to school in a summer morn,
O ! it drives all joy away ;
Under a cruel eye outworn,
The little ones spend the day
In sighing and dismay.

Ah ! then at times I drooping sit,
And spend many an anxious hour,
Nor in my book can I take delight,
Nor sit in learning's bower,
Worn thro' with the dreary shower.

How can the bird that is born for joy
Sit in a cage and sing ?
How can a child, when fears annoy,
But droop his tender wing,
And forget his youthful spring ?

O ! father and mother, if buds are nipped,
And blossoms blown away,
And if the tender plants are stripped
Of their joy in the springing day,
By sorrow and care's dismay,

How shall the summer arise in joy,
Or the summer fruits appear ?
Or how shall we gather what griefs destroy,
Or bless the mellowing year,
When the blasts of winter appear ?

WILLIAM BLAKE

145   A BOY'S SONG

WHERE the pools are bright and deep,
Where the grey trout lies asleep,
Up the river and over the lea,
That's the way for Billy and me.

Where the blackbird sings the latest,
Where the hawthorn blooms the sweetest,
Where the nestlings chirp and flee,
That's the way for Billy and me.

Where the mowers mow the cleanest,
Where the hay lies thick and greenest,
There to track the homeward bee,
That's the way for Billy and me.

Where the hazel bank is steepest,
Where the shadow falls the deepest,
Where the clustering nuts fall free,
That's the way for Billy and me.

Why the boys should drive away
Little sweet maidens from their play,
Or love to banter and fight so well,
That's the thing I never could tell.

But this I know, I love to play
Through the meadow, among the hay ;
Up the water and over the lea,
That's the way for Billy and me.

                       JAMES HOGG

146   MARKET DAY

WHO'LL walk the fields with us to town,
In an old coat and a faded gown ?
We take our roots and country sweets,
Where high walls shade the steep old streets,
And golden bells and silver chimes
Ring up and down the sleepy times.

SUMMER : GREENWOOD : SOLITUDE

The morning mountains smoke like fires ;
The sun spreads out his shining wires ;
The mower in the half-mown lezza
Sips his tea and takes his pleasure.
Along the lane slow waggons amble.
The sad-eyed calves awake and gamble ;
The toad that lay so sorrowful
Is playing in the grasses cool.
By slanting ways, in slanting sun,
Through startled lapwings now we run
Along the pale green hazel-path,
Through April's lingering aftermath
Of lady's smock and lady's slipper ;
We stay to watch a nesting dipper.
The rabbits eye us while we pass,
Out of the sorrel-crimson grass ;
The blackbird sings, without a fear,
Where honeysuckle horns blow clear—
Cool ivory stained with true vermilion,
And here, within a silk pavilion,
Small caterpillars lie at ease.
The endless shadows of the trees
Are painted purple and cobalt ;
Grandiloquent, the rook-files halt,
Each one aware of you and me,
And full of conscious dignity.
Our shoes are golden as we pass
With pollen from the pansied grass.
Beneath an elder—set anew
With large clean plates to catch the dew—
On fine white cheese and bread we dine.
The clear brook-water tastes like wine.
If all folk lived with labour sweet
Of their own busy hands and feet,
Such marketing, it seems to me,
Would make an end of poverty.

MARY WEBB

147 UNDER THE GREENWOOD TREE

UNDER the greenewood tree,
Who loves to lye with me,
And turne his merrie Note
Unto the sweet Bird's throte :
Come hither, come hither, come hither,
    Heere shall he see no enemie
But Winter and rough Weather.

Who doth ambition shunne
And loves to live i' the Sunne,
Seeking the food he eates
And pleased with what he gets :
Come hither, come hither, come hither,
    Here shall he see no enemie
But Winter and rough Weather.
                        WILLIAM SHAKESPEARE

148 IN SUMMER

IN somer when the shawes be sheyne,[1]
    And leves be large and long,
Hit [2] is full merry in feyre foreste
    To here the foulys [3] song.

To se the dere draw to the dale
    And leve the hilles hee,
And shadow him in the leves grene
    Under the green-wode tree.

Hit befell on Whitsontide
    Early in a May mornyng,
The Sonne up faire gan shyne,
    And the briddis mery gan syng.

" This is a mery mornyng," said Litulle Johne,
    " By Hym that dyed on tree ;

[1] When the woods are fresh and fair   [2] It   [3] Small birds'

143

SUMMER : GREENWOOD : SOLITUDE

A more mery man than I am one
Lyves not in Christianté.

" Pluk up thi hert, my dere mayster,"
Litulle Johne can say,
" And thynk hit is a fulle fayre tyme
In a mornynge of May."

140   LUBBER BREEZE

The four sails of the mill
Like stocks stand still ;
Their lantern-length is white
On blue more bright.

Unruffled is the mead,
Where lambkins feed
And sheep and cattle browse
And donkeys drowse.

Never the least breeze will
The wet thumb chill
That the anxious miller lifts,
Till the vane shifts.

The breeze in the great flour-bin
Is snug tucked in ;
The lubber, while rats thieve,
Laughs in his sleeve.

                              T. STURGE MOORE

150   A SUMMER'S DAY

" The ample heaven of fabrik sure,
    In cleannes dois surpas
The chrystall and the silver pure,
    Or clearest poleist [1] glas.

The shadow of the earth anon
    Removes and drawes by,

[1] Polished

                144

A SUMMER'S DAY

Sine in the east, when it is gon,
  Appears a clearer sky.

Quhilk sune [1] perceives the little larks,
  The lapwing and the snyp,
And tune their sangs, like Nature's clarks
  Our medow, mure and stryp. [2]

The time sa tranquil is and still,
  That na where sall ye find,
Saife on ane high and barren hill,
  Ane aire of peeping wind.

All trees and simples [3] great and small,
  That balmie leife do beir,
Nor thay were painted on a wall,
  Na mair they move or steir [4] . . ."

ALEXANDER HUME

151   LEISURE

WHAT is this life if, full of care,
We have no time to stand and stare ?

No time to stand beneath the boughs
And stare as long as sheep or cows.

No time to see, when woods we pass,
Where squirrels hide their nuts in grass.

No time to see, in broad daylight,
Streams full of stars, like skies at night.

No time to turn at Beauty's glance,
And watch her feet, how they can dance.

No time to wait till her mouth can
Enrich that smile her eyes began.

A poor life this if, full of care,
We have no time to stand and stare.

WILLIAM H. DAVIES

[1] Which soon   [2] O'er meadow, moor and stream
[3] Herbs, wild flowers   [4] Stir

152   THE HAPPY COUNTRYMAN

Who can live in heart so glad
As the merry country lad ?
Who upon a fair green balk [1]
May at pleasure sit and walk,
And amid the azure skies
See the morning sun arise, —
While he hears in every spring
How the birds do chirp and sing :
Or before the hounds in cry
See the hare go stealing by :
Or along the shallow brook,
Angling with a baited hook,
See the fishes leap and play
In a blessèd sunny day :
Or to hear the partridge call,
Till she have her covey all :
Or to see the subtle fox,
How the villain plies the box :
After feeding on his prey,
How he closely sneaks away,
Through the hedge and down the furrow
Till he gets into his burrow :
Then the bee to gather honey,
And the little black-haired coney,
On a bank for sunny place,
With her forefeet wash her face :
Are not these, with thousands moe [2]
Than the courts of kings do know,
The true pleasing spirit's sights
That may breed true love's delights ? . . .

                              NICHOLAS BRETON

[1] A bank between ploughlands   [2] More

146

153   "O FOR A BOOKE"

O for a Booke and a shadie nooke,
    eyther in-a-doore or out ;
With the grene leaves whispering overhede,
    or the Streete cryes all about.
Where I maie Reade all at my ease,
    both of the Newe and Olde ;
For a jollie goode Booke whereon to looke,
    is better to me than Golde.

154   GREEN BROOM

THERE was an old man lived out in the wood,
    His trade was a-cutting of Broom, green Broom ;
He had but one son without thrift, without good,
    Who lay in his bed till 'twas noon, bright noon.

The old man awoke, one morning and spoke,
    He swore he would fire the room, that room,
If his John would not rise and open his eyes,
    And away to the wood to cut Broom, green Broom.

So Johnny arose, and he slipped on his clothes,
    And away to the wood to cut Broom, green Broom,
He sharpened his knives, for once he contrives
    To cut a great bundle of Broom, green Broom.

When Johnny passed under a lady's fine house,
    Passed under a lady's fine room, fine room,
She called to her maid, " Go fetch me," she said,
    " Go fetch me the boy that sells Broom, green Broom."

When Johnny came in to the lady's fine house,
    And stood in the lady's fine room, fine room ;
" Young Johnny," she said, " Will you give up your trade,
    And marry a lady in bloom, full bloom ? "

Johnny gave his consent, and to church they both went,
  And he wedded the lady in bloom, full bloom,
At market and fair, all folks do declare,
  There is none like the Boy that sold Broom, green Broom.

155   THE TWELVE OXEN

I HAVE twelfé oxen that be faire and brown,
And they go a grasing down by the town.
  With hey ! with how ! with hoy !
Saweste not you mine oxen, you litill prety boy ?

I have twelfé oxen, and they be faire and white,
And they go a grasing down by the dyke.
  With hey ! with how ! with hoy !
Saweste not you mine oxen, you litill prety boy ?

I have twelfé oxen, and they be faire and blak,
And they go a grasing down by the lake.
  With hey ! with how ! with hoy !
Saweste not you mine oxen, you litill prety boy ?

I have twelfé oxen, and they be faire and rede,
And they go a grasing down by the mede
  With hey ! with how ! with hoy !
Saweste not you mine oxen, you litill prety boy ?

156   LAVENDER'S BLUE

LAVENDER'S blue, dilly dilly, lavender's green,
When I am king, dilly dilly, you shall be queen
Who told you so, dilly dilly, who told you so ?
'Twas mine one heart, dilly dilly, that told me so.

Call up your men, dilly dilly, set them to work,
Some with a rake, dilly dilly, some with a fork,
Some to make hay, dilly dilly, some to thresh corn,
Whilst you and I, dilly dilly, keep ourselves warm. . . .

THE GARDEN

157

. . . WHAT wondrous life is this I lead !
Ripe apples drop about my head ;
The luscious clusters of the vine
Upon my mouth do crush their wine ;
The nectarine and curious peach
Into my hands themselves do reach ;
Stumbling on melons, as I pass,
Ensnared with flowers, I fall on grass.

Meanwhile the mind, from pleasure less,
Withdraws into its happiness ;
The mind, that ocean where each kind
Does straight its own resemblance find ;
Yet it creates, transcending these,
Far other worlds and other seas,
Annihilating all that's made
To a green thought in a green shade.

Here at the fountain's sliding foot
Or at some fruit-tree's mossy root,
Casting the body's vest aside
My soul into the boughs does glide :
There, like a bird, it sits and sings,
Then whets [1] and claps its silver wings,
And, till prepared for longer flight,
Waves in its plumes the various light. . . .

Such was the happy Garden-state
While man there walked without a mate :
After a place so pure and sweet,
What other help could yet be meet !
But 'twas beyond a mortal's share
To wander solitary there :
Two paradises 'twere in one,
To live in Paradise alone. . . .

ANDREW MARVELL

[1] Preens

149

158   CHERRY-RIPE

CHERRIE Ripe, Ripe, Ripe, I cry,
Full and faire ones ; come and buy :
If so be you ask me where
They doe grow ? I answer, There,
Where my *Julia's* lips doe smile ;
There's the Land, or Cherrie Ile :
Whose Plantations fully show
All the yeare, where Cherries grow.

                                    ROBERT HERRICK

159   CHERRY-RIPE

THERE is a Garden in her face
Where Roses and white Lillies grow ;
    A heav'nly paradice is that place,
Wherein all pleasant fruits doe flow.
        There Cherries grow, which none may buy,
        Till *Cherry Ripe* themselves doe cry.

Those Cherries fayrely doe enclose
Of Orient Pearle a double row,
    Which when her lovely laughter showes,
They look like Rose-buds filled with snow.
        Yet them nor Peere nor Prince can buy,
        Till *Cherry Ripe* themselves doe cry.

Her Eyes like Angels watch them still ;
Her Browes like bended bowes doe stand,
    Threat'ning with piercing frownes to kill
All that approach with eye or hand
        These sacred Cherries to come nigh,
        Till *Cherry Ripe* themselves do cry.

                                    THOMAS CAMPION

160   SONG

What is there hid in the heart of a rose,
          Mother-mine ?
Ah, who knows, who knows, who knows ?
A Man that died on a lonely hill
May tell you, perhaps, but none other will,
          Little child.

What does it take to make a rose,
          Mother-mine ?
The God that died to make it knows
It takes the world's eternal wars,
It takes the moon and all the stars,
It takes the might of heaven and hell
And the everlasting Love as well,
          Little child.
                                        ALFRED NOYES

161   THE MYSTERY

He came and took me by the hand
          Up to a red rose tree,
He kept His meaning to Himself
          But gave a rose to me.
I did not pray Him to lay bare
          The mystery to me,
Enough the rose was Heaven to smell,
          And His own face to see.
                                        RALPH HODGSON

162   THE ROSE

A Rose, as fair as ever saw the North,
Grew in a little garden all alone ;
A sweeter flower did Nature ne'er put forth,
Nor fairer garden yet was never known :

The maidens danced about it morn and noon,
And learnèd bards of it their ditties made ;
                    151

SUMMER : GREENWOOD : SOLITUDE

The nimble fairies by the pale-faced moon
Watered the root and kissed her pretty shade.

But well-a-day !—the gardener careless grew ;
The maids and fairies both were kept away,
And in a drought the caterpillars threw
Themselves upon the bud and every spray.

God shield the stock ! If heaven send no supplies,
The fairest blossom of the garden dies.

WILLIAM BROWNE

163   SONG

Ask me no more, where Jove bestows
When June is past the fading rose ;
For in your beauty's orient deep
These flowers, as in their causes, sleep.

Ask me no more, whither do stray
The golden atoms of the day ;
For in pure love heaven did prepare
Those powders to enrich your hair.

Ask me no more, whither doth haste
The nightingale when May is past ;
For in your sweet dividing throat
She winters and keeps warm her note.

Ask me no more, where those stars light [1]
That downwards fall in dead of night ;
For in your eyes they sit and there
Fixèd become as in their sphere.

Ask me no more if east or west
The Phœnix builds her spicy nest ;
For unto you at last she flies,
And in your fragrant bosom dies.

THOMAS CAREW

[1] Stay

164

THE BOWER OF BLISS

(The "daintie Paradise of the Enchauntresse" whereinto the Palmer brought Sir Guyon.)

. . . And in the midst of all, a fountaine stood,
Of richest substaunce that on earth might bee,
So pure and shiny, that the silver flood
Through every channell running, one might see ;
Most goodly it with pure imageree
Was over-wrought, and shapes of naked boyes,
Of which some seemed with lively jollitee
To fly about, playing their wanton toyes,
Whiles others did them selves embay in liquid joyes.

And over all, of purest gold was spred
A trayle of yvie in his native hew :
For the rich mettall was so colouréd,
That wight, who did not well-advised it vew,
Would surely deeme it to be yvie treu.
Lowe his lascivious arms adown did creepe,
That themselves dipping in the silver dew,
Their fleecy flowres they tenderly did steepe,
Which drops of Cristall seemd for wantonnes to weepe.

Infinit streames continually did well
Out of this fountaine, sweet and faire to see,
The which into an ample laver fell,
And shortly grew to so great quantitie,
That like a little lake it seemed to bee ;
Whose depth exceeded not three cubits hight,
That through the waves one might the bottom see,
All paved beneath with Jaspar shining bright
That seemd the fountaine in that sea did sayle upright.

And all the margent round about was set
With shady lawrell-trees, thence to defend
The sunny beames, which on the billows bet,
And those which therein bathèd, mote [1] offend . . .

[1] Might

153

SUMMER : GREENWOOD : SOLITUDE

Eftsoones they heard a most melodious sound,
Of all that mote delight a daintie eare,
Such as att once might not on living ground,
Save in this Paradise, be heard elswhere :
Right hard it was, for wight, which did it heare,
To read, what manner musicke that mote bee :
For all that pleasing is to living eare,
Was there consorted in one harmonie,
Birdes, voyces, instruments, windes, waters, all agree.

The joyous birdes, shrouded in cheareful shade,
Their notes unto the voice attempred sweet ;
Th' Angelicall soft trembling voyces made
To th' instruments divine respondence meet :
The silver sounding instruments did meet
With the base murmure of the waters fall :
The waters fall with difference discreet,
Now soft, now loud, unto the wind did call :
The gentle warbling wind low answerèd to all.

EDMUND SPENSER

165   SMALL FOUNTAINS

. . . JARRING the air with rumour cool,
Small fountains played into a pool
With sound as soft as the barley's hiss
When its beard just sprouting is ;
Whence a young stream, that trod on moss,
Prettily rimpled the court across.
And in the pool's clear idleness,
Moving like dreams through happiness,
Shoals of small bright fishes were ;
In and out weed-thickets bent
Perch and carp, and sauntering went
With mounching jaws and eyes a-stare ;
Or on a lotus leaf would crawl,
A brinded loach to bask and sprawl,

154

SMALL FOUNTAINS

Tasting the warm sun ere it dipt
Into the water; but quick as fear
Back his shining brown head slipt
To crouch on the gravel of his lair,
Where the cooled sunbeams broke in wrack,
Spilt shattered gold about his back. . . .

LASCELLES ABERCROMBIE

166   THE INVITATION, TO JANE

BEST and brightest, come away!
Fairer far than this fair Day,
Which, like thee to those in sorrow,
Comes to bid a sweet good-morrow
To the rough Year just awake
In its cradle on the brake.
The brightest hour of unborn Spring,
Through the winter wandering,
Found, it seems, the halcyon Morn
To hoar February born;
Bending from Heaven, in azure mirth,
It kissed the forehead of the Earth,
And smiled upon the silent sea,
And bade the frozen streams be free,
And waked to music all their fountains,
And breathed upon the frozen mountains,
And like a prophetess of May
Strewed flowers upon the barren way,
Making the wintry world appear
Like one on whom thou smilest, dear. . . .

Radiant sister of the Day,
Awake! arise! and come away!
To the wild woods and the plains,
And the pools where winter rains
Image all their roof of leaves,
Where the pine its garland weaves
Of sapless green and ivy dun
Round stems that never kiss the sun;

SUMMER : GREENWOOD : SOLITUDE

Where the lawns and pastures be,
And the sand-hills of the sea ; —
Where the melting hoar-frost wets
The daisy-star that never sets,
The wind-flowers, and violets,
Which yet join not scent to hue,
Crown the pale year weak and new ;
When the night is left behind
In the deep east, dun and blind,
And the blue noon is over us,
And the multitudinous
Billows murmur at our feet,
Where the earth and ocean meet,
And all things seem only one
In the universal sun.

PERCY BYSSHE SHELLEY

167   THE RECOLLECTION

... WE wandered to the Pine Forest
   That skirts the Ocean's foam ;
The lightest wind was in its nest,
   The tempest in its home.
The whispering waves were half asleep,
   The clouds were gone to play,
And on the bosom of the deep
   The smile of Heaven lay ;
It seemed as if the hour were one
   Sent from beyond the skies,
Which scattered from above the sun
   A light of Paradise !

We paused amid the pines that stood
   The giants of the waste,
Tortured by storms to shapes as rude
   As serpents interlaced,
And soothed by every azure breath,
   That under heaven is blown,

156

THE RECOLLECTION

To harmonies and hues beneath,
  As tender as its own :
Now all the tree-tops lay asleep
  Like green waves on the sea,
As still as in the silent deep
  The ocean woods may be.

How calm it was !—The silence there
  By such a chain was bound
That even the busy woodpecker
  Made stiller with her sound
The inviolable quietness ;
  The breath of peace we drew
With its soft motion made not less
  The calm that round us grew.
There seemed, from the remotest seat
  Of the white mountain waste
To the soft flower beneath our feet,
  A magic circle traced,—
A spirit interfused around,
  A thrilling, silent life—
To momentary peace it bound
  Our mortal nature's strife ;—
And still I felt the centre of
  The magic circle there
Was one fair form that filled with love
  The lifeless atmosphere. . . .
                    PERCY BYSSHE SHELLEY

THE GOAT PATHS

THE crooked paths go every way
  Upon the hill—they wind about
  Through the heather in and out
Of the quiet sunniness.
And there the goats, day after day,
  Stray in sunny quietness,

SUMMER : GREENWOOD : SOLITUDE

Cropping here and cropping there,
  As they pause and turn and pass,
Now a bit of heather spray,
  Now a mouthful of the grass.

In the deeper sunniness,
  In the place where nothing stirs,
Quietly in quietness,
  In the quiet of the furze,
For a time they come and lie
Staring on the roving sky.

If you approach they run away,
  They leap and stare, away they bound,
  With a sudden angry sound,
To the sunny quietude ;
  Crouching down where nothing stirs
  In the silence of the furze,
Couching down again to brood
In the sunny solitude.

If I were as wise as they,
  I would stray apart and brood,
I would beat a hidden way
Through the quiet heather spray
  To a sunny solitude ;

And should you come I'd run away,
  I would make an angry sound,
  I would stare and turn and bound
To the deeper quietude,
  To the place where nothing stirs
  In the silence of the furze.

In that airy quietness
  I would think as long as they ;
Through the quiet sunniness
  I would stray away to brood
By a hidden beaten way
  In a sunny solitude,

I would think until I found
Something I can never find,
Something lying on the ground,
In the bottom of my mind.

JAMES STEPHENS

169　UNDER A WILTSHIRE APPLE TREE

SOME folks as can afford,
So I've heard say,
Set up a sort of cross
Right in the garden way
To mind 'em of the Lord.
But I, when I do see
Thik [1] apple tree
An' stoopin' limb
All spread wi' moss,
I think of Him
And how He talks wi' me.

I think of God
And how He trod
That garden long ago ;
He walked, I reckon, to and fro
And then sat down
Upon the groun'
Or some low limb
What suited Him,
Such as you see
On many a tree,
And on thik very one
Where I at set o' sun
Do sit and talk wi' He.

And, mornings, too, I rise and come
An' sit down where the branch be low ;
A bird do sing, a bee do hum,
The flowers in the border blow,

[1] This

And all my heart's so glad and clear
As pools be when the sun do peer,
As pools a-laughing in the light
When mornin' air is swep' an' bright,
As pools what got all Heaven in sight,
So's my heart's cheer
When He be near.

He never pushed the garden door,
He left no footmark on the floor ;
I never heard 'Un stir nor tread
And yet His Hand do bless my head,
And when 'tis time for work to start
I takes Him with me in my heart.
And when I die, pray God I see
At very last thik apple tree
An' stoopin' limb,
And think of Him
And all He been to me.

ANNA BUNSTON DE BARY

170   WONDER

How like an Angel came I down !
How bright were all things here !
When first among His works I did appear
O how their Glory me did crown !
The world resembled His ETERNITY,
In which my soul did walk ;
And every thing that I did see
Did with me talk.

The skies in their magnificence,
The lively, lovely air,
Oh how divine, how soft, how sweet, how fair !
The stars did entertain my sense,

WONDER

And all the works of God, so bright and pure,
    So rich and great did seem,
  As if they ever must endure
    In my esteem. . . .

  The streets were paved with golden stones,
    The boys and girls were mine,
Oh how did all their lovely faces shine !
  The sons of men were holy ones,
In joy and beauty they appeared to me,
    And every thing which here I found,
  While like an Angel I did see,
    Adorned the ground.

  Rich diamond and pearl and gold
    In every place was seen ;
Rare splendours, yellow, blue, red, white and green,
  Mine eyes did everywhere behold.
Great wonders clothed with glory did appear,
    Amazement was my bliss,
  That and my wealth was everywhere ;
    No joy to this ! . . .
              THOMAS TRAHERNE

171   SONG

How sweet I roamed from field to field
And tasted all the summer's pride,
Till I the Prince of Love beheld
Who in the sunny beams did glide !

He showed me lilies for my hair,
And blushing roses for my brow ;
He led me through his gardens fair
Where all his golden pleasures grow.

With sweet May dews my wings were wet,
And Phoebus fired my vocal rage ;
He caught me in his silken net,
And shut me in his golden cage.

SUMMER : GREENWOOD : SOLITUDE

He loves to sit and hear me sing,
Then, laughing, sports and plays with me ;
Then stretches out my golden wing,
And mocks my loss of liberty.

WILLIAM BLAKE

172   THE BOOK

Of this fair volume which we World do name
If we the sheets and leaves could turn with care,
Of Him who it corrects and did it frame,
We clear might read the art and wisdom rare :

Find out His power which wildest powers doth tame,
His providence extending everywhere,
His justice which proud rebels doth not spare,
In every page, no period of the same.

But silly we, like foolish children, rest
Well pleased with coloured vellum, leaves of gold,
Fair dangling ribbands, leaving what is best,
On the great Writer's sense ne'er taking hold ;

Or, if by chance we stay our minds on aught, .
It is some picture on the margin wrought.

WILLIAM DRUMMOND

173   TETHY'S FESTIVAL

Are they shadows that we see ?
And can shadows pleasure give ?
Pleasures only shadows be,
Cast by bodies we conceive ;
And are made the things we deem
In those figures which they seem.

But those pleasures vanish fast,
Which by shadows are exprest ;

TETHY'S FESTIVAL

Pleasures are not, if they last ;
In their passing is their best :
Glory is more bright and gay
In a flash, and so away.

Feed apace then, greedy eyes,
On the wonder you behold :
Take it sudden, as it flies,
Though you take it not to hold.
When your eyes have done their part
Thought must length'n it in the heart.

SAMUEL DANIEL

WAR

A WAR SONG TO ENGLISHMEN

PREPARE, prepare the iron helm of War,
Bring forth the lots, cast in the spacious orb ;
The Angel of Fate turns them with mighty hands,
And casts them out upon the darkened earth !
                              Prepare, prepare !

Prepare your hearts for Death's cold hand ! prepare
Your souls for flight, your bodies for the earth ;
Prepare your arms for glorious victory ;
Prepare your eyes to meet a holy God !
                              Prepare, prepare !

Whose fatal scroll is that ?   Methinks 'tis mine !
Why sinks my heart, why faltereth my tongue ?
Had I three lives, I'd die in such a cause,
And rise, with ghosts, over the well-fought field.
                              Prepare, prepare !

The arrows of Almighty God are drawn !
Angels of Death stand in the lowering heavens !
Thousands of souls must seek the realms of light,
And walk together on the clouds of heaven !
                              Prepare, prepare !

Soldiers, prepare !   Our cause is Heaven's cause ;
Soldiers, prepare !   Be worthy of our cause :
Prepare to meet our fathers in the sky :
Prepare, O troops, that are to fall to-day !
                              Prepare, prepare !

WAR

Alfred shall smile, and make his harp rejoice ;
The Norman William, and the learnèd Clerk,
And Lion Heart, and black-browed Edward, with
His loyal Queen, shall rise, and welcome us !
Prepare, prepare !
WILLIAM BLAKE

175   FOR SOLDIERS

YE buds of Brutus' land, courageous youths, now play your
    parts ;
Unto your tackle stand, abide the brunt with valiant hearts.
For news is carried to and fro, that we must forth to warfare
    go :
Men muster now in every place, and soldiers are prest forth
    apace.
          Faint not, spend blood,
        To do your Queen and country good ;
          Fair words, good pay,
        Will make men cast all care away.

The time of war is come, prepare your corslet, spear and
    shield ;
Methinks I hear the drum strike doleful marches to the field ;
Tantarâ, tantarâ, ye trumpets sound, which makes our
    hearts with joy abound.
The roaring guns are heard afar, and everything denounceth
    war.
          Serve God ; stand stout ;
        Bold courage brings this gear about.
          Fear not ; fate run [1] ;
        Faint heart fair lady never won.

Ye curious [2] carpet-knights, that spend the time in sport and
    play ;
Abroad and see new sights, your country's cause calls you
    away ;

[1] Risk, hazard, dare.   [2] Dainty ; luxurious.

168

FOR SOLDIERS

Do not to make your ladies' game, bring blemish to your
worthy name.
Away to field and win renown, with courage beat your
enemies down.
    Stout hearts gain praise,
    When dastards sail in Slander's seas ;
    Hap what hap shall,
    We sure shall die but once for all.

Alarm methinks they cry, Be packing, mates, begone with
speed ;
Our foes are very nigh ; shame have that man that shrinks
at need !
Unto it boldly let us stand, God will give Right the upper
hand.
Our cause is good, we need not doubt, in sign of coming
give a shout.
    March forth, be strong,
    Good hap will come ere it be long.
    Shrink not, fight well,
    For lusty lads must bear the bell.

All you that will shun evil, must dwell in warfare every day ;
The world, the flesh, and devil, always do seek our soul's
decay ;
Strive with these foes with all your might, so shall you fight
a worthy fight.
That conquest doth deserve most praise, where vice do yield
to virtue's ways.
    Beat down foul sin,
    A worthy crown then shall ye win ;
    If ye live well,
    In heaven with Christ our souls shall dwell.
                 HUMPHREY GIFFORD

WAR

BATTLE-HYMN OF THE REPUBLIC

MINE eyes have seen the glory of the coming of the Lord;
He is trampling out the vintage where the grapes of wrath
are stored;
He hath loosed the fateful lightning of His terrible swift
sword;
His truth is marching on.

I have seen Him in the watch-fires of a hundred circling
camps;
They have builded Him an altar in the evening dews and
damps;
I can read his righteous sentence by the dim and flaring
lamps;
His day is marching on.

I have read a fiery gospel, writ in burnished rows of steel:
"As ye deal with my contemners, so with you my grace
shall deal;
Let the Hero, born of woman, crush the serpent with his
heel,
Since God is marching on."

He has sounded forth the trumpet that shall never call
retreat;
He is sifting out the hearts of men before His judgment-seat;
Oh, be swift, my soul, to answer Him! be jubilant, my feet!
Our God is marching on.

In the beauty of the lilies Christ was born across the sea,
With a glory in His bosom that transfigures you and me:
As He died to make men holy, let us die to make men free,
While God is marching on.

JULIA WARD HOWE

"I HEARD A SOLDIER"

I HEARD a soldier sing some trifle
  Out in the sun-dried veldt alone :
He lay and cleaned his grimy rifle
  Idly, behind a stone.

" If after death, love, comes a waking,
  And in their camp so dark and still
The men of dust hear bugles, breaking
  Their halt upon the hill,

" To me the slow, the silver pealing
  That then the last high trumpet pours
Shall softer than the dawn come stealing,
  For, with its call, comes yours ! "

What grief of love had he to stifle,
  Basking so idly by his stone,
That grimy soldier with his rifle
  Out in the veldt, alone ?

HERBERT TRENCH

THE DUG-OUT

WHY do you lie with your legs ungainly huddled,
And one arm bent across your sullen cold
Exhausted face ?   It hurts my heart to watch you,
Deep-shadowed from the candle's guttering gold ;
And you wonder why I shake you by the shoulder ;
Drowsy, you mumble and sigh and turn your head . . .
You are too young to fall asleep for ever ;
And when you sleep you remind me of the dead.

SIEGFRIED SASSOON

179   NOCTURNE

Be thou at peace this night
    Wherever be thy bed,
Thy slumbering be light,
    The fearful dreams be dead
    Within thy lovely head ;
God keep thee in His sight.

No hint of love molest
    Thy quiet mind again ;
Night fold thee to her breast
    And hush thy crying pain ;
    Let memory in vain
Conspire against thy rest.

So may thy thoughts be lost
    In the full hush of sleep.
Lest any sight accost
    Thine eyes to make them weep,
    In darkness buried deep
For ever be my ghost.

                         EDWARD L. DAVISON

180   THE DEAD

THESE hearts were woven of human joys and cares,
    Washed marvellously with sorrow, swift to mirth.
The years had given them kindness. Dawn was theirs,
    And sunset, and the colours of the earth.

These had seen movement, and heard music ; known
    Slumber and waking ; loved ; gone proudly friended ;
Felt the quick stir of wonder ; sat alone ;
    Touched flowers and furs and cheeks. All this is
        ended.

There are waters blown by changing winds to laughter
And lit by the rich skies, all day. And after,
    Frost, with a gesture, stays the waves that dance

172

And wandering loveliness. He leaves a white
Unbroken glory, a gathered radiance,
A width, a shining peace, under the night.

RUPERT BROOKE

181   THE END

AFTER the blast of lightning from the east,
The flourish of loud clouds, the Chariot throne ;
After the drums of time have rolled and ceased,
And, from the bronze west, long retreat is blown—

Shall Life renew these bodies ?   Of a truth
All death will he annul, all tears assuage ?—
Or fill these void veins full again with youth,
And wash, with an immortal water, Age ?

When I do ask white Age, he saith, " Not so :
My head hangs weighed with snow."
And when I hearken to the Earth, she saith :
" My fiery heart sinks aching.   It is death.
Mine ancient scars shall not be glorified.
Nor my titanic tears, the seas, be dried."

WILFRED OWEN

182   THE CROWNS

CHERRY and pear are white,
Their snows lie sprinkled on the land like light
On darkness shed.
Far off and near
The orchards toss their crowns of delight,
And the sun casts down
Another shining crown.

The wind tears and throws down
Petal by petal the crown
Of cherry and pear till the earth is white,
And all the brightness is shed
In the orchards far off and near,
That tossed by the road and under the green hill ;
And the wind is fled.

173

WAR

Far, far off the wind
Has shaken down
A brightness that was as the brightness of cherry or pear
When the orchards shine in the sun.
—Oh there is no more fairness
Since this rareness,
The radiant blossom of English earth—is dead !

John Freeman

183   CORONACH[1]

He is gone on the mountain,
   He is lost to the forest,
Like a summer-dried fountain,
   When our need was the sorest.
The font, reappearing,
   From the rain-drops shall borrow,
But to us comes no cheering,
   To Duncan no morrow !

The hand of the reaper
   Takes the ears that are hoary,
But the voice of the weeper
   Wails manhood in glory.
The autumn winds rushing
   Waft the leaves that are serest,
But our flower was in flushing,
   When blighting was nearest.

Fleet foot on the correi,[2]
   Sage counsel in cumber,[3]
Red hand in the foray,
   How sound is thy slumber !
Like the dew on the mountain,
   Like the foam on the river,
Like the bubble on the fountain,
   Thou art gone, and for ever.

Sir Walter Scott

[1] Dirge, lament   [2] Vast hill-hollow   [3] Danger or defeat

184   THE CHILDREN'S BELLS

WHERE are your Oranges?
Where are your Lemons?
What, are you silent now,
Bells of St. Clement's? *
You, of all bells that rang
Once in old London,
You, of all bells that sang,
Utterly undone?
You whom all children know
Ere they know letters,
Making Big Ben himself
Call you his betters?
Where are your lovely tones
Fruitful and mellow,
Full-flavoured orange-gold,
Clear lemon-yellow?
Ring again, sing again,
Bells of St. Clement's!
Call as you swing again,
" Oranges! Lemons!"
Fatherless children
Are listening near you—
Sing for the children,
The fathers will hear you.

                    ELEANOR FARJEON

185   MEN WHO MARCH AWAY

WE be the King's men, hale and hearty,
Marching to meet one Buonaparty;
If he won't sail, lest the wind should blow,
We shall have marched for nothing, O!
                    Right fol-lol!

(*When the half-muffled City Bells rang in commemoration of the
Bell-Ringers who fell in the war, the bells of St. Clement Danes could
not take part owing to a defect in the framework.)

WAR

We be the King's men, hale and hearty,
Marching to meet one Buonaparty ;
If he be sea-sick, says " No, no ! "
We shall have marched for nothing, O !
                    Right fol-lol !

We be the king's men hale and hearty,
Marching to meet one Buonaparty ;
Never mind, mates ; we'll be merry, though
We may have marched for nothing, O !
                    Right fol-lol !

                              THOMAS HARDY

186   BUDMOUTH DEARS

WHEN we lay where Budmouth Beach is,
O, the girls were fresh as peaches,
With their tall and tossing figures and their eyes of blue and
        brown !
        And our hearts would ache with longing
        As we paced from our sing-songing,
With a smart *Clink ! Clink !* up the Esplanade and down.

        They distracted and delayed us
        By the pleasant pranks they played us,
And what marvel, then, if troopers, even of regiments of
        renown,
        On whom flashed those eyes divine, O,
        Should forget the countersign, O,
As we tore *Clink ! Clink !* back to camp above the town.

        Do they miss us much, I wonder,
        Now that war has swept us sunder,
And we roam from where the faces smile to where the faces
        frown ?
        And no more behold the features
        Of the fair fantastic creatures,
And no more *Clink ! Clink !* past the parlours of the town ?

Shall we once again there meet them ?
Falter fond attempts to greet them ?
Will the gay sling-jacket glow again beside the muslin
gown ?
    Will they archly quiz and con us
    With a sideway glance upon us,
While our spurs *Clink! Clink!* up the Esplanade and
down ?

THOMAS HARDY

187   TRAFALGAR

In the wild October night-time, when the wind raved round
    the land,
And the Back-sea met the Front-sea, and our doors were
    blocked with sand,
And we heard the drub of Dead-man's Bay, where bones of
    thousands are,
We knew not what the day had done for us at Trafalgár.
        (*All*) Had done,
              Had done,
       For us at Trafalgar !

" Pull hard, and make the Nothe, or down we go !" one says,
    says he.
We pulled ; and bedtime brought the storm ; but snug at
    home slept we.
Yet all the while our gallants after fighting through the
    day,
Were beating up and down the dark, sou'-west of Cadiz Bay.
           The dark,
           The dark,
      Sou'-west of Cadiz Bay !

The victors and the vanquished then the storm it tossed and
    tore,
As hard they strove, those worn-out men, upon that surly
    shore ;

WAR

Dead Nelson and his half-dead crew, his foes from near and
    far,
Were rolled together on the deep that night at Trafalgar !
            The deep,
            The deep,
        That night at Trafalgar !

THOMAS HARDY

MESSMATES

He gave us all a good-bye cheerily
    At the first dawn of day ;
We dropped him down the side full drearily
    When the light died away.
It's a dead dark watch that he's a-keeping there,
And a long, long night that lags a-creeping there,
Where the Trades and the tides roll over him
    And the great ships go by.

He's there alone with green seas rocking him
    For a thousand miles round ;
He's there alone with dumb things mocking him,
    And we're homeward bound.
It's a long, lone watch that he's a-keeping there,
And a dead cold night that lags a-creeping there,
While the months and the years roll over him
    And the great ships go by.

I wonder if the tramps come near enough
    As they thrash to and fro,
And the battle-ships' bells ring clear enough
    To be heard down below ;
If through all the lone watch that he's a-keeping
        there,
And the long, cold night that lags a-creeping there,
The voices of the sailor-men shall comfort him
    When the great ships go by.

HENRY NEWBOLT

189   SONG FOR ALL SEAS, ALL SHIPS

To-day a rude brief recitative,
Of ships sailing the seas, each with its special flag or ship-
    signal,
Of unnamed heroes in the ships—of waves spreading and
    spreading far as the eye can reach,
Of dashing spray, and the winds piping and blowing,
And out of these a chant for the sailors of all nations,
Fitful, like a surge.

Of sea-captains young or old, and the mates, and of all
    intrepid sailors,
Of the few, very choice, taciturn, whom fate can never
    surprise nor death dismay,
Picked sparingly without noise by thee, old ocean, chosen
    by thee,
Thou sea that pickest and cullest the race in time, and
    unitest nations,
Suckled by thee, old husky nurse, embodying thee,
Indomitable, untamed as thee. . . .

Flaunt out, O sea, your separate flags of nations !
Flaunt out visible as ever the various ship-signals !
But do you reserve especially for yourself and for the soul
    of man one flag above all the rest,
A spiritual woven signal for all nations, emblem of man elate
    above death,
Token of all brave captains and all intrepid sailors and
    mates,
And all that went down doing their duty,
Reminiscent of them, twined from all intrepid captains young
    or old,
A pennant universal, subtly waving all time, o'er all, brave
    sailors,
All seas, all ships.

                                        WALT WHITMAN

HOHENLINDEN

On Linden, when the sun was low,
All bloodless lay the untrodden snow ;
And dark as winter was the flow
    Of Iser, rolling rapidly.

But Linden saw another sight,
When the drum beat at dead of night
Commanding fires of death to light
    The darkness of her scenery.

By torch and trumpet fast arrayed
Each horseman drew his battle-blade,
And furious every charger neighed
    To join the dreadful revelry.

Then shook the hills with thunder riven ;
Then rushed the steed, to battle driven ;
And louder than the bolts of Heaven
    Far flashed the red artillery.

But redder yet that light shall glow
On Linden's hills of stainèd snow ;
And bloodier yet the torrent flow
    Of Iser, rolling rapidly.

'Tis morn ; but scarce yon level sun
Can pierce the war-clouds, rolling dun,
Where furious Frank and fiery Hun
    Shout in their sulphurous canopy.

The combat deepens. On, ye Brave,
Who rush to glory or the grave !
Wave, Munich ! all thy banners wave,
    And charge with all thy chivalry !

Few, few shall part, where many meet !
The snow shall be their winding-sheet,
And every turf beneath their feet
    Shall be a soldier's sepulchre.
              THOMAS CAMPBELL

HAME, HAME, HAME

HAME, HAME, HAME

HAME, hame, hame, hame, fain wad I be :
O hame, hame, hame to my ain countrie !
When the flower is in the bud, and the leaf is on the tree,
The lark shall sing me hame to my ain countrie.
Hame, hame, hame ! O hame fain wad I be !
O hame, hame, hame to my ain countrie !

The green leaf o' loyalty's beginning now to fa' ;
The bonnie white rose it is withering an' a' ;
But we'll water it with the blude of usurping tyrannie,
And fresh it shall blaw in my ain countrie !

O, there's nocht now frae ruin my countrie can save,
But the keys o' kind heaven, to open the grave,
That a' the noble martyrs wha died for loyaltie
May rise again and fight for their ain countrie.

The great now are gane, who attempted to save ;
The green grass is growing abune their graves ;
Yet the sun through the mirk seems to promise to me—
I'll shine on ye yet in your ain countrie.
Hame, hame, hame, hame, fain wad I be ;
O hame, hame, hame to my ain countrie !

ALLAN CUNNINGHAM

DARK ROSALEEN

O MY dark Rosaleen,
  Do not sigh, do not weep !
The priests are on the ocean green,
  They march along the deep.
There's wine from the royal Pope
  Upon the ocean green,
And Spanish ale shall give you hope,
  My dark Rosaleen !
  My own Rosaleen !
Shall glad your heart, shall give you hope,
Shall give you health, and help, and hope,
  My dark Rosaleen !

WAR

Over hills and through dales
  Have I roamed for your sake ;
All yesterday I sailed the sails
  On river and on lake.
The Erne, at its highest flood,
  I dashed across unseen,
For there was lightning in my blood,
  My dark Rosaleen !
  My own Rosaleen !
Oh ! there was lightning in my blood,
Red lightning lightened through my blood,
  My dark Rosaleen !

All day long, in unrest,
  To and fro do I move.
The very soul within my breast
  Is wasted for you, love !
The heart in my bosom faints
  To think of you, my Queen,
My life of life, my saint of saints,
  My dark Rosaleen !
  My own Rosaleen !
To hear your sweet and sad complaints,
My life, my love, my saint of saints,
  My dark Rosaleen !

Woe and pain, pain and woe,
  Are my lot, night and noon,
To see your bright face clouded so,
  Like to the mournful moon.
But yèt will I rear your throne
  Again in golden sheen ;
'Tis you shall reign, shall reign alone
  My dark Rosaleen !
  My own Rosaleen !
'Tis you shall have the golden throne,
'Tis you shall reign, and reign alone,
  My dark Rosaleen !

DARK ROSALEEN

Over dews, over sands,
  Will I fly for your weal :
Your holy delicate white hands
  Shall girdle me with steel.
At home, in your emerald bowers,
  From morning's dawn till e'en,
You'll pray for me, my flower of flowers,
  My dark Rosaleen !
  My fond Rosaleen !
You'll think of me through daylight hours,
My virgin flower, my flower of flowers,
  My dark Rosaleen !

I could scale the blue air,
  I could plough the high hills,
Oh, I could kneel all night in prayer,
  To heal your many ills !
And one beamy smile from you
  Would float like light between
My toils and me, my own, my true,
  My dark Rosaleen !
  My fond Rosaleen !
Would give me life and soul anew,
A second life, a soul anew,
  My dark Rosaleen !

Oh ! the Erne shall run red
  With redundance of blood,
The earth shall rock beneath our tread,
  And flames wrap hill and wood,
And gun-peal and slogan-cry
  Wake many a glen serene,
Ere you shall fade, ere you shall die,
  My dark Rosaleen !
  My own Rosaleen !
The Judgment Hour must first be nigh,
Ere you shall fade, ere you can die,
  My dark Rosaleen !

JAMES CLARENCE MANGAN

WAR

MY LUVE'S IN GERMANY

" My Luve's in Germany ;
  Send him hame, send him hame ;
My Luve's in Germany,
  Send him hame :
My Luve's in Germany,
  Fighting for Royalty ;
He may ne'er his Jeanie see ;
  Send him hame, send him hame ;
He may ne'er his Jeanie see,
  Send him hame.

" He's brave as brave can be,
  Send him hame, send him hame ;
He's brave as brave can be,
  Send him hame.
He's brave as brave can be,
He wad rather fa' than flee ;
But his life is dear to me,
  Send him hame, send him hame ;
Oh ! his life is dear to me,
  Send him hame.

" Our faes are ten to three,
  Send him hame, send him hame ;
Our faes are ten to three,
  Send him hame.
Our faes are ten to three,
He maun either fa' or flee,
In the cause o' Loyalty ;
  Send him hame, send him hame ;
In the cause o' Loyalty,
  Send him hame."

" Your luve ne'er learnt to flee,
  Bonnie Dame, winsome Dame ;
Your luve ne'er learnt to flee,
  Winsome Dame.

184

MY LUVE'S IN GERMANY

Your luve ne'er learnt to flee,
But he fell in Germany,
Fighting brave for Loyalty,
    Mournfu' Dame, bonnie Dame,
Fighting brave for Loyalty,
    Mournfu' Dame !"

" He'll ne'er come owre the sea,
    Willie's slain, Willie's slain ;
He'll ne'er come owre the sea,
    Willie's gane !
He'll ne'er come owre the sea,
To his Love and ain Countrie—
This warld's nae mair for me,
    Willie's gane, Willie's gane !
This warld's nae mair for me
    Willie's slain !"

A WEARY LOT IS THINE

" A WEARY lot is thine, fair maid,
    A weary lot is thine !
To pull the thorn thy brow to braid,
    And press the rue for wine.
A lightsome eye, a soldier's mien,
    A feather of the blue,
A doubtlet of the Lincoln green—
    No more of me you knew,
                My love !
No more of me you knew.

" This morn is merry June, I trow,
    The rose is budding fain ;
But she shall bloom in winter snow
    Ere we two meet again."
He turned his charger as he spake
    Upon the river shore,

WAR

He gave the bridle-reins a shake,
  Said, " Adieu for evermore,
          My love !
And adieu for evermore."

SIR WALTER SCOTT

105   CHARLIE HE'S MY DARLING

  An' Charlie he's my darling,
    My darling, my darling !
  Charlie he's my darling,
    The young Chevalier !

'Twas on a Monday morning,
  Right early in the year,
That Charlie cam' to our town,
  The young Chevalier !

As he was walking up the street,
  The city for to view,
O, there he spied a bonnie lass
  The window lookin' through.

Sae light's he jimpèd up the stair,
  An' tirlèd at the pin ;
An' wha sae ready as hersel
  To let the laddie in ?

He set Jenny on his knee,
  A' in his Highland dress ;
For brawlie weel he kenned the way
  To please a lassie best.

It's up yon heathery mountain,
  An' down yon scroggy glen,
We daur na gang a-milking
  For Charlie an' his men !

  An' Charlie he's my darling,
    My darling, my darling !
  Charlie he's my darling,
    The young Chevalier !

THE FAREWELL

It was a' for our rightfu' king
   We left fair Scotland's strand ;
It was a' for our rightfu' king
   We e'er saw Irish land,
      My dear,
   We e'er saw Irish land.

Now a' is done that man can do,
   And a' is done in vain ;
My love, and native land, farewell,
   For I maun cross the main,
      My dear,
   For I maun cross the main.

He turned him right and round about
   Upon the Irish shore ;
And gae his bridle-reins a shake,
   With Adieu for evermore,
      My dear,
   Adieu for evermore.

The sodger frae the wars returns,
   The sailor frae the main ;
But I hae parted frae my love,
   Never to meet again,
      My dear,
   Never to meet again.

When day is gane, and night is come,
   And a' folks bound to sleep ;
I think on him that's far awa',
   The lee-lang night, and weep,
      My dear,
   The lee-lang night, and weep.

                              ROBERT BURNS

WAR

THE FLOWERS OF THE FOREST

I've heard them lilting at our ewe-milking,
Lasses a-lilting before the dawn of day ;
But now they are moaning on ilka green loaning :—
The Flowers of the Forest are a' wede away.

At bughts in the morning nae blythe lads are scorning ;
The lasses are lanely, and dowie, and wae ;
Nae daffing, nae gabbing, but sighing and sabbing,
Ilk ane lifts her leglin, and hies her away.

In hairst, at the shearing, nae youths now are jeering :
The bandsters are lyart, and runkled, and gray.
At fair or at preaching, nae wooing, nae fleeching—
The Flowers of the Forest are a' wede away.

At e'en, in the gloaming, nae swankies are roaming
'Bout stacks wi' the lasses at bogle to play ;
But ilk ane sits drearie, lamenting her dearie—
The Flowers of the Forest are a' wede away.

Dool and wae for the order sent our lads to the Border !
The English, for ance, be guile wan the day ;
The Flowers of the Forest, that fought aye the foremost,
The prime of our land, lie cauld in the clay.

We'll hear nae mair lilting at our ewe-milking ;
Women and bairns are heartless and wae ;
Sighing and moaning on ilka green loaning :
The Flowers of the Forest are a' wede away.

                                        JEAN ELLIOT

198   ## "AS I WAS GOING"

As I was going by Charing Cross,
I saw a black man upon a black horse :
They told me it was King Charles the First ;
Oh dear, my heart was ready to burst !

199   OF THE GREAT AND FAMOUS

EVER TO BE HONOURED KNIGHT, SIR FRANCIS DRAKE,
AND OF MY LITTLE-LITTLE SELFE.

THE Dragon that our Seas did raise his Crest
And brought back heapes of gold unto his nest,
Unto his Foes more terrible than Thunder,
Glory of his age, After-ages' wonder,
Excelling all those that excelled before ;
It's feared we shall have none such any more ;
Effecting all he sole did undertake,
Valiant, just, wise, milde, honest, Godly *Drake*.
This man when I was little I did meete
As he was walking up Totnes' long street.
He asked me whose I was ?   I answered him.
He asked me if his good friend were within ?
A faire red Orange in his hand he had,
He gave it me whereof I was right glad,
Takes and kist me, and prayes *God blesse my boy* :
Which I record *with comfort* to this day.
Could he on me have breathèd with his breath,
His gifts, Elias-like, after his death,
Then had I beene enabled for to doe
Many brave things I have a heart unto.
I have as great desire as e're had *hee*
To joy, annoy, friends, foes ; but 'twill not be.
                             ROBERT HAYMAN

200   A LAMENTATION

ALL looks be pale, hearts cold as stone,
For Hally now is dead and gone.
     Hally in whose sight,
       Most sweet sight,
All the earth late took delight.
     Every eye, weep with me,
     Joys drowned in tears must be.

WAR

His ivory skin, his comely hair,
His rosy cheeks so clear and fair,
 Eyes that once did grace
  His bright face,
Now in him all want their place.
 Eyes and hearts, weep with me,
 For who so kind as he?

His youth was like an April flower,
Adorned with beauty, love, and power.
 Glory strewed his way,
  Whose wreaths gay
Now are all turnèd to decay.
 Then, again, weep with me,
 None feel more cause than we.

No more may his wished sight return.
His golden lamp no more can burn.
 Quenched is all his flame,
  His hoped fame
Now hath left him nought but name.
 For him all weep with me,
 Since more him none shall see.

THOMAS CAMPION

201 WHAT IF SOME LITTLE PAIN THE PASSAGE HAVE

 . . . What if some little paine the passage have,
That makes fraile flesh to feare the bitter wave?
Is not short paine well borne, that brings long ease,
And layes the soule to sleepe in quiet grave?
Sleep after toyle, port after stormie seas,
Ease after warre, death after live does greatly please. . . .

EDMUND SPENSER

202   HENRY BEFORE AGINCOURT : October 25,
1415

... Our King went up upon a hill high
And looked down to the valleys low :
He saw where the Frenchmen came hastily
As thick as ever did hail or snow.
Then kneeled our King down, in that stound,[1]
And all his men on every side :
Every man made a cross and kissed the ground,
And on their feet fast gan abide.
Our King said, " Sirs, what time of the day ? "
" My Liege," they said, " it is nigh Prime."
" Then go we to our journey,
By the grace of Jesu, it is good time :
For saints that lie in their shrine
To God for us be praying.
All the Religious of England, in this time,
Ora pro nobis for us they sing."
St. George was seen over the host :
Of very truth this sight men did see.
Down was he sent by the Holy Ghost,
To give our King the victory. . . .

John Lydgate

203   ALEXANDER THE GREAT

Four men stood by the grave of a man,
The grave of Alexander the Proud :
They sang words without falsehood
Over the prince from fair Greece.

Said the first man of them :
" Yesterday there were around the king
The men of the world—a sad gathering !
Though to-day he is alone."

[1] For a moment

WAR

" Yesterday the king of the brown world
Rode upon the heavy earth :
Though to-day it is the earth
That rides upon his neck."

" Yesterday," said the third wise author,
" Philip's son owned the whole world :
To-day he has nought
Save seven feet of earth."

" Alexander the liberal and great
Was wont to bestow silver and gold :
To-day," said the fourth man,
" The gold is here, and it is nought."

Thus truly spoke the wise men
Around the grave of the high-king :
It was not foolish women's talk
What those four sang.

204   THE MYRTLE BUSH GREW SHADY

" THE myrtle bush grew shady
Down by the ford."—
" Is it even so ?" said my lady.
" Even so !" said my lord.
" The leaves are set too thick together
For the point of a sword."

" The arras in your room hangs close,
No light between !
You wedded one of those
That see unseen."—
" Is it even so ?" said the King's Majesty.
" Even so !" said the Queen.
                                    MARY COLERIDGE

205 ## THE FORT OF RATHANGAN

The fort over against the oak-wood,
Once it was Bruidge's, it was Cathal's,
It was Aed's, it was Ailill's,
It was Conaing's, it was Cuiline's,
And it was Maelduin's ;
The fort remains after each in his turn—
And the kings asleep in the ground.

DANCE, ⊕ ⊕ ⊕ ⊕
MUSIC AND BELLS.

206   A PIPER

A PIPER in the streets to-day
Set up, and tuned, and started to play,
And away, away, away on the tide
Of his music we started ; on every side
Doors and windows were opened wide,
And men left down their work and came,
And women with petticoats coloured like flame.
And little bare feet that were blue with cold,
Went dancing back to the age of gold,
And all the world went gay, went gay,
For half an hour in the street to-day.

SEUMAS O'SULLIVAN

207   THE LITTLE DANCERS

LONELY, save for a few faint stars, the sky
Dreams ; and lonely, below, the little street
Into its gloom retires, secluded and shy.
Scarcely the dumb roar enters this soft retreat ;
And all is dark, save where come flooding rays
From a tavern window : there, to the brisk measure
Of an organ that down in an alley merrily plays,
Two children, all alone and no one by,
Holding their tattered frocks, through an airy maze
Of motion, lightly threaded with nimble feet,
Dance sedately : face to face they gaze,
Their eyes shining, grave with a perfect pleasure.

LAURENCE BINYON

208   TWO NUT TREES

i

I HAD a little nut tree,
Nothing would it bear,
But a silver nutmeg,
And a golden pear.
The King of Spain's daughter
Came to visit me,
And all was because of
My little nut tree.
I skipped over water
I danced over sea,
And all the birds in the air
Could not catch me.

THOMAS ANON

ii

THE King of China's daughter
So beautiful to see
With her face like yellow water, left
Her nutmeg tree.
Her little rope for skipping
She kissed and gave it me—
Made of painted notes of singing-birds
Among the fields of tea.
I skipped across the nutmeg grove,—
I skipped across the sea ;
But neither sun nor moon, my dear,
Has yet caught me.

EDITH SITWELL

209   WHEN THE GREEN WOODS LAUGH

WHEN the green woods laugh with the voice of joy,
And the dimpling stream runs laughing by ;
When the air does laugh with our merry wit,
And the green hill laughs with the noise of it ;

WHEN THE GREEN WOODS LAUGH

When the meadows laugh with lively green,
And the grasshopper laughs in the merry scene,
When Mary and Susan and Emily
With their sweet round mouths sing " Ha, Ha, He !"

When the painted birds laugh in the shade,
Where our table with cherries and nuts is spread,
Come live, and be merry, and join with me,
To sing the sweet chorus of " Ha, Ha, He !"

WILLIAM BLAKE

210   FA LA LA

My mistress frowns when she should play ;
I'll please her with a *Fa la la.*
Sometimes she chides, but I straightway
Present her with a *Fa la la.*

You lovers that have loves astray
May win them with a *Fa la la.*
Quick music's best, for still they say
None pleaseth like your *Fa la la.*

211   IT WAS A LOVER

It was a Lover, and his lasse,
 With a hey, and a ho, and a hey nonino,
That ore the greene corne-field did passe,
 In spring time, the onely pretty ring time,
When Birds do sing, *hey ding a ding, ding :*
Sweet Lovers love the spring.

Between the acres of the Rie,
 With a hey, and a ho, and a hey nonino,
These prettie Country folks would lie,
 In spring time, the onely pretty ring time,
When Birds do sing, *hey ding a ding, ding :*
Sweet Lovers love the spring.

199

This Carroll they began that houre,
  With a hey, and a ho, and a hey nonino,
How that a life was but a Flower,
  In spring time, the only pretty ring time,
When Birds do sing, *hey ding a ding, ding :*
Sweet Lovers love the spring.

And therefore take the present time,
  With a hey, and a ho, and a hey nonino ;
For love is crownèd with the prime
  In spring time, the only pretty ring time,
When birds do sing, *hey ding a ding, ding :*
Sweet lovers love the spring.

WILLIAM SHAKESPEARE

212   HEY, NONNY NO !

  Hey, nonny no !
  Men are fools that wish to die !
  Is't not fine to dance and sing
  When the bells of death do ring ?
  Is't not fine to swim in wine,
  And turn upon the toe,
  And sing *Hey nonny no !*

  When the winds blow   and the seas flow ?
  Hey, nonny no !

213   TARANTELLA

Do you remember an Inn,
Miranda ?
Do you remember an Inn ?
And the tedding and the spreading
Of the straw for a bedding,
And the fleas that tease in the High Pyrenees,
And the wine that tasted of the tar ?
And the cheers and the jeers of the young muleteers
(Under the dark of the vine verandah) ?

TARANTELLA

Do you remember an Inn, Miranda,
Do you remember an Inn?
And the cheers and the jeers of the young muleteers
Who hadn't got a penny,
And who weren't paying any,
And the hammer at the doors and the Din?
And the Hip! Hop! Hap!
Of the clap
Of the hands to the twirl and the swirl
Of the girl gone chancing,
Glancing,
Dancing,
Backing and advancing,
.Snapping of the clapper to the spin
Out and in—
And the Ting, Tong, Tang of the guitar!
Do you remember an Inn,
Miranda?
Do you remember an Inn?

Never more;
Miranda,
Never more.
Only the high peaks hoar:
And Aragon a torrent at the door.
No sound
In the walls of the Halls where falls
The tread
Of the feet of the dead to the ground.
No sound:
Only the boom
Of the far Waterfall like Doom.

HILAIRE BELLOC

"I LOVED A LASS"

I LOVED a lass, a fair one,
    As fair as e'er was seen ;
She was indeed a rare one,
    Another Sheba Queen :
But, fool as then I was,
    I thought she loved me too :
But now, alas ! she has left me,
    Falero, lero, loo ! . . .

And as abroad we walkèd
    As lovers' fashion is,
Oft as we sweetly talkèd
    The sun would steal a kiss.
The wind upon her lips
    Likewise most sweetly blew ;
But now, alas ! she has left me
    Falero, lero, loo !

Many a merry meeting
    My love and I have had ;
She was my only sweeting,
    She made my heart full glad ;
The tears stood in her eyes
    Like to the morning dew :
But now, alas ! she has left me,
    Falero, lero, loo !

Her cheeks were like the cherry,
    Her skin was white as snow ;
When she was blithe and merry
    She angel-like did show ;
Her waist exceeding small,
    The fives did fit her shoe :
But now, alas ! she has left me,
    Falero, lero, loo !

In summer time or winter
    She had her heart's desire ;

"I LOVED A LASS"

I still did scorn to stint her
    From sugar, sack, or fire ;
The world went round about,
    No cares we ever knew :
But now, alas ! she has left me,
    Falero, lero, loo ! . . .

No riches now can raise me,
    No want make me despair ;
No misery amaze me,
    Nor yet for want I care.
I have lost a world itself,
    My earthly heaven, adieu,
Since she, alas ! hath left me,
    Falero, lero, loo. . . .

GEORGE WITHER

215   GREEN GRASS

A dis, a dis, a green grass,
    A dis, a dis, a dis ;
Come all you pretty fair maids
    And dance along with us.

For we are going roving,
    A roving in this land ;
We take this pretty fair maid,
    We take her by the hand.

She shall get a duke, my dear,
    As duck do get a drake ;
And she shall have a young prince,
    For her own fair sake.

And if this young prince chance to die,
    She shall get another ;
The bells will ring, and the birds will sing,
    And we clap hands together.

203

DANCE, MUSIC AND BELLS

210   THE LINCOLNSHIRE POACHER

WHEN I was bound apprentice in famous Lincolnshire,
Full well I served my master for more than seven year,
Till I took up to poaching—as you shall quickly hear :
  Oh, 'tis my delight on a shining night
  In the season of the year !

As me and my comrade were setting of a snare,
'Twas then we spied the gamekeeper, for him we did not care,
For we can wrestle and fight, my boys, and jump o'er any-
  where :
  Oh, 'tis my delight on a shining night
  In the season of the year !

As me and my comrade were setting four or five,
And taking on 'em up again we caught a hare alive,
We took the hare alive, my boys, and through the woods did
  steer :
  Oh, 'tis my delight on a shining night
  In the season of the year !

I threw him on my shoulder, and then we trudged home,
We took him to a neighbour's house and sold him for a
  crown
We sold him for a crown, my boys, but I did not tell you
  where :
  Oh, 'tis my delight on a shining night
  In the season of the year !

Success to every gentleman that lives in Lincolnshire,
Success to every poacher that wants to sell a hare,
Bad luck to every gamekeeper that will not sell his deer : [1]
  Oh, 'tis my delight on a shining night
  In the season of the year !

---

[1] Game

217   THE MEN OF GOTHAM

SEAMEN three ! What men be ye ?
Gotham's three wise men we be.
Whither in your bowl so free ?
To rake the moon from out the sea.
The bowl goes trim. The moon doth shine.
And our ballast is old wine—
And your ballast is old wine.

Who art thóu, so fast adrift ?
I am he they call Old Care.
Here on board we will thee lift.
No : I may not enter there.
Wherefore so ?   'Tis Jove's decree,
In a bowl Care may not be—
In a bowl Care may not be.

Fear ye not the waves that roll ?
No ; in charmèd bowl we swim.
What the charm that floats the bowl ?
Water may not pass the brim.
The bowl goes trim. The moon doth shine.
And our ballast is old wine—
And your ballast is old wine.

THOMAS LOVE PEACOCK

218   EARLY MORNING MEADOW SONG

Now some may drink old vintage wine
    To ladies gowned with rustling silk,
But we will drink to dairymaids,
    And drink to them in rum and milk—
O, it's up in the morning early,
    When the dew is on the grass,
And St. John's bell rings for matins,
    And St. Mary's rings for mass !

DANCE, MUSIC AND BELLS

The merry skylarks soar and sing,
    And seem to Heaven very near
Who knows what blessed inns they see,
    What holy drinking songs they hear?
O, it's up in the morning early,
    When the dew is on the grass,
And St. John's bell rings for matins,
    And St. Mary's rings for mass!

The mushrooms may be priceless pearls
    A queen has lost beside the stream;
But rum is melted rubies when
    It turns the milk to golden cream!
O, it's up in the morning early,
    When the dew is on the grass,
And St. John's bell rings for matins,
    And St. Mary's rings for mass!

CHARLES DALMON

219   DABBLING IN THE DEW

On, where are you going to, my pretty little dear,
With your red rosy cheeks and your coal-black hair?
I'm going a-milking, kind sir, she answered me:
And it's dabbling in the dew makes the milkmaids fair!

Suppose I were to clothe you, my pretty little dear,
In a green silken gown and the amethyst rare?
O no, sir, O no, sir, kind sir, she answered me,
For it's dabbling in the dew makes the milkmaids fair!

Suppose I were to carry you, my pretty little dear,
In a chariot with horses, a grey gallant pair?
O no, sir, O no, sir, kind sir, she answered me,
For it's dabbling in the dew makes the milkmaids fair!

Suppose I were to feast you, my pretty little dear,
With dainties on silver, the whole of the year?
O no, sir, O no, sir, kind sir, she answered me,
For it's dabbling in the dew makes the milkmaids fair!

DABBLING IN THE DEW

O but London's a city, my pretty little dear,
And all men are gallant and brave that are there—
O no, sir, O no, sir, kind sir, she answered me,
For it's dabbling in the dew makes the milkmaids fair !

O fine clothes and dainties and carriages so rare
Bring grey to the cheeks and silver to the hair ;
What's a ring on the finger if rings are round the eye ?
But it's dabbling in the dew makes the milkmaids fair !

220   BONNY LASSIE O !

O THE evening's for the fair, bonny lassie O !
To meet the cooler air and walk an angel there,
  With the dark dishevelled hair,
   Bonny lassie O !

The bloom's on the brere, bonny lassie O !
Oak apples on the tree ; and wilt thou gang to see
  The shed I've made for thee,
   Bonny lassie O !

'Tis agen the running brook, bonny lassie O !
In a grassy nook hard by, with a little patch of sky,
  And a bush to keep us dry,
   Bonny lassie O !

There's the daisy all the year, bonny lassie O !
There's the king-cup bright as gold, and the speedwell never
 cold,
  And the arum leaves unrolled,
   Bonny lassie O !

O meet me at the shed, bonny lassie O !
With the woodbine peeping in, and the roses like thy skin
  Blushing, thy praise to win,
   Bonny lassie O !

I will meet thee there at e'en, bonny lassie O !
When the bee sips in the bean, and grey willow branches lean,
   And the moonbeam looks between,
     Bonny lassie O !

                           JOHN CLARE

221   THE MAD MAID'S SONG

GOOD-MORROW to the Day so fair,
  Good-morning, Sir, to you :
Good-morrow to mine own torn hair,
  Bedabbled with the dew.

Good-morning to this Prim-rose too,
  Good-morrow to each maid,
That will with flowers the *Tomb* bestrew
  Wherein my Love is laid.

Ah ! woe is me, woe, woe is me,
  Alack and welladay !
For pitty, Sir, find out that Bee
  Which bore my Love away.

Ile seek him in your Bonnet brave,
  Ile seek him in your eyes ;
Nay, now, I think they've made his grave
  I' the bed of strawburies.

Ile seek him there ; I know, ere this,
  The cold, cold Earth doth shake him ;
But I will go, or send a kiss
  By you, Sir, to awake him.

Pray hurt him not, though he be dead,
  He knowes well who do love him,
And who with green-turfes reare his head,
  And who do rudely move him.

THE MAD MAID'S SONG

He's soft and tender (Pray take heed) ;
    With bands of Cowslips bind him,
And bring him home—but 't is decreed
    That I shall never find him.

ROBERT HERRICK

222   TELL ME WHERE IS FANCIE BRED

TELL me where is Fancie bred,
Or in the heart or in the head ?
How begot, how nourishèd ?
            Replie, replie !
It is engendered in the eyes,
With gazing fed ; and Fancie dies
In the cradle where it lies.
Let us all ring Fancie's knell :
Ile begin it :
            Ding, dong, bell.
All.   *Ding, dong, bell.*

WILLIAM SHAKESPEARE

223   MUSIC

MUSIC, when soft voices die,
Vibrates in the memory—
Odours, when sweet violets sicken,
Live within the sense they quicken.
Rose leaves, when the rose is dead,
Are heaped for the belovèd's bed ;
And so thy thoughts, when thou art gone,
Love itself shall slumber on.

PERCY BYSSHE SHELLEY

DANCE, MUSIC AND BELLS

THE BELLS OF SHANDON

With deep affection and recollection
I often think of the Shandon bells,
Whose sounds so wild would, in the days of childhood,
Fling around my cradle their magic spells.
On this I ponder where'er I wander,
And thus grow fonder, sweet Cork, of thee ;
       With thy bells of Shandon,
       That sound so grand on
The pleasant waters of the river Lee.

I've heard bells chiming full many a clime in,
Tolling sublime in cathedral shrine,
While at a glib rate brass tongues would vibrate ;
But all their music spoke naught to thine ;
For memory, dwelling on each proud swelling
Of thy belfry, knelling its bold notes free,
       Made the bells of Shandon
       Sound more grand on
The pleasant waters of the river Lee.

I've heard bells tolling old " Adrian's Mole " in,
Their thunder rolling from the Vatican,
And cymbals glorious, swinging uproarious
In the gorgeous turrets of Notre Dame ;
But thy sounds were sweeter than the dome of Peter
Flings o'er the Tiber, pealing solemnly.
       O ! the bells of Shandon
       Sound far more grand on
The pleasant waters of the river Lee.

There's a bell in Moscow ; while on Tower and
       Kiosk, O !
In St. Sophia the Turkman gets,
And loud in air, calls men to prayer,
From the tapering summit of tall minarets.
Such empty phantom I freely grant them ;

THE BELLS OF SHANDON

But there is an anthem more dear to me,—
    'Tis the bells of Shandon,
    That sound so grand on
The pleasant waters of the river Lee.

        FRANCIS MAHONY (FATHER PROUT)

225   UPON A RING OF BELLS

BELLS have wide mouths and tongues, but are too weak,
Have they not help, to sing, or talk or speak.
But if you move them they will mak't appear,
By speaking they'l make all the Town to hear.
When Ringers handle them with Art and Skill,
They then the ears of their Observers fill,
With such brave Notes, they ting and tang so well
As to out strip all with their ding, dong, Bell.

Comparison

These Bells are like the Powers of my Soul;
Their Clappers to the Passions of my mind;
The Ropes by which my Bells are made to tole,
Are Promises (I by experience find.)
    My body is the Staple where they hang,
My graces they which do ring ev'ry Bell:
Nor is there any thing gives such a tang,
When by these Ropes these Ringers ring them well.
    Let not my Bells these Ringers want, nor Ropes;
Yea let them have room for to swing and sway:
To toss themselves deny them not their Scopes.
Lord! in my Steeple give them room to play.
If they do tole, ring out, or chime all in,
They drown the tempting tinckling Voice of Vice:
Lord! when my Bells have gone, my Soul has bin
As 'twere a tumbling in this Paradice!
    Or if these Ringers do the Changes ring,
Upon my Bells, they do such Musick make,
My Soul then (Lord) cannot but bounce and sing,
So greatly her they with their Musick take.

DANCE, MUSIC AND BELLS

But Boys (my Lusts) into my Belfry go,
And pull these Ropes, but do no Musick make
They rather turn my Bells by what they do,
Or by disorder make my Steeple shake.

  Then, Lord! I pray thee keep my Belfry Key,
Let none but Graces meddle with these Ropes:
And when these naughty Boys come, say them Nay.
From such Ringers of Musick there's no hopes.

  O Lord! If thy poor Child might have his will,
And might his meaning freely to thee tell;
He never of this Musick has his fill,
There's nothing to him like thy ding, dong, Bell.

John Bunyan

226   THE BELFRY

Dark is the stair, and humid the old walls
Wherein it winds, on worn stones, up the tower.
Only by loophole chinks at intervals
Pierces the late glow of this August hour.

Two truant children climb the stairway dark,
With joined hands, half in glee and half in fear,
The boy mounts brisk, the girl hangs back to hark
If the gruff sexton their light footsteps hear.

Dazzled at last they gain the belfry-room.
Barred rays through shutters hover across the floor
Dancing in dust; so fresh they come from gloom
That breathless they pause wondering at the door.

How hushed it is! what smell of timbers old
From cobwebbed beams! The warm light here and there
Edging a darkness, sleeps in pools of gold,
Or weaves fantastic shadows through the air.

How motionless the huge bell! Straight and stiff,
Ropes through the floor rise to the rafters dim.
The shadowy round of metal hangs, as if
No force could ever lift its gleamy rim.

THE BELFRY

A child's awe, a child's wonder, who shall trace
What dumb thoughts on its waxen softness write
In such a spell-brimmed, time-forgotten place,
Bright in that strangeness of approaching night ?

As these two gaze, their fingers tighter press ;
For suddenly the slow bell upward heaves
Its vast mouth, the cords quiver at the stress,
And ere the heart prepare, the ear receives

Full on its delicate sense the plangent stroke
Of violent, iron, reverberating sound.
As if the tower in all its stones awoke,
Deep echoes tremble, again in clangour drowned,

That starts without a whir of frighted wings
And holds these young hearts shaken, hushed, and thrilled,
Like frail reeds in a rushing stream, like strings
Of music, or like trees with tempest filled,

And rolls in wide waves out o'er the lone land,
Tone following tone toward the far-setting sun,
Till where in fields long shadowed reapers stand
Bowed heads look up, and lo, the day is done. . . .

Laurence Binyon

227   IL PENSEROSO

. . . Sweet bird that shunn'st the noise of folly,
Most musicall, most melancholy !
Thee chauntress of the Woods among
I woo to hear thy eeven-song ;
And missing thee, I walk unseen
On the dry smooth-shaven green,
To behold the wandering moon
Riding near her highest noon,
Like one that had been led astray
Through the Heaven's wide pathles way,
And oft, as if her head she bowed,
Stooping through a fleecy cloud.

DANCE, MUSIC AND BELLS

Oft on a Plat of rising ground,
I hear the far-off *Curfeu* sound
Over some wide-watered shoar,
Swinging slow with sullen roar :
Or if the Ayr will not permit,
Som still removèd place will fit,
Where glowing Embers through the room
Teach light to counterfeit a gloom,
Far from all resort of mirth,
Save the Cricket on the hearth,
Or the Belman's drousie charm
To bless the dores from nightly harm. . . .

JOHN MILTON

228   CHIMES

Brief, on a flying night,
    From the shaken tower,
A flock of bells take flight,
    And go with the hour.

Like birds from the cote to the gales,
    Abrupt—O hark !
A fleet of bells set sails,
    And go to the dark.

Sudden the cold airs swing,
    Alone, aloud,
A verse of bells takes wing
    And flies with the cloud.

ALICE MEYNELL

229   CITIES DROWNED

Cities drowned in olden time
Keep, they say, a magic chime
Rolling up from far below
When the moon-led waters flow.

CITIES DROWNED

So within me, ocean deep,
Lies a sunken world asleep.
Lest its bells forget to ring,
Memory ! set the tide a-swing !

HENRY NEWBOLT

230 ## THE BELL-MAN

From noise of Scare-fires rest ye free,
From Murders—*Benedicite*.
From all mischances, that may fright
Your pleasing slumbers in the night :
Mercie secure ye all, and keep
The Goblin from ye, while ye sleep.
Past one aclock, and almost two,
My Masters all, *Good day to you !*

ROBERT HERRICK

AUTUMN LEAVES :
WINTER SNOW.

TO MEADOWS

Ye have been fresh and green,
  Ye have been filled with flowers :
And ye the Walks have been
  Where Maids have spent their houres.

You have beheld, how they
  With *Wicker Arks* did come
To kisse, and beare away
  The richer Couslips home.

Ye have heard them sweetly sing
  And seen them in a Round :
Each Virgin, like a Spring,
  With Hony-succles crowned.

But now, we see, none here,
  Whose silverie feet did tread,
And with dishevelled Haire,
  Adorned this smoother Mead.

Like Unthrifts, having spent,
  Your stock, and needy grown,
Ye are left here to lament
  Your poore estates, alone.

ROBERT HERRICK

232   THE COTTAGER TO HER INFANT

The days are cold, the nights are long,
The North wind sings a doleful song ;
Then hush again upon my breast ;
All merry things are now at rest,
    Save thee, my pretty love !

The kitten sleeps upon the hearth,
The crickets long have ceased their mirth ;
There's nothing stirring in the house
Save one wee, hungry, nibbling mouse,
    Then why so busy thou ?
Nay ! start not at the sparkling light ;
'Tis but the moon that shines so bright
    On the window-pane
    Bedropped with rain :
Then, little darling ! sleep again,
    And wake when it is day.
                    DOROTHY WORDSWORTH

233   TO AUTUMN

SEASON of mists and mellow fruitfulness,
    Close bosom-friend of the maturing sun ;
Conspiring with him how to load and bless
    With fruit the vines that round the thatch-eaves run :
To bend with apples the mossed cottage-trees,
    And fill all fruit with ripeness to the core ;
    To swell the gourd, and plump the hazel shells
With a sweet kernel ; to set budding more,
And still more, later flowers for the bees,
Until they think warm days will never cease,
    For Summer has o'er-brimmed their clammy cells—

Who hath not seen thee oft amid thy store ?
    Sometimes whoever seeks abroad may find
Thee sitting careless on a granary floor,
    Thy hair soft-lifted by the winnowing wind ;

Or on a half-reaped furrow sound asleep,
  Drowsed with the fume of poppies, while thy hook
    Spares the next swath and all its twinèd flowers :
And sometimes like a gleaner thou dost keep
  Steady thy laden head across a brook ;
    Or by a cyder-press, with patient look,
      Thou watchest the last oozings hours by hours.

Where are the songs of Spring ?   Ay, where are they ?
  Think not of them, thou hast thy music too,—
While barred clouds bloom the soft-dying day,
  And touch the stubble-plains with rosy hue ;
Then in a wailful choir the small gnats mourn
  Among the river-sallows, borne aloft
    Or sinking as the light wind lives or dies ;
And full-grown lambs loud bleat from hilly bourn ;
  Hedge-crickets sing ; and now with treble soft
  The red-breast whistles from a garden-croft ;
    And gathering swallows twitter in the skies.

John Keats

234   THE SOLITARY REAPER

Behold her, single in the field,
Yon solitary Highland Lass !
Reaping and singing by herself ;
Stop here, or gently pass !
Alone she cuts and binds the grain,
And sings a melancholy strain ;
O listen ! for the vale profound
Is overflowing with the sound.

No nightingale did ever chaunt
More welcome notes to weary bands
· Of travellers in some shady haunt,
Among Arabian sands :
A voice so thrilling ne'er was heard
In spring-time from the cuckoo bird.

AUTUMN LEAVES : WINTER SNOW

Breaking the silence of the seas
Among the farthest Hebrides.

Will no one tell me what she sings ?—
Perhaps the plaintive numbers flow
For old, unhappy, far-off things,
And battles long ago ;
Or is it some more humble lay,
Familiar matter of to-day ?
Some natural sorrow, loss, or pain,
That has been, and may be again ?

Whate'er the theme, the maiden sang
As if her song could have no ending ;
I saw her singing at her work,
And o'er the sickle bending ;—
I listened, motionless and still ;
And, as I mounted up the hill,
The music in my heart I bore
Long after it was heard no more.

WILLIAM WORDSWORTH

235 "THE HEAVING ROSES OF THE HEDGE ARE STIRRED"

THE heaving roses of the hedge are stirred
By the sweet breath of summer, and the bird
Makes from within his jocund voice be heard.

The winds that kiss the roses sweep the sea
Of uncut grass, whose billows rolling free
Half drown the hedges which part lea from lea.

But soon shall look the wondering roses down
Upon an empty field cut close and brown,
That lifts no more its height against their own.

And in a little while those roses bright,
Leaf after leaf, shall flutter from their height,
And on the reapèd fields lie pink and white.

"THE ROSES OF THE HEDGE ARE STIRRED"

And yet again the bird that sings so high
Shall ask the snow for alms with piteous cry ;
Take fright in his bewildering bower, and die.

CANON DIXON

AUTUMN

A DIRGE

THE warm sun is failing, the bleak wind is wailing,
The bare boughs are sighing, the pale flowers are dying ;
  And the year
On the earth her death-bed, in a shroud of leaves dead,
  Is lying.
   Come, months, come away,
   From November to May,
   In your saddest array ;
   Follow the bier
   Of the dead cold year,
And like dim shadows watch by her sepulchre.

The chill rain is falling, the nipped worm is crawling,
The rivers are swelling, the thunder is knelling
  For the year ;
The blithe swallows are flown, and the lizards each gone
  To his dwelling.
   Come, months, come away ;
   Put on white, black, and grey ;
   Let your light sisters play—
   Ye, follow the bier
   Of the dead cold year,
And make her grave green with tear on tear.

PERCY BYSSHE SHELLEY

237 "WHEN THAT I WAS AND A LITTLE TINY
BOY"

When that I was and a little tinie boy,
With hey, ho, the winde and the raine :
A foolish thing was but a toy,
For the raine it raineth every day.

But when I came to man's estate,
With hey, ho, the winde and the raine :
'Gainst Knaves and Theeves men shut their gate,
For the raine it raineth every day.

But when I came, alas, to wive,
With hey, ho, the winde and the raine :
By swaggering could I never thrive,
For the raine it raineth every day.

But when I came unto my beds,
With hey, ho, the wind and the raine,
With tos-pottes still had drunken heades,—
For the raine it raineth every day.

A great while ago the world begon,
With hey, ho, the winde and the raine,
But that's all one, our Play is done,
And we'll strive to please you every day.
WILLIAM SHAKESPEARE

238 SONG

The feathers of the willow
Are half of them grown yellow
  Above the swelling stream ;
And ragged are the bushes,
And rusty are the rushes
  And wild the clouded gleam.

SONG

The thistle now is older,
His stalk begins to moulder,
His head is white as snow ;
The branches all are barer,
The linnet's song is rarer
The robin pipeth now.

CANON DIXON

239 ## FALL, LEAVES, FALL

FALL, leaves, fall ; die, flowers, away ;
Lengthen night and shorten day ;
Every leaf speaks bliss to me,
Fluttering from the autumn tree.

I shall smile when wreaths of snow
Blossom where the rose should grow ;
I shall sing when night's decay
Ushers in a drearier day.

EMILY BRONTË

240 ## THE SANDS OF DEE

" O MARY, go and call the cattle home,
And call the cattle home,
And call the cattle home
Across the sands of Dee ; "
The western wind was wild and dank with foam,
And all alone went she.

The western tide crept up along the sand,
And o'er and o'er the sand,
And round and round the sand,
As far as eye could see.
The rolling mist came down and hid the land :
And never home came she.

AUTUMN LEAVES : WINTER SNOW

" Oh ! is it weed, or fish, or floating hair—
    A tress of golden hair,
    A drownèd maiden's hair
  Above the nets at sea ?
Was never salmon yet that shone so fair
  Among the stakes on Dee."

They rowed her in across the rolling foam,
    The cruel crawling foam,
    The cruel hungry foam,
  To her grave beside the sea :
But still the boatmen hear her call the cattle home
  Across the sands of Dee.

CHARLES KINGSLEY

BREAK, BREAK, BREAK

241

Break, break, break,
  On thy cold grey stones, O Sea !
And I would that my tongue could utter
  The thoughts that arise in me.

O well for the fisherman's boy,
  That he shouts with his sister at play !
O well for the sailor lad,
  That he sings in his boat on the bay !

And the stately ships go on
  To their haven under the hill ;
But O for the touch of a vanished hand,
  And the sound of a voice that is still !

Break, break, break,
  At the foot of thy crags, O Sea !
But the tender grace of a day that is dead
  Will never come back to me.

ALFRED, LORD TENNYSON

I

O, WILD West Wind, thou breath of Autumn's being,
Thou, from whose unseen presence the leaves dead
Are driven, like ghosts from an enchanter fleeing,

Yellow, and black, and pale, and hectic red,
Pestilence-stricken multitudes : O, thou,
Who chariotest to their dark wintry bed

The wingèd seeds, where they lie cold and low,
Each like a corpse within its grave, until
Thine azure sister of the spring shall blow

Her clarion o'er the dreaming earth, and fill
(Driving sweet buds like flocks to feed in air)
With living hues and odours plain and hill :

Wild Spirit, which art moving everywhere ;
Destroyer and preserver ; hear, O hear !

II

Thou on whose stream, mid the steep sky's commotion,
Loose clouds like earth's decaying leaves are shed,
Shook from the tangled boughs of Heaven and Ocean,

Angels of rain and lightning : there are spread
On the blue surface of thine airy surge,
Like the bright hair uplifted from the head

Of some fierce Maenad, even from the dim verge
Of the horizon to the zenith's height
The locks of the approaching storm.   Thou dirge

Of the dying year, to which this closing night
Will be the dome of a vast sepulchre,
Vaulted with all thy congregated might

Of vapours, from whose solid atmosphere
Black rain, and fire, and hail will burst : O hear !

AUTUMN LEAVES : WINTER SNOW

III

Thou who didst waken from his summer dreams
The blue Mediterranean, where he lay,
Lulled by the coil of his crystalline streams,

Beside a pumice isle in Baiae's bay,
And saw in sleep old palaces and towers
Quivering within the wave's intenser day,

All overgrown with azure moss and flowers
So sweet, the sense faints picturing them ! Thou
For whose path the Atlantic's level powers

Cleave themselves into chasms, while far below
The sea-blooms and the oozy woods which wear
The sapless foliage of the ocean, know

Thy voice, and suddenly grow grey with fear,
And tremble and despoil themselves : O hear !

IV

If I were a dead leaf thou mightest bear ;
If I were a swift cloud to fly with thee ;
A wave to pant beneath thy power, and share

The impulse of thy strength, only less free
Than thou, O, uncontrollable ! If even
I were as in my boyhood, and could be

The comrade of thy wanderings over heaven,
As then, when to outstrip thy skiey speed
Scarce seemed a vision ; I would ne'er have striven

As thus with thee in prayer in my sore need.
Oh ! lift me as a wave, a leaf, a cloud !
I fall upon the thorns of life ! I bleed !

A heavy weight of hours has chained and bowed
One too like thee : tameless, and swift, and proud.

228

ODE TO THE WEST WIND

V

Make me thy lyre, even as the forest is :
What if my leaves are falling like its own !
The tumult of thy mighty harmonies

Will take from both a deep, autumnal tone,
Sweet though in sadness.   Be thou, spirit fierce,
My spirit !   Be thou me, impetuous one !

Drive my dead thoughts over the universe
Like withered leaves to quicken a new birth !
And, by the incantation of this verse,

Scatter, as from an unextinguished hearth
Ashes and sparks, my words among mankind !
Be through my lips to unawakened earth

The trumpet of a prophecy ! O, wind,
If Winter comes, can Spring be far behind ?

PERCY BYSSHE SHELLEY

243

THAT WIND

THAT wind, I used to hear it swelling ;
With joy divinely deep ;
You might have seen my hot tears welling,
But rapture made me weep.

I used to love on winter nights
To lie and dream alone
Of all the rare and real delights
My lonely years had known ;

And oh !—above the best—of those
That coming time should bear,
Like heaven's own glorious stars they rose,
Still beaming bright and fair.

EMILY BRONTË

A FROSTY NIGHT

Mother.	Alice, dear, what ails you,
	Dazed and white and shaken ?
	Has the chill night numbed you ?
	Is it fright you have taken ?
Alice.	Mother I am very well,
	I felt never better ;
	Mother, do not hold me so,
	Let me write my letter.
Mother.	Sweet, my dear, what ails you ?
Alice.	No, but I am well.
	The night was cold and frosty,
	There's no more to tell.
Mother.	Ay, the night was frosty,
	Coldly gaped the moon,
	Yet the birds seemed twittering
	Through green boughs of June.

Soft and thick the snow lay,
Stars danced in the sky,
Not all the lambs of May-day
Skip so bold and high.

Your feet were dancing, Alice,
Seemed to dance on air,
You looked a ghost or angel
In the starlight there.

Your eyes were frosted starlight,
Your heart, fire, and snow.
Who was it said " I love you ?"
Alice.   Mother, let me go !

                                        ROBERT GRAVES

245 IN A DREAR-NIGHTED DECEMBER

In a drear-nighted December,
  Too happy, happy tree,
Thy branches ne'er remember
  Their green felicity :
The north cannot undo them
With a sleety whistle through them ;
Nor frozen thawings glue them
    From budding at the prime.

In a drear-nighted December,
  Too happy, happy brook,
Thy bubblings ne'er remember
  Apollo's summer look ;
But with a sweet forgetting,
They stay their crystal fretting,
Never, never petting
    About the frozen time.

Ah ! would 'twere so with many
  A gentle girl and boy !
But were there ever any
  Writhed not at passèd joy ?
To know the change and feel it,
When there is none to heal it
Nor numbèd sense to steal it,
    Was never said in rhyme.

JOHN KEATS

246 A SONG OF WINTER

Cold cold !
Cold to-night is broad Moylurg,
Higher the snow than the mountain-range,
The deer cannot get at their food.

Cold till Doom !
The storm has spread over all :

231

AUTUMN LEAVES : WINTER SNOW

A river is each furrow upon the slope,
Each ford a full pool.

A great tidal sea is each loch,
A full loch is each pool :
Horses cannot get over the ford of Ross,
No more can two feet get there.

The fish of Ireland are a-roaming,
There is no strand which the wave does not pound,
Not a town there is in the land,
Not a bell is heard, no crane talks.

The wolves of Cuan-wood get
Neither rest nor sleep in their lair,
The little wren cannot find
Shelter in her nest on the slope of Lon.

Keen wind and cold ice
Has burst upon the little company of birds,
The blackbird cannot get a lee to her liking,
Shelter for its side in Cuan-wood.

Cosy our pot on its hook,
Crazy the hut on the slope of Lon :
The snow has crushed the wood here,
Toilsome to climb up Ben-bo.

Glenn Rye's ancient bird
From the bitter wind gets grief ;
Great her misery and her pain,
The ice will get into her mouth.

From flock and from down to rise—
Take it to heart !—were folly for thee ;
Ice in heaps on every ford—
That is why I say " cold " !

247

COLD BLOWS THE WIND

CAULD blows the wind frae north to south,
　　And drift is driving sairly ;
The sheep are couring [1] in the heugh,[2]
　　Oh sirs ! it's winter fairly.
Now up in the morning's no' for me,
　　Up in the morning early ;
I'd rather gae supperless to my bed,
　　Than rise in the morning early.

Loud rairs the blast amang the woods,
　　The branches tirling barely,
Amang the chimley taps it thuds,
　　And frost is nippin sairly.
Now up in the morning's no' for me,
　　Up in the morning early ;
To sit a' the night I'd rather agree,
　　Than rise in the morning early.

The sun peeps o'er the southlan' hill,
　　Like ony tim'rous carlie [3] ;
Just blinks a wee, then sinks again,
　　And that we find severely.
Now up in the morning's no' for me,
　　Up in the morning early ;
When snaw blaws into the chimley cheek,
　　Wha'd rise in the morning early.

Nae linties [4] lilt on hedge or bush,
　　Poor things, they suffer sairly ;
In cauldrife [5] quarters a' the night,
　　A' day they feed but sparely.
Now up in the morning's no' for me,
　　Up in the morning early ;
Nae fate can be waur,[6] in winter time,
　　Than rise in the morning early.

JOHN HAMILTON

[1] Cowering　　[2] Glen　　[3] Wee bit lassikin
[4] No linnets　　[5] Freezing　　[6] Worse

233

248   SKATING

... So through the darkness and the cold we flew,
And not a voice was idle ; with the din
Smitten, the precipices rang aloud ;
The leafless trees and every icy crag
Tinkled like iron ; while far distant hills
Into the tumult sent an alien sound
Of melancholy not unnoticed, while the stars
Eastward were sparkling clear, and in the west
The orange sky of evening died away.
Not seldom from the uproar I retired
Into a silent bay, or sportively
Glanced sideway, leaving the tumultuous throng,
To cut across the reflex of a star
That fled, and, flying still before me, gleamed
Upon the glassy plain ; and oftentimes,
When we had given our bodies to the wind,
And all the shadowy banks on either side
Came sweeping through the darkness, spinning still
In rapid line of motion, then at once
Have I, reclining back upon my heels,
Stopped short ; yet still the solitary cliffs
Wheeled by me—even as if the earth had rolled
With visible motion her diurnal round !
Behind me did they stretch in solemn train,
Feebler and feebler, and I stood and watched
Till all was tranquil as a dreamless sleep. . . .

WILLIAM WORDSWORTH

249   LONDON SNOW

WHEN men were all asleep the snow came flying,
In large white flakes falling on the city brown,
Stealthily and perpetually settling and loosely lying,
    Hushing the latest traffic of the drowsy town ;
Deadening, muffling, stifling its murmurs failing ;
Lazily and incessantly floating down and down :

LONDON SNOW

Silently sifting and veiling road, roof and railing ;
Hiding difference, making unevenness even,
Into angles and crevices softly drifting and sailing.
   All night it fell, and when full inches seven
It lay in the depth of its uncompacted lightness,
The clouds blew off from a high and frosty heaven ;
   And all woke earlier for the unaccustomed brightness
Of the winter dawning, the strange unheavenly glare :
The eye marvelled—marvelled at the dazzling whiteness ;
   The ear hearkened to the stillness of the solemn air ;
No sound of wheel rumbling nor of foot falling,
And the busy morning cries came thin and spare.
   Then boys I heard, as they went to school, calling,
They gathered up the crystal manna to freeze
Their tongues with tasting, their hands with snowballing ;
   Or rioted in a drift, plunging up to the knees ;
Or peering up from under the white-mossed wonder,
" O look at the trees !" they cried, " O look at the trees !"
   With lessened load a few carts creak and blunder,
Following along the white deserted way,
A country company long dispersed asunder :
   When now already the sun, in pale display
Standing by Paul's high dome, spread forth below
His sparkling beams, and awoke the stir of the day.
   For now doors open, and war is waged with the snow ;
And trains of sombre men, past tale of number,
Tread long brown paths, as toward their toil they go :
   But even for them awhile no cares encumber
Their minds diverted ; the daily word is unspoken,
The daily thoughts of labour and sorrow slumber
At the sight of the beauty that greets them, for the charm
   they have broken.

ROBERT BRIDGES

250 ## FOR SNOW

On the falling Snow !
Oh the falling Snow !
Where does it all come from ?
Whither does it go ?
Never never laughing,
Never never weeping,
Falling in its Sleep,
Forever ever sleeping—
From what Sleep of Heaven
Does it flow, and go
Into what Sleep of Earth,
The falling falling Snow ?

ELEANOR FARJEON

251 ## VELVET SHOES

Let us walk in the white snow
    In a soundless space ;
With footsteps quiet and slow,
    At a tranquil pace,
    Under veils of white lace.

I shall go shod in silk,
    And you in wool,
White as a white cow's milk,
    More beautiful
    Than the breast of a gull.

We shall walk through the still town
    In a windless peace ;
We shall step upon white down,
    Upon silver fleece,
    Upon softer than these.

We shall walk in velvet shoes :
    Wherever we go
Silence will fall like dews
    On white silence below.
    We shall walk in the snow.

ELINOR WYLIE

236

LUCY GRAY

Oft I had heard of Lucy Gray :
And when I crossed the wild,
I chanced to see at break of day
The solitary child.

No mate, no comrade Lucy knew ;
She dwelt on a wide moor,
The sweetest thing that ever grew
Beside a human door !

You yet may spy the fawn at play,
The hare upon the green ;
But the sweet face of Lucy Gray
Will never more be seen.

" To-night will be a stormy night—
You to the town must go ;
And take a lantern, Child, to light
Your mother through the snow."

" That, Father ! will I gladly do :
'Tis scarcely afternoon—
The minster-clock has just struck two,
And yonder is the moon !"

At this the father raised his hook,
And snapped a faggot-band ;
He plied his work ;—and Lucy took
The lantern in her hand.

Not blither is the mountain roe :
With many a wanton stroke
Her feet disperse the powdery snow,
That rises up like smoke.

The storm came on before its time :
She wandered up and down ;
And many a hill did Lucy climb :
But never reached the town.

AUTUMN LEAVES: WINTER SNOW

The wretched parents all that night
Went shouting far and wide ;
But there was neither sound nor sight
To serve them for a guide.

At day-break on a hill they stood
That overlook'd the moor ;
And thence they saw the bridge of wood
A furlong from their door.

They wept—and, turning homeward, cried
" In heaven we all shall meet !"
— When in the snow the mother spied
The print of Lucy's feet.

Then downwards from the steep hill's edge
They tracked the footmarks small ;
And through the broken hawthorn hedge,
And by the long stone-wall :

And then an open field they crossed,
The marks were still the same ;
They tracked them on, nor ever lost ;
And to the bridge they came :

They followed from the snowy bank
Those footmarks, one by one,
Into the middle of the plank ;
And further there were none !

—Yet some maintain that to this day
She is a living child ;
That you may see sweet Lucy Gray
Upon the lonesome wild.

O'er rough and smooth she trips along,
And never looks behind ;
And sings a solitary song
That whistles in the wind.

WILLIAM WORDSWORTH

253   GONE WERE BUT THE WINTER COLD

" GANE were but the winter cauld,
    And gane were but the snaw,
I could sleep in the wild woods,
    Where primroses blaw.

" Cauld's the snaw at my head,
    And cauld at my feet,
And the finger o' death is at my e'en
    Closing them to sleep,

" Let nane tell my father,
    Or my mither sae dear ;
I'll meet them baith in heaven
    At the Spring o' the year."

                    ALLAN CUNNINGHAM

254   A CHILD'S WINTER EVENING

THE smothering dark engulfs relentlessly
With nightmare tread approaching steadfastly ;
All horrors thicken as the daylight fails
And, is it wind, or some lost ghost that wails ?

Tongue cannot tell the stories that beset,
With livid pictures blackness dense as jet,
Or that wild questioning—whence we are ; and why ;
If death is darkness ; and why I am I.

The children look through the uneven pane
Out to the world, to bring them joy again ;
But only snowflakes melting into mire
Without, within the red glow of the fire.

They long for something wonderful to break
This long-drawn winter wistfulness, and take
Shape in the darkness ; threatening like Fate
There comes a hell-like crackling from the grate.

AUTUMN LEAVES : WINTER SNOW

But hand in hand they urge themselves anear
And watch the cities burning bright and clear ;
Faces diabolical and cliffs and halls
And strangely-pinnacled, molten castle walls.

Tall figures flicker on the ceiling stark
Then grimly fade into one ominous dark ;
Dream terrors iron-bound throng on them apace,
And dusk with fire, and flames with shadows race.

GWEN JOHN

255   A CAROL FOR SAINT STEPHEN'S DAY

SEYNT STEVENE was a clerk,
    In kyng Herowdes halle,
And servyd him of bred and cloth,
    As every kyng befalle.

Stevyn out of Kechoun cam,
    Wyth boris hed on honde,
He saw a sterr was fayr and bryght
    Over Bedlem stonde.

He kyst adoun the bores hed,
    And went into the halle :
" I forsake the, kyng Herowde,
    And thi werkes alle.

" I forsak the, kyng Herowde,
    And thi werkes alle :
Ther is a chyld, in Bedlem born,
    Is better than we alle."

" Quhat eylyt the, Stevene ?
    Quhat is the befalle ?
Lakkyt the eyther mete or drynk
    In kyng Herowdes halle ? "

240

A CAROL FOR SAINT STEPHEN'S DAY

" Lakyt me neyther mete ne drynk
   In kyng Herowdès halle ;
Ther is a chyld, in Bedlem born,
   Is better than we alle."

" Quhat eylyt the, Stevyn, art thu wod ?
   Or thu gynnyst to brede ?
Lakkyt the eyther gold or fe,
   Or ony rychè wede ?"

" Lakyt me neyther gold ne fe,
   Ne non rychè wede ;
Ther is a chyld, in Bedlem born,
   Shal helpyn us at our nede."

" That is al so soth, Stevyn,
   Al so soth, I wys,
As this capon crowè schel
   That lyth her in myn dych."

That word was not so sonè seyd,
   That wordè in that halle,
The capon crew, *Christus natus est !*
   Among the lordès alle.

" Rysyt up, myn túrmentowres
   Be to and al be on,
And ledyt Stevyn out of this town,
   And stonyt hym wyth ston."

Tokyn hem Stevene,
   And stonyd hym in the way :
And therfor is his evyn
   On Crystès owyn day.

THE BURNING BABE

As I in hoary winter's night
  Stood shivering in the snow,
Surprised I was with sudden heat,
  Which made my heart to glow ;
And lifting up a fearful eye
  To view what fire was near,
A pretty babe all burning bright,
  Did in the air appear :
Who, scorchèd with excessive heat,
  Such floods of tears did shed,
As though his floods should quench his flames,
  Which with his tears were fed :
" Alas ! " quoth he, " but newly born,
  In fiery heats I fry,[1]
Yet none approach to warm their hearts
  Or feel my fire, but I !

My faultless breast the furnace is,
  The fuel wounding thorns ;
Love is the fire, and sighs the smoke,
  The ashes shames and scorns ;
The fuel Justice layeth on,
  And Mercy blows the coals ;
The metal in this furnace wrought
  Are men's defilèd souls :
For which, as now on fire I am,
  To work them to their good,
So will I melt into a bath,
  To wash them in my blood."
With this he vanished out of sight,
  And swiftly shrunk away,
And straight I called unto my mind
  That it was Christmas Day.
                    ROBERT SOUTHWELL

[1] Burn

THE HOLLY AND THE IVY

THE holly and the ivy,
  Now both are full-well grown,
Of all the trees that are in the wood,
  The holly bears the crown.
     O the rising of the sun,
      Thé running of the deer,
     The playing of the merry Organ,
      Sweet singing in the quire.
      Sweet singing in the quire.

The holly bears a blossom,
  As white as lily-flower ;
And Mary bore sweet Jesus Christ,
  To be our sweet Saviour.
     O the rising of the sun, . . .

The holly bears a berry,
  As red as any blood ;
And Mary bore sweet Jesus Christ,
  To do poor sinners good.
     O the rising of the sun, . . .

The holly bears a prickle,
  As sharp as any thorn ;
And Mary bore sweet Jesus Christ,
  On Christmas Day in the morn.
     O the rising of the sun, . . .

The holly bears a bark,
  As bitter as any gall ;
And Mary bore sweet Jesus Christ,
  For to redeem us all.
     O the rising of the sun, . . .

The holly and the ivy,
  Now both are full well grown,

AUTUMN LEAVES : WINTER SNOW

Of all the trees that are in the wood,
The holly bears the crown.

O the rising of the sun,
  The running of the deer,
The playing of the merry Organ,
Sweet singing in the quire.
Sweet singing in the quire.

WELCOME YULE !

. . . Wolcum be thu, hevene kyng,
Wolcum, born in on morwenyng,
Wolcum for home [1] we shal syng,
  Wolcum yol.

Wolcum be ye Stefne and Jon,
Wolcum Innocentes everychon,
Wolcum Thomas martyr on,
  Wolcum yol.

Wolcum be ye, good newe yere,
Wolcum twelthe-day, bothe infer, [2]
Wolcum syentes lef [3] and der,
  Wolcum yol.

Wolcum be ye Candylmesse,
Wolcum be ye qwyn of blys,
Wolcum both to mor and lesse,
  Wolcum yol.

Wolcum be ye that arn her, [4]
Wolcum alle and mak good cher,
Wolcum alle another yer,
  Wolcum yol.

[1] Him   [2] Together   [3] Loved   [4] Are here

259   NAY, IVY, NAY

Nay, Ivy, nay,
  Hyt shal not be, I wys ;
Let Holy hafe the maystry,
  As the maner [1] ys.

HOLY stond in the halle,
  Fayre to behold ;
Ivy stond wythout the dore,
  She ys ful sore a-cold.
    Nay, Ivy, nay . . .

Holy and hys mery men,
  They dawnsyn and they syng ;
Ivy and hur maydenys,
  They wepyn and they wryng.
    Nay, Ivy, nay . . .

Ivy hath a kybe,[2]
  She kaght yt wyth the colde,
So mot thay all haf ae,
  That wyth Ivy hold.
    Nay, Ivy, nay . . .

Holy hath berys,
  As rede as any rose,
The foster [3] and the hunter
  Kepe hem [4] fro the doos.
    Nay, Ivy, nay . . .

Ivy hath berys,
  As blake as any slo,
Ther com the oulé,
  And ete hym as she goo.
    Nay, Ivy, nay . . .

[1] Custom   [2] Chilblain   [3] Forester   [4] Them

Holy hath byrdys,
A ful fayre flok,
The nyghtyngale, the poppynguy,
The gayntyl lavyrok.
Nay, Ivy, nay . . .

Gode Ivy [tell me]
What byrdys ast thu ? [1]
Non but the howlat,
That kreye [2] how, how !

Nay, Ivy, nay,
Hyt shal not be, I wys,
Let Holy hafe the maystry,
As the maner ys.

260   TU-WHIT TO-WHO

WHEN Isicles hang by the wall,
    And Dicke the shepheard blowes his naile,
And Tom beares Logges into the hall,
    And Milke comes frozen home in paile :
When blood is nipt, and waies be fowle,
Then nightly sings the staring Owle,
        Tu-whit to-who
    A merrie note,
While greasie Jone doth keele [3] the pot.

When all aloud the winde doth blow,
    And coffing drownes the Parson's saw ;
And birds sit brooding in the snow,
    And Marrian's nose lookes red and raw ;
When roasted Crabs [4] hisse in the bowle,
Then nightly sings the staring Owle,
        Tu-whit to-who
    A merrie note,
While greasy Jone doth keele the pot.
                              WILLIAM SHAKESPEARE

[1] Hast thou   [2] Cries   [3] Skim   [4] Apples

261 BLOW, BLOW, THOU WINTER WIND

Blow, blow, thou winter winde,
Thou art not so unkinde
    As man's ingratitude ;
Thy tooth is not so keene,
Because thou art not seene,
    Although thy breath be rude.
Heigh ho ! sing heigh ho, unto the green holly,
Most friendship is fayning, most Loving meere folly :
    Then heigh ho, the holly,
    This Life is most jolly.

Freize, freize, thou bitter skie,
That dost not bight so nigh
    As benefitts forgot ;
Though thou the waters warpe,
Thy sting is not so sharpe,
    As friend remembered not.
Heigh ho ! sing heigh ho ! unto the green holly,
Most friendship is fayning, most Loving meere folly :
    Then heigh ho, the holly,
    This Life is most jolly.
            WILLIAM SHAKESPEARE

"LIKE STARS UPON SOME
GLOOMY GROVE" ⊗ ⊗

SPRING QUIET

GONE were but the Winter,
    Come were but the Spring,
I would go to a covert
    Where the birds sing.

Where in the whitethorn
    Singeth a thrush,
And a robin sings
    In the holly-bush.

Full of fresh scents
    Are the budding boughs
Arching high over
    A cool green house :

Full of sweet scents,
    And whispering air
Which sayeth softly :
    " We spread no snare ;

" Here dwell in safety,
    Here dwell alone,
With a clear stream
    And a mossy stone.

" Here the sun shineth
    Most shadily ;
Here is heard an echo
    Of the far sea,
    Though far off it be."

CHRISTINA ROSSETTI

263   A WIDOW BIRD

A widow bird sat mourning for her love
          Upon a wintry bough ;
The frozen wind crept on above,
          The freezing stream below.

There was no leaf upon the forest bare,
          No flower upon the ground,
And little motion in the air
          Except the mill-wheel's sound.
                              PERCY BYSSHE SHELLEY

264   ECHO'S LAMENT FOR NARCISSUS

SLOW, slow, fresh fount, keep time with my salt tears ;
    Yet, slower yet ; O faintly, gentle springs ;
List to the heavy part the music bears ;
    Woe weeps out her division when she sings.
          Droop herbs and flowers ;
          Fall grief in showers,
          Our beauties are not ours ;
              O, I could still,
Like melting snow upon some craggy hill,
          Drop, drop, drop, drop,
Since nature's pride is now a withered daffodil.
                              BEN JONSON

265   THIS LIFE

This Life, which seems so fair,
Is like a bubble blown up in the air
          By sporting children's breath,
          Who chase it everywhere,
And strive who can most motion it bequeath.
And though it sometimes seem of its own might
Like to an eye of gold to be fixed there,
And firm to hover in that empty height,

That only is because it is so light.
But in that pomp it doth not long appear ;
For when 'tis most admirèd—in a thought,
Because it erst [1] was nought, it turns to nought.

WILLIAM DRUMMOND

266   SWEET CONTENT

ART thou poor, yet hast thou golden slumbers ?
          O, sweet content !
Art thou rich, yet is thy mind perplexed ?
          O, punishment !
Dost thou laugh to see how fools are vexed
To add to golden numbers golden numbers ?
O, sweet content !   O, sweet, O sweet content !

   Work apace, apace, apace, apace ;
   Honest labour bears a lovely face ;
   Then hey nonny, hey nonny, nonny !

Canst drink the waters of the crispèd spring ?
          O, sweet content !
Swimm'st thou in wealth, yet sink'st in thine own tears ?
          O, punishment !
Then he that patiently want's burden bears,
No burden bears, but is a king, a king !
O, sweet content !   O, sweet, O, sweet content !

   Work apace, apace, apace, apace ;
   Honest labour bears a lovely face ;
   Then hey nonny, hey nonny, nonny !

THOMAS DEKKER

[1] Once

253

267   OH, SWEET CONTENT

Oh, sweet content, that turns the labourer's sweat
    To tears of joy, and shines the roughest face ;
How often have I sought you high and low,
    And found you still in some lone quiet place ;

Here, in my room, when full of happy dreams,
    With no life heard beyond that merry sound
Of moths that on my lighted ceiling kiss
    Their shadows as they dance and dance around ;

Or in a garden, on a summer's night,
    When I have seen the dark and solemn air
Blink with the blind bats' wings, and heaven's bright face
Twitch with the stars that shine in thousands there.
                                WILLIAM H. DAVIES

268   RARELY, RARELY, COMEST THOU

            RARELY, rarely, comest thou,
                Spirit of Delight !
            Wherefore hast thou left me now
                Many a day and night ?
            Many a weary night and day
            'Tis since thou art fled away.

            How shall ever one like me
                Win thee back again ?
            With the joyous and the free
                Thou wilt scoff at pain.
            Spirit false ! thou hast forgot
            All but those who need thee not.

            As a lizard with the shade
                Of a trembling leaf,
            Thou with sorrow art dismayed ;
                Even the sighs of grief
            Reproach thee, that thou art not near,
            And reproach thou wilt not hear.
                        254

RARELY, RARELY, COMEST THOU

Let me set my mournful ditty
    To a merry measure,
Thou wilt never come for pity,
    Thou wilt come for pleasure.
Pity then will cut away,
Those cruel wings, and thou wilt stay.

I love all that thou lovest,
    Spirit of Delight !
The fresh Earth in new leaves drest,
    And the starry night,
Autumn evening, and the morn
When the golden mists are born.

I love snow, and all the forms
    Of the radiant frost ;
I love waves, and winds, and storms,
    Everything almost
Which is Nature's, and may be
Untainted by man's misery.

I love tranquil solitude
    And such society
As is quiet, wise, and good ;
    Between thee and me
What difference ? but thou dost possess
The things I seek, not love them less.

I love Love—though he has wings,
    And like light can flee,
But above all other things,
    Spirit, I love thee—
Thou art love and life ! O come,
Make once more my heart thy home !
                    PERCY BYSSHE SHELLEY

269   BIRTHRIGHT

LORD RAMESES of Egypt sighed
Because a summer evening passed ;
And little Ariadne cried
That summer fancy fell at last
To dust ; and young Verona died
When beauty's hour was overcast.

Theirs was the bitterness we know
Because the clouds of hawthorn keep
So short a state, and kisses go
To tombs unfathomably deep,
While Rameses and Romeo
And little Ariadne sleep.

                              JOHN DRINKWATER

270   O SORROW !

. . . " O SORROW,
        Why dost borrow
The natural hue of health, from vermeil lips ?--
            To give maiden blushes
            To the white rose bushes ?
Or is't thy dewy hand the daisy tips ?

        " O Sorrow,
        Why dost borrow
The lustrous passion from a falcon-eye ?--
            To give the glow-worm light ?
            Or, on a moonless night,
To tinge, on siren shores, the salt sea-spry ?

        " O Sorrow,
        Why dost borrow
The mellow ditties from a mourning tongue ?--
            To give at evening pale
            Unto the nightingale,
That thou mayst listen the cold dews among ?

O SORROW!

" O sorrow,
Why dost borrow
Heart's lightness from the merriment of May ? —
A lover would not tread
A cowslip on the head,
Though he should dance from eve till peep of day—
Nor any drooping flower
Held sacred for thy bower,
Wherever he may sport himself and play.

" To Sorrow,
I bade good-morrow,
And thought to leave her far away behind ;
But cheerly, cheerly,
She loves me dearly ;
She is so constant, to me, and so kind :
I could deceive her
And so leave her,
But oh ! she is so constant and so kind. . . .

" Come then, Sorrow !
Sweetest Sorrow !
Like an own babe I nurse thee on my breast :
I thought to leave thee
And deceive thee,
But now of all the world I love thee best.

" There is not one,
No, no, not one
But thee to comfort a poor lonely maid ;
Thou art her mother,
And her brother,
Her playmate, and her wooer in the shade.". . .

JOHN KEATS

271   WHEN THE LAMP IS SHATTERED

When the lamp is shattered,
The light in the dust lies dead —
When the cloud is scattered
The rainbow's glory is shed.
When the lute is broken,
Sweet tones are remembered not ;
When the lips have spoken,
Loved accents are soon forgot.

As music and splendour
Survive not the lamp and the lute,
The heart's echoes render
No song when the spirit is mute :—
No song but sad dirges,
Like the wind through a ruined cell,
Or the mournful surges
That ring the dead seaman's knell.

When hearts have once mingled
Love first leaves the well-built nest ;
The weak one is singled
To endure what it once possest.
O Love, who bewailest
The frailty of all things here,
Why choose you the frailest
For your cradle, your home, and your bier ?

Its passions will rock thee
As the storm rocks the ravens on high :
Bright reason will mock thee,
Like the sun from a wintry sky.
From thy nest every rafter
Will rot, and thine eagle home
Leave thee to naked laughter,
When leaves fall and cold winds come.

PERCY BYSSHE SHELLEY

272

He sees them pass
    As the light is graying,
Each lad and lass
    In their beauty gaying
And a voice in his aching heart is saying :

" Once—once even I
    Was straight as these,
As clear of eye,
    And as apt to please
When I tuned my voice to balladries.

Now my eyes are dim,
    Their old fires forsaking,
And each wasted limb
    As a branch is shaking,
And my grief-bowed heart will soon be breaking.

—Ah, if One comes not
    Beckoning nigh
To that land where hums not
    One small fly,
These Strong and Fair shall be as I."

                                    Eric N. Batterham

273   UPON THE IMAGE OF DEATH

Before my face the picture hangs
    That dailie should put me in minde
Of those cold qualms and bitter pangs
    That shortly I am like to finde :
        But yet, alas ! full little I
        Do think hereon, that I must die.

I often look upon a face
    Most uglie, grislie, bare, and thin ;
I often view the hollow place
    Where eyes and nose have sometime been ;

"LIKE STARS UPON SOME GLOOMY GROVE"

I see the bones across that lie ;
Yet little think, that I must die.

I read the label underneathe,
That telleth me whereto I must :
I see the sentence eke that saithe
    " Remember, man, that thou art duste ; "
    But yet, alas, but seldom I
    Do think indeed, that I must die !

Continually at my bed's head
    An hearse doth hang, which doth me tell
That I, ere morning, may be dead,
    Though now I feel myself full well :
    But yet, alas, for all this, I
    Have little minde that I must die !

The gowne which I do use to weare,
    The knife, wherewith I cut my meate,
And eke that old and ancient chair
    Which is my only usual seate,
    All these do tell me I must die ;
    And yet my life amende not I !

My ancestors are turned to clay,
    And many of my mates are gone ;
My youngers daily drop away ;—
    And can I think to 'scape alone ?
    No, no, I know that I must die ;
    And yet my life amende not I !

Not Solomon, for all his wit,
    Nor Samson, though he were so strong,
No king, nor ever person yet,
    Could 'scape, but Death laid him along !
    Wherefore I know that I must die ;
    And yet my life amende not I !

Though all the east did quake to hear
    Of Alexander's dreadful name,
And all the west did likewise fear
    The sound of Julius Caesar's fame,

UPON THE IMAGE OF DEATH

Yet both by death in duste now lie ;
Who then can 'scape, but he must die ?

If none can 'scape Death's dreadful darte,
If rich and poor his beck obey,
If strong, if wise, if all do smarte,
Then I to 'scape shall have no way.
O grant me grace, O God, that I
My life may mende, sith I must die !

ROBERT SOUTHWELL

274   ADIEU ! FAREWELL EARTH'S BLISS !

ADIEU ! farewell earth's bliss !
This world uncertain is :
Fond are life's lustful joys,
Death proves them all but toys.
None from his darts can fly :
I am sick, I must die—
    Lord, have mercy on us !

Rich men, trust not in wealth,
Gold cannot buy you health ;
Physic himself must fade ;
All things to end are made ;
The plague full swift goes by :
I am sick, I must die—
    Lord, have mercy on us !

Beauty is but a flower
Which wrinkles will devour :
Brightness falls from the air ;
Queens have died young and fair
Dust hath closed Helen's eye :
I am sick, I must die—
    Lord, have mercy on us !

Strength stoops unto the grave
Worms feed on Hector brave ;

"LIKE STARS UPON SOME GLOOMY GROVE"

Swords may not fight with fate ;
Earth still holds ope her gate ;
Come ! come ! the bells do cry :
I am sick, I must die —
Lord, have mercy on us !

Wit with his wantonness,
Tasteth death's bitterness ·
Hell's executioner
Hath no ears for to hear
What vain art can reply.
I am sick, I must die—
Lord, have mercy on us !

Haste, therefore, each degree
To welcome destiny !
Heaven is our heritage ;
Earth but a player's stage.
Mount we unto the sky !
I am sick, I must die—
Lord, have mercy on us !

THOMAS NASH

275

MESSAGES

What shall I your true-love tell,
Earth-forsaking maid ?
What shall I your true-love tell,
When life's spectre's laid ?

" Tell him that, our side the grave,
Maid may not conceive
Life should be so sad to have,
That's so sad to leave !"

What shall I your true-love tell,
When I come to him ?
What shall I your true-love tell—
Eyes growing dim !

262

MESSAGES

" Tell him this, when you shall part
   From a maiden pined ;
That I see him with my heart,
   Now my eyes are blind."

What shall I your true-love tell ?
   Speaking-while is scant.
What shall I your true-love tell,
   Death's white postulant ?

" Tell him—love, with speech at strife,
   For last utterance saith :
I, who loved with all my life,
   Love with all my death."

Francis Thompson

276   DOUBTS

When she sleeps, her soul, I know,
Goes a wanderer on the air,
Wings where I may never go,
Leaves her lying, still and fair,
Waiting, empty, laid aside,
Like a dress upon a chair. . . .
This I know, and yet I know
Doubts that will not be denied.

For if the soul be not in place,
What has laid trouble in her face ?
And, sits there nothing ware and wise
Behind the curtains of her eyes,
What is it, in the self's eclipse,
Shadows, soft and passingly,
About the corners of her lips,
The smile that is essential she ?

And if the spirit be not there,
Why is fragrance in the hair ?

Rupert Brooke

277   HARK

Hark! now everything is still,
The screech-owl and the whistler shrill
Call upon our dame aloud,
And bid her quickly don her shroud.

Much you had of land and rent ;
Your length in clay's now competent.
A long war disturbed your mind ;
Here your perfect peace is signed.
Of what is't fools make such vain keeping ?—
Sin their conception, their birth weeping,
Their life a general mist of error,
Their death a hideous storm of terror.
Strew your hair with powders sweet,
Don clean linen, bathe your feet,
And (the foul fiend more to check)
A crucifix let bless your neck :
'Tis now full tide 'tween night and day ;
End your groan, and come away.
                                    JOHN WEBSTER

278   A LYKE-WAKE DIRGE

This ae nighte, this ae nighte,
        Every nighte and alle,
Fire and sleet and candle-lighte,
        And Christe receive thy saule.

When thou from hence away art past,
        Every nighte and alle,
To Whinny-muir thou comest at last ;
        And Christe receive thy saule.

If ever thou gavest hosen and shoon,
        Every nighte and alle,
Sit thee down and put them on ;
        And Christe receive thy saule.

                    264

A LYKE-WAKE DIRGE

If hosen and shoon thou ne'er gav'st nane,
  Every nighte and alle,
The whinnes sall prick thee to the bare bane ;
  And Christe receive thy saule.

From Whinny-muir that thou may'st pass,
  Every nighte and alle,
To Brig o' Dread thou comest at last,
  And Christe receive thy saule.

From Brig o' Dread that thou may'st pass,
  Every nighte and alle,
To Purgatory fire thou com'st at last,
  And Christe receive thy saule.

If ever thou gavest meat or drink,
  Every nighte and alle,
The fire sall never make thee shrink ;
  And Christe receive thy saule.

If meat and drink thou ne'er gav'st nane
  Every nighte and alle,
The fire will burn thee to the bare bane,
  And Christe receive thy saule.

This ae nighte, this ae nighte,
  Every nighte and alle,
Fire and sleet and candle-lighte,
  And Christe receive thy saule.

279   HE IS THE LONELY GREATNESS

HE is the lonely greatness of the world—
        (His eyes are dim),
His power it is holds up the Cross
        That holds up Him.

He takes the sorrow of the threefold hour—
        (His eyelids close),
Round Him and round, the wind—His Spirit—where
        It listeth blows.

"LIKE STARS UPON SOME GLOOMY GROVE"

And so the wounded greatness of the World
In silence lies —
And death is shattered by the light from out
Those darkened eyes.

MADELEINE CARON ROCK

"O SING UNTO MY ROUNDELAY"

O SING unto my roundelay,
    O drop the briny tear with me,
Dance no more at holyday
    Like a running river be !
        My love is dead,
            Gone to his death-bed,
                All under the willow-tree.

Black his cryne [1] as the winter night,
    White his rode [2] as the summer snow,
Red his face as the morning light,
    Cold he lies in the grave below :
        My love is dead,
            Gone to his death-bed,
                All under the willow-tree. . . .

See, the white moon shines on high ;
    Winter is my true-love's shroud,
Whiter than the morning sky,
    Whiter than the evening cloud.
        My love is dead,
            Gone to his death-bed,
                All under the willow-tree. . . .

With my hands I'll dent [3] the briars
Round his holy corse to gre ; [4]
Ouph [5] and fairy, light your fires,
Here my body still shall be.
        My love is dead,
            Gone to his death-bed,
                All under the willow-tree. . . .

THOMAS CHATTERTON

[1] Locks   [2] Skin   [3] Set   [4] Grow   [5] Elf

281 FEAR NO MORE

FEARE no more the heate o' th' Sun,
Nor the fureous Winters rages,
Thou thy worldly task hast don,
Home art gon, and tane thy wages.
Golden Lads and Girles all must,
As Chimney-Sweepers, come to dust.

Feare no more the frowne o' th' Great,
Thou art past the Tirants stroake,
Care no more to cloath, and eate,
To thee the Reede is as the Oake :
The Scepter, Learning, Physicke must,
All follow this, and come to dust.

Feare no more the Lightning flash,
Nor the all-dreaded Thunder-stone,
Feare not Slander, Censure rash,
Thou hast finished joy and mone.
All Lovers young, all Lovers must,
Consigne to thee, and come to dust. . . .
WILLIAM SHAKESPEARE

282 A LAND DIRGE

CALL for the robin-redbreast and the wren,
Since o'er shady groves they hover,
And with leaves and flowers do cover
The friendless bodies of unburied men.
Call unto his funeral dole
The ant, the field-mouse, and the mole,
To rear him hillocks that shall keep him warm,
And (when gay tombs are robbed) sustain no harm ;
But keep the wolf far thence, that's foe to men,
For with his nails he'll dig them up again.
JOHN WEBSTER

283   THE GRAVE OF LOVE

I DUG, beneath the cypress shade,
   What well might seem an elfin's grave ;
And every pledge in earth I laid,
   That erst thy false affection gave.

I pressed them down the sod beneath ;
   I placed one mossy stone above ;
And twined the rose's fading wreath
   Around the sepulchre of love.

Frail as thy love, the flowers were dead
   Ere yet the evening sun was set :
But years shall see the cypress spread,
   Immutable as my regret.

                       THOMAS LOVE PEACOCK

284   THE BURIAL

ALL the flowers of the spring
Meet to perfume our burying ;
These have but their growing prime,
And man does flourish but his time.
Survey our progress from our birth—
We are set, we grow, we turn to earth,
Courts adieu, and all delights,
All bewitching appetites !
Sweetest breath and clearest eye,
Like perfumes go out and die ;
And consequently this is done
As shadows wait upon the sun.
Vain the ambition of kings
Who seek by trophies and dead things
To leave a living name behind,
And weave but nets to catch the wind.

                         JOHN WEBSTER

285   ON THE TOMBS IN WESTMINSTER ABBEY

MORTALITY, behold and fear !
What a change of flesh is here !
Think how many royal bones
Sleep within these heaps of stones ;
Here they lie had realms and lands,
Who now want strength to stir their hands ;
Where from their pulpits sealed with dust
They preach :—" In greatness is no trust."
Here's an acre sown indeed
With the richest royallest seed
That the Earth did e'er suck in
Since the first man died for sin :
Here the bones of birth have cried :—
" Though gods they were, as men they died !"
Here are sands, ignoble things,
Dropt from the ruined sides of Kings :
Here's a world of pomp and state
Buried in dust, once dead by fate.

FRANCIS BEAUMONT

286   A FUNERALL SONG

(*Lamenting Syr Phillip Sidney*)

COME to me, grief, for ever ;
Come to me, tears, day and night ;
Come to me, plaint, ah, helpless ;
Just grief, heart tears, plaint worthy.

Go from me dread to die now ;
Go from me care to live more ;
Go from me joys all on earth ;
Sidney, O Sidney is dead.

He whom the court adornèd,
He whom the country courtesied,
He who made happy his friends,
He that did good to all men.

Sidney, the hope of land strange,
Sidney, the flower of England,
Sidney, the spirit heroic,
Sidney is dead, O dead.

Dead ? no, no, but renownèd,
With the Anointed onèd ; [1]
Honour on earth at his feet,
Bliss everlasting his seat.

Come to me, grief, for ever ;
Come to me, tears, day and night ;
Come to me, plaint, ah, helpless ;
Just grief, heart tears, plaint worthy.

287   ON JOHN DONNE'S BOOK OF POEMS

I SEE in his last preached and printed Booke,
His Picture in a sheet. In Pauls I looke,
And see his Statue in a sheete of stone,
And sure his body in the grave hath one.
Those sheetes present him dead ; these, if you buy,
You have him living to Eternity.

JOHN MARRIOT

288   O, LIFT ONE THOUGHT

STOP, Christian passer-by !—Stop, child of God,
And read with gentle breast. Beneath this sod
A poet lies, or that which once seemed he.
O, lift one thought in prayer for S.T.C. ;
That he who many a year with toil of breath
Found death in life, may here find life in death.
Mercy for praise—to be forgiven for fame
He asked, and hoped, through Christ. Do thou the same !

SAMUEL TAYLOR COLERIDGE

[1] Made one

270

289 ELEGY

To the Memory of an unfortunate Lady.

. . . Most souls, 'tis true, but peep out once an age,
Dull, sullen prisoners in the body's cage ;
Dim lights of life, that burn a length of years,
Useless, unseen, as lamps in sepulchres ;
Like eastern kings, a lazy state they keep,
And close confined to their own palace, sleep. . . .
Yet shall thy grave with rising flowers be dressed,
And the green turf lie lightly on thy breast :
There shall the morn her earliest tears bestow,
There the first roses of the year shall blow ;
While angels with their silver wings o'ershade
The ground, now sacred by thy relics made.
  So peaceful rests, without a stone, a name,
What once had beauty, titles, wealth and fame.
How loved, how honoured once, avails thee not
To whom related, or by whom begot ;
A heap of dust alone remains of thee :
'Tis all thou art, and all the proud shall be !
  Poets themselves must fall, like those they sung,
Deaf the praised ear, and mute the tuneful tongue.
Ev'n he whose soul now melts in mournful lays
Shall shortly want the generous tear he pays ;
Then from his closing eyes thy form shall part,
And the last pang shall tear thee from his heart :
Life's idle business at one gasp be o'er,
The Muse forgot, and thou beloved no more !

ALEXANDER POPE

290 UPON A CHILD THAT DIED

Here she lies, a pretty bud,
Lately made of flesh and blood :
Who, as soone, fell fast asleep,
As her little eyes did peep.
Give her strewings ; but not stir
The earth, that lightly covers her.

ROBERT HERRICK

THE TURNSTILE

291

Ah ! sad wer we as we did peäce
The wold church road, wi' downcast feäce,
The while the bells, that mwoaned so deep
Above our child a-left asleep,
Wer now a-zingèn all alive
Wi' tother bells to meäke the vive.
But up at woone pleäce we come by,
'Twer hard to keep woone's two eyes dry ;
On Steän-cliff road, 'ithin the drong,
Up where, as vo'k do pass along,
The turnèn stile, a-painted white,
Do sheen by day an' show by night.

Vor always there, as we did goo
To church, thik stile did let us drough,
Wi' spreadèn eärms that wheeled to guide
Us each in turn to tother zide.
An' vu'st ov all the traïn he took
My wife, wi' winsome gaït an' look ;
An' then zent on my little maïd,
A-skippen onward, over-jaÿ'd
To reach ageän the pleäce o' pride,
Her comely mother's left han' zide.
An' then, a-wheelèn roun', he took
On me, 'ithin his third white nook.
An' in the fourth, a-sheäken wild,
He zent us on our giddy child.

But eesterday he guided slow
My downcast Jenny, vull o' woe,
An' then my little maïd in black,
A-walkèn softly on her track ;
An' after he'd a-turned ageän,
To let me goo along the leäne,
He had noo little bwoy to vill
His last white eärms, an' they stood still.

WILLIAM BARNES

272

292   THE EXEQUY

... Sleep on, my Love, in thy cold bed
Never to be disquieted !
My last good-night ! Thou wilt not wake
Till I thy fate shall overtake :
Till age, or grief, or sickness must
Marry my body to that dust
It so much loves ; and fill the room
My heart keeps empty in that tomb.
Stay for me there : I will not fail
To meet thee in that hollow vale.
And think not much of my delay :
I am already on the way,
And follow thee with all the speed
Desire can make, or sorrows breed.
Each minute is a short degree
And every hour a step towards thee. . . .
                              Henry King

293   " I FOUND HER OUT THERE "

I found her out there
On a slope few see,
That falls westwardly
To the salt-edged air,
Where the ocean breaks
On the purple strand,
And the hurricane shakes
The solid land.

I brought her here,
And have laid her to rest
In a noiseless nest
No sea beats near.
She will never be stirred
In her loamy cell
By the waves long heard
And loved so well.

273   8

" LIKE STARS UPON SOME GLOOMY GROVE "

So she does not sleep
By those haunted heights
The Atlantic smites
And the blind gales sweep,
Whence she often would gaze
At Dundagel's famed head,
While the dipping blaze
Dyed her face fire-red ;

And would sigh at the tale
Of sunk Lyonnesse,
As a wind-tugged tress
Flapped her cheek like a flail ;
Or listen at whiles
With a thought-bound brow
To the murmuring miles
She is far from now.

Yet her shade, maybe,
Will creep underground
Till it catch the sound
Of that western sea
As it swells and sobs
Where she once domiciled,
And joys in its throbs
With the heart of a child.

THOMAS HARDY

294 I NEVER SHALL LOVE THE SNOW AGAIN

I NEVER shall love the snow again
    Since Maurice died :
With corniced drift it blocked the lane
And sheeted in a desolate plain
    The country side.

The trees with silvery rime bedight
    Their branches bare.
By day no sun appeared ; by night
The hidden moon shed thievish light
    In the misty air.

274

I NEVER SHALL LOVE THE SNOW AGAIN

We fed the birds that flew around
    In flocks to be fed :
No shelter in holly or brake they found.
The speckled thrush on the frozen ground
    Lay frozen and dead.

We skated on stream and pond ; we cut
    The crinching snow
To Doric temple or Arctic hut ;
We laughed and sang at nightfall, shut
    By the fireside glow.

Yet grudged we our keen delights before
    Maurice should come.
We said, In-door or out-of-door
We shall love life for a month or more,
    When he is home.

They brought him home ; 'twas two days late
    For Christmas day :
Wrapped in white, in solemn state,
A flower in his hand, all still and straight
    Our Maurice lay.

And two days ere the year outgave
    We laid him low.
The best of us truly were not brave,
When we laid Maurice down in his grave
    Under the snow.
                  ROBERT BRIDGES

295   THE COMFORTERS

WHEN I crept over the hill, broken with tears,
    When I crouched down on the grass, dumb in despair,
I heard the soft croon of the wind bend to my ears,
    I felt the light kiss of the wind touching my hair.

When I stood lone on the height my sorrow did speak,
    As I went down the hill, I cried and I cried,

"LIKE STARS UPON SOME GLOOMY GROVE"

The soft little hands of the rain stroking my cheek,
  The kind little feet of the rain ran by my side.

When I went to thy grave, broken with tears,
  When I crouched down in the grass, dumb in despair,
I heard the sweet croon of the wind soft in my ears,
  I felt the kind lips of the wind touching my hair.

When I stood lone by thy cross, sorrow did speak,
  When I went down the long hill, I cried and I cried,
The soft little hands of the rain stroked my pale cheek,
  The kind little feet of the rain ran by my side.

DORA SIGERSON SHORTER

296   THE CHILDLESS FATHER

" Up, Timothy, up with your staff and away !
Not a soul in the village this morning will stay ;
The hare has just started from Hamilton's grounds,
And Skiddaw is glad with the cry of the hounds."

—Of coats and of jackets grey, scarlet, and green,
On the slopes of the pastures all colours were seen ;
With their comely blue aprons, and caps white as snow,
The girls on the hills made a holiday show.

Fresh sprigs of green boxwood, not six months before,
Filled the funeral basin at Timothy's door ;
A coffin through Timothy's threshold had passed ;
One child did it bear, and that child was his last.

Now fast up the dell came the noise and the fray,
The horse and the horn, and the " hark ! hark away !"
Old Timothy took up his staff, and he shut,
With a leisurely motion, the door of his hut.

Perhaps to himself at that moment he said,
" The key I must take, for my Helen is dead."
But of this in my ears not a word did he speak,
And he went to the chase with a tear on his cheek.

WILLIAM WORDSWORTH

297   "LYDIA IS GONE THIS MANY A YEAR "

LYDIA is gone this many a year,
    Yet when the lilacs stir,
In the old gardens far or near,
    This house is full of her.

They climb the twisted chamber stair ;
    Her picture haunts the room ;
On the carved shelf beneath it there,
    They heap the purple bloom.

A ghost so long has Lydia been,
    Her cloak upon the wall,
Broidered, and gilt, and faded green,
    Seems not her cloak at all.

The book, the box on mantle laid,
    The shells in a pale row,
Are those of some dim little maid,
    A thousand years ago.

And yet the house is full of her,
    She goes and comes again ;
And longings thrill, and memories stir,
    Like lilacs in the rain.

Out in their yards the neighbours walk,
    Among the blossoms tall ;
Of Anne, of Phyllis do they talk,
    Of Lydia not at all.
                    LIZETTE WOODWORTH REESE

298   REMEMBRANCE

COLD in the earth—and the deep snow piled above thee,
    Far, far removed, cold in the dreary grave !
Have I forgot, my only Love, to love thee,
    Severed at last by Time's all-severing wave ?

"LIKE STARS UPON SOME GLOOMY GROVE"

Now—when alone—do my thoughts no longer hover
 Over the mountains, on that northern shore,
Resting their wings where heath and fern-leaves cover
 Thy noble heart for ever, ever more ?

Cold in the earth—and fifteen wild Decembers,
 From those brown hills, have melted into spring :
Faithful, indeed, is the spirit that remembers
 After such years of change and suffering !

Sweet Love of youth, forgive, if I forget thee,
 While the world's tide is bearing me along ;
Other desires and other hopes beset me,
 Hopes which obscure, but cannot do thee wrong !

No later light has lightened up my heaven,
 No second morn has ever shone for me ;
All my life's bliss from thy dear life was given,
 All my life's bliss is in the grave with thee.

But, when the days of golden dreams had perished,
 And even Despair was powerless to destroy ;
Then did I learn how existence could be cherished,
 Strengthened, and fed, without the aid of joy.

Then did I check the tears of useless passion—
 Weaned my young soul from yearning after thine ;
Sternly denied its burning wish to hasten
 Down to that tomb already more than mine.

And, even yet, I dare not let it languish,
 Dare not indulge in memory's rapturous pain ;
Once drinking deep of that divinest anguish,
 How could I seek the empty world again ?

EMILY BRONTË

299   SONG

When I am dead, my dearest,
    Sing no sad songs for me ;
Plant thou no roses at my head,
    Nor shady cypress-tree :
Be the green grass above me
    With showers and dewdrops wet ;
And if thou wilt, remember,
    And if thou wilt, forget.

I shall not see the shadows,
    I shall not feel the rain ;
I shall not hear the nightingale
    Sing on, as if in pain :
And dreaming through the twilight
    That doth not rise nor set,
Haply I may remember
    And haply may forget.
                    Christina Rossetti

300   " WHERE SHALL THE LOVER REST "

Where shall the lover rest
    Whom the fates sever
From his true maiden's breast
    Parted for ever ? —
Where, through groves deep and high
    Sounds the far billow,
Where early violets die
    Under the willow.
        Eleu loro
    Soft shall be his pillow.

There through the summer day
    Cool streams are laving :
There, while the tempests sway,
    Scarce are boughs waving ;
279

There thy rest shalt thou take,
    Parted for ever,
Never again to wake
    Never, O never !
        Eleu loro
    Never, O never !

SIR WALTER SCOTT

301   REMEMBER

REMEMBER me when I am gone away,
    Gone far away into the silent land ;
    When you can no more hold me by the hand,
Nor I half turn to go yet turning stay.
Remember me when no more day by day
    You tell me of our future that you planned :
    Only remember me ;   you understand
It will be late to counsel then or pray.

Yet if you should forget me for a while
    And afterwards remember, do not grieve :
    For if the darkness and corruption leave
A vestige of the thoughts that once I had,
Better by far you should forget and smile
    Than that you should remember and be sad.

CHRISTINA ROSSETTI

302   READEN OV A HEAD-STWONE

As I wer readèn ov a stwone,
    In Grenley church-yard, all alwone,
A little maïd ran up, wi' pride
To zee me there ; an' pushed azide
A bunch o' bennets, that did hide
    A verse her father, as she zaïd,
    Put up above her mother's head
        To tell how much he loved her.

READEN OV A HEAD-STWONE

The verse wer short, but very good,
I stood an' larn'd en where I stood :—
" Mid [1] God, dear Meäry, gi'e me greäce
" To vind, lik' thee, a better pleäce,
" Where I, oonce mwore, mid zee thy feäce ;
  " An' bring thy children up, to know
  " His word, that they mid come an' show
   " Thy soul how much I loved thee."
" Where's father, then," I zaid, " my chile ?"
" Dead, too," she answered wi' a smile ;
" An' I an' brother Jem do bide
" At Betty White's, o'tother zide
  " O' road." " Mid He, my chile," I cried,
  " That's father to the fatherless,
  " Become thy father now, an' bless
   " An' keep, an' leäd, an' love thee." ·
—Though she've a-lost, I thought, so much,
Still He don't let the thoughts o't touch
Her litsome heart, by day or night ;
An' zoo, if we could teäke it right,
  Do show He'll meäke his burdens light
  To weaker souls ; an' that his smile,
  Is sweet upon a harmless chile,
   When they be dead that loved it.
WILLIAM BARNES

GOLDEN SLUMBERS

303

GOLDEN slumbers kiss your eyes,
Smiles awake you when you rise.
Sleep, pretty wantons, do not cry,
And I will sing a lullaby.
Rock them, rock them, lullaby.

Care is heavy, therefore sleep you ;
You are care, and care must keep you.
Sleep, pretty wantons, do not cry,
And I will sing a lullaby :
Rock them, rock them, lullaby.
THOMAS DEKKER

[1] May

281

304   MATER DOLOROSA

I'D a dream to-night
    As I fell asleep,
O ! the touching sight
    Makes me still to weep :
Of my little lad,
Gone to leave me sad,
Ay, the child I had,
    But was not to keep.

As in heaven high,
    I my child did seek,
There in train came by
    Children fair and meek,
Each in lily white,
With a lamp alight ;
Each was clear to sight,
    But they did not speak.

Then, a little sad,
    Came my child in turn,
But the lamp he had
    O it did not burn !
He, to clear my doubt,
Said, half-turned about,
" Your tears put it out ;
    Mother, never mourn."
                        WILLIAM BARNES

305   WEEP YOU NO MORE

WEEP you no more, sad fountains !
    What need you flow so fast ?
Look how the snowy mountains
    Heaven's sun doth gently waste !
But my sun's heavenly eyes
    View not your weeping,
    That now lies sleeping
Softly, now softly lies
        Sleeping.

282

WEEP YOU NO MORE

Sleep is a reconciling,
  A rest that peace begets :
Doth not the sun rise smiling
  When fair at even he sets ?
Rest you then, rest, sad eyes !
  Melt not in weeping,
  While she lies sleeping
Softly, now softly lies
        Sleeping.

306   FAERY SONG

SHED no tear—O shed no tear !
The flower will bloom another year.
Weep no more—O weep no more !
Young buds sleep in the root's white core.
Dry your eyes—O dry your eyes !
For I was taught in Paradise
To ease my breast of melodies—
        Shed no tear.

Overhead—look overhead
'Mong the blossoms white and red—
Look up, look up—I flutter now
On this flush pomegranate bough—
See me—'tis this silvery bill
Ever cures the good man's ill—
Shed no tear—O shed no tear !
The flower will bloom another year.
Adieu—Adieu—I fly, adieu,
I vanish in the heaven's blue—
        Adieu, Adieu !
              JOHN KEATS

307   THE WORLD OF LIGHT

THEY are all gone into the world of light !
  And I alone sit lingering here ;
Their very memory is fair and bright,
  And my sad thoughts doth clear.

283

It glows and glitters in my cloudy breast
  Like stars upon some gloomy grove,
Or those faint beams in which this hill is drest
  After the Sun's remove.

I see them walking in an Air of glory,
  Whose light doth trample on my days ;
My days, which are at best but dull and hoary,
  Mere glimmering and decays.

O holy hope ! and high humility,
  High as the Heavens above !
These are your walks, and you have showed them me,
  To kindle my cold love.

Dear, beauteous Death ! the Jewel of the Just !
  Shining nowhere but in the dark ;
What mysteries do lie beyond thy dust,
  Could man outlook that mark !

He that hath found some fledged bird's nest may know
  At first sight if the bird be flown ;
But what fair Well, or Grove he sings in now,
  That is to him unknown.

And yet, as Angels in some brighter dreams
  Call to the soul, when man doth sleep,
So some strange thoughts transcend our wonted themes,
  And into glory peep. . . .

                                    HENRY VAUGHAN

308   SILENT IS THE HOUSE

SILENT is the house : all are laid asleep :
One alone looks out o'er the snow-wreaths deep,
Watching every cloud, dreading every breeze
That whirls the wildering drift, and bends the groaning trees.

Cheerful is the hearth, soft the matted floor ;
Not one shivering gust creeps through pane or door ;
The little lamp burns straight, its rays shoot strong and far :
I trim it well, to be the wanderer's guiding-star.

SILENT IS THE HOUSE

Frown, my haughty sire ; chide, my angry dame ;
Set your slaves to spy ; threaten me with shame !
But neither sire, nor dame, nor prying serf shall know,
What angel nightly tracks that waste of frozen snow.

What I love shall come like visitant of air,
Safe in secret power from lurking human snare ;
What loves me, no word of mine shall e'er betray,
Though for faith unstained my life must forfeit pay.

Burn, then, little lamp ; glimmer straight and clear—
Hush ! a rustling wing   stirs, methinks, the air :
He for whom I wait, thus ever comes to me ;
Strange Power ! I trust thy might ; trust thou my constancy.

EMILY BRONTË

309   THE MISTRESS OF VISION

. . . SECRET was the garden ;
Set i' the pathless awe
Where no star its breath can draw.
Life, that is its warden,
Sits behind the fosse of death.   Mine eyes saw not, and I saw.

It was a mazeful wonder ;
Thrice three times it was enwalled
With an emerald—
Sealèd so asunder.
All its birds in middle air hung a-dream, their music thralled.

The Lady of fair weeping,
At the garden's core,
Sang a song of sweet and sore
And the after-sleeping ;
In the land of Luthany, and the tracts of Elenore.

With sweet-pangèd singing,
Sang she through a dream-night's day ;
That the bowers might stay,
Birds bate their winging,
Nor the wall of emerald float in wreathèd haze away. . . .

Her song said that no springing
Paradise but evermore
Hangeth on a singing
That has chords of weeping,
And that sings the after-sleeping
To souls which wake too sore.
" But woe the singer, woe !" she said ; " beyond the dead
his singing-lore,
All its art of sweet and sore
He learns, in Elenore !"
Where is the land of Luthany,
Where is the tract of Elenore ?
I am bound therefor.

" Pierce thy heart to find the key ;
With thee take
Only what none else would keep ;
Learn to dream when thou dost wake,
Learn to wake when thou dost sleep.
Learn to water joy with tears,
Learn from fears to vanquish fears ;
To hope, for thou dar'st not despair,
Exult, for that thou dar'st not grieve ;
Plough thou the rock until it bear ;
Know, for thou else couldst not believe ;
Lose, that the lost thou may'st receive ;
Die, for none other way canst live.
When earth and heaven lay down their veil,
And that apocalypse turns thee pale ;
When thy seeing blindeth thee
To what thy fellow-mortals see ;
When their sight to thee is sightless ;
Their living, death ; their light, most light-
less ;
Search no more—
Pass the gates of Luthany, tread the region Elenore."

Where is the land of Luthany ,
And where the region Elenore ?
I do faint therefor.

THE MISTRESS OF VISION

" When to the new eyes of thee
All things by immortal power,
Near or far,
Hiddenly
To each other linkèd are,
That thou canst not stir a flower
Without troubling of a star ;
When thy song is shield and mirror
To the fair snake-curlèd Pain,
Where thou dar'st affront her terror
That on her thou may'st attain
Perséan conquest ; seek no more,
O seek no more!
Pass the gates of Luthany, tread the region Elenore."

So sang she, so wept she,
Through a dream-night's day ;
And with her magic singing kept she—
Mystical in music—
The garden of enchanting
In visionary May ;
Songless from my spirits' haunting,
Thrice-threefold walled with emerald from our mortal
    mornings grey. . . .

Francis Thompson

FAR 🍃 🍃 🍃 🍃 🍃

TOM O' BEDLAM

THE moon's my constant mistress,
  And the lovely owl my marrow ;
    The flaming drake,
    And the night-crow, make
  Me music to my sorrow.

I know more than Apollo ;
  For oft, when he lies sleeping,
    I behold the stars
    At mortal wars,
  And the rounded welkin weeping.

The moon embraces her shepherd,
  And the Queen of Love her warrior ;
    While the first does horn
    The stars of the morn,
  And the next the heavenly farrier.

With a heart of furious fancies,
  Whereof I am commander :
    With a burning spear,
    And a horse of air,
  To the wilderness I wander ;

With a Knight of ghosts and shadows,
  I summoned am to Tourney :
    Ten leagues beyond
    The wide world's end ;
  Methinks it is no journey.

311   THE NIGHT-PIECE

Her Eyes the Glow-worme lend thee,
The Shooting Starres attend thee ;
        And the Elves also,
        Whose little eyes glow,
Like the sparks of fire, befriend thee.

No *Will-o' th'-Wispe* mis-light thee ;
Nor Snake, or Slow-worme bite thee :
        But on, on thy way
        Not making a stay,
Since Ghost ther's none to affright thee.

Let not the darke thee cumber ;
What though the Moon does slumber ?
        The Starres of the night
        Will lend thee their light,
Like Tapers cleare without number. . . .
                              ROBERT HERRICK

312   MY PLAID AWA'

" My plaid awa', my plaid awa',
    And ore the hill and far awa',
    And far awa' to Norrowa,
My plaid shall not be blown awa'."

The elphin knight sits on yon hill,
        Ba, ba, lilli ba,
He blowes it east, he blowes it west,
He blowes it where he lyketh best . . .
" My plaid awa', my plaid awa',
    And ore the hill and far awa'."

313   BUCKEE BENE

Buckee, Buckee, biddy Bene,
Is the way now fair and clean ?
Is the goose ygone to nest,
And the fox ygone to rest ?
Shall I come away ?

314   WHAT'S IN THERE ?

FAHT'S in there ?
Gold and money.
Fahr's [1] my share o't ?
The moosie ran awa' wi't.
Fahr's the moosie ?
In her hoosie.
Fahr's her hoosie ?
In the wood.
Fahr's the wood ?
The fire brunt it.
Fahr's the fire ?
The water quencht it.
Fahr's the water ?
The broon bull drank it.
Fahr's the broon bull ?
Back a Burnie's hill.
Fahr's Burnie's hill ?
A' claid wi' snaw.
Fahr's the snaw ?
The sun meltit it.
Fahr's the sun ?
Heigh, heigh up i' the air ! "

315   THE WEE WEE MAN

As I was wa'king all alone,
    Between a water and a wa',
And there I spy'd a Wee Wee Man,
    And he was the least that ere I saw.

His legs were scarce a shathmont's length
    And thick and thimber was his thigh ;
Between his brows there was a span,
    And between his shoulders there was three.

He took up a meikle stane,
    And he flang't as far as I could see ;

---

[1] Where's

FAR

Though I had been a Wallace wight,
  I couldna' liften't to my knee.

"O Wee Wee Man, but thou be strang !
  O tell me where thy dwelling be ?"
"My dwelling's down at yon bonny bower ;
  O will you go with me and see ?"

On we lap, and awa' we rade,
  Till we came to yon bonny green ;
We lighted down for to bait our horse,
  And out there came a lady fine.

Four and twenty at her back,
  And they were a' clad out in green ;
Though the King of Scotland had been there,
  The warst o' them might hae been his queen.

On we lap, and awa' we rade,
  Till we came to yon bonny ha',
Whare the roof was o' the beaten gould,
  And the floor was o' the cristal a'.

When we came to the stair-foot,
  Ladies were dancing, jimp and sma',
But in the twinkling of an eye,
  My Wee Wee Man was clean awa'.

316   I SAW A PEACOCK

I saw a peacock with a fiery tail
I saw a blazing comet drop down hail
I saw a cloud wrappèd with ivy round
I saw an oak creep on along the ground
I saw a pismire swallow up a whale
I saw the sea brim full of ale
I saw a Venice glass five fathom deep
I saw a well full of men's tears that weep

I SAW A PEACOCK

I saw red eyes all of a flaming fire
I saw a house bigger than the moon and higher
I saw the sun at twelve o'clock at night
I saw the Man that saw this wondrous sight.

317

GIRAFFE AND TREE

Upon a dark ball spun in Time
   Stands a Giraffe beside a Tree :
Of what immortal stuff can that
   The fading picture be ?

So, thought I, standing by my love
   Whose hair, a small black flag,
Broke on the universal air
   With proud and lovely brag :

It waved among the silent hills,
   A wind of shining ebony
In Time's bright glass, where mirrored clear
   Stood the Giraffe beside a Tree.
                              WALTER J. TURNER

318

THE WATER LADY

Alas, the moon should ever beam
   To show what man should never see !
I saw a maiden on a stream,
   And fair was she !

I stayed awhile, to see her throw
   Her tresses back, that all beset
The fair horizon of her brow
   With clouds of jet

I stayed a little while to view
   Her cheek, that wore in place of red
The bloom of water, tender blue,
   Daintily spread.

295

I stayed to watch, a little space,
Her parted lips if she would sing ;
The waters closed above her face
With many a ring.

And still I stayed a little more,
Alas ! she never comes again ;
I throw my flowers from the shore,
And watch in vain.

I know my life will fade away,
I know that I must vainly pine,
For I am made of mortal clay,
But she's divine !

THOMAS HOOD

319   THE SONG OF WANDERING AENGUS

I WENT out to the hazel wood,
Because a fire was in my head,
And cut and peeled a hazel wand,
And hooked a berry to a thread ;
And when white moths were on the wing,
And moth-like stars were flickering out,
I dropped the berry in a stream
And caught a little silver trout.

When I had laid it on the floor
I went to blow the fire a-flame,
But something rustled on the floor,
And someone called me by my name :
It had become a glimmering girl
With apple blossom in her hair
Who called me by my name and ran
And faded through the brightening air.

Though I am old with wandering
Through hollow lands and hilly lands,
I will find out where she has gone,
And kiss her lips and take her hands ;

THE SONG OF WANDERING AENGUS

And walk among long dappled grass,
And pluck till time and times are done
The silver apples of the moon,
The golden apples of the sun.

W. B. Yeats

320   THE WAY THROUGH THE WOODS

They shut the road through the woods
Seventy years ago.
Weather and rain have undone it again,
And now you would never know
There was once a road through the woods
Before they planted the trees.
It is underneath the coppice and heath,
And the thin anemones.
Only the keeper sees
That, where the ring-dove broods,
And the badgers roll at ease,
There was once a road through the woods.

Yet, if you enter the woods
Of a summer evening late,
When the night-air cools on the trout-ringed pools
Where the otter whistles his mate.
(They fear not men in the woods,
Because they see so few)
You will hear the beat of a horse's feet,
And the swish of a skirt in the dew,
Steadily cantering through
The misty solitudes,
As though they perfectly knew
The old lost road through the woods . . .
But there is no road through the woods !

Rudyard Kipling

321 THE FALLOW DEER AT THE LONELY HOUSE

ONE without looks in to-night
    Through the curtain-chink
From the sheet of glistening white ;
One without looks in to-night
    As we sit and think
    By the fender-brink.

We do not discern those eyes
    Watching in the snow ;
Lit by lamps of rosy dyes
We do not discern those eyes
    Wondering, aglow,
    Fourfooted, tiptoe.

THOMAS HARDY

322   DEER

SHY in their herding dwell the fallow deer.
They are spirits of wild sense. Nobody near
Comes upon their pastures. There a life they live,
Of sufficient beauty, phantom, fugitive,
Treading as in jungles free leopards do,
Printless as evelight, instant as dew.
The great kine are patient, and home-coming sheep
Know our bidding. The fallow deer keep
Delicate and far their counsels wild,
Never to be folded reconciled
To the spoiling hand as the poor flocks are ;
Lightfoot, and swift, and unfamiliar,
These you may not hinder, unconfined
Beautiful flocks of the mind.

JOHN DRINKWATER

323

THE TWO SWANS

(A FAIRY TALE)

IMMORTAL Imogen, crowned queen above
The lilies of thy sex, vouchsafe to hear
A fairy dream in honour of true love—
True above ills, and frailty, and all fear—
Perchance a shadow of his own career
Whose youth was darkly prisoned and long twined
By serpent-sorrow, till white Love drew near,
And sweetly sang him free, and round his mind
A bright horizon threw, wherein no grief may wind.

I saw a tower builded on a lake,
Mocked by its inverse shadow, dark and deep—
That seemed a still intenser night to make,
Wherein the quiet waters sunk to sleep,—
And, whatsoe'er was prisoned in that keep,
A monstrous Snake was warden :—round and round
In sable ringlets I beheld him creep,
Blackest amid black shadows, to the ground,
Whilst his enormous head the topmost turret crowned :

From whence he shot fierce light against the stars,
Making the pale moon paler with affright ;
And with his ruby eye out-threatened Mars—
That blazed in the mid-heavens, hot and bright—
Nor slept, nor winked, but with a steadfast spite
Watched their wan looks and tremblings in the skies ;
And that he might not slumber in the night,
The curtain-lids were plucked from his large eyes,
So he might never drowse, but watch his secret prize.

Prince or princess in dismal durance pent,
Victims of old Enchantment's love or hate,
Their lives must all in painful sighs be spent,
Watching the lonely waters soon and late,
And clouds that pass and leave them to their fate,

Or company their grief with heavy tears :—
Meanwhile that Hope can spy no golden gate
For sweet escapement, but in darksome fears
They weep and pine away as if immortal years.

No gentle bird with gold upon its wing
Will perch upon the grate—the gentle bird
Is safe in leafy dell, and will not bring
Freedom's sweet keynote and commission-word
Learned of a fairy's lips, for pity stirred—
Lest while he trembling sings, untimely guest !
Watched by that cruel Snake and darkly heard,
He leave a widow on her lonely nest,
To press in silent grief the darlings of her breast.

No gallant knight, adventurous, in his bark,
Will seek the fruitful perils of the place,
To rouse with dipping oar the waters dark
That bear that serpent-image on their face.
And Love, brave Love ! though he attempt the base,
Nerved to his loyal death, he may not win
His captive lady from the strict embrace
Of that foul Serpent, clasping her within
His sable folds—like Eve enthralled by the old Sin.

But there is none—no knight in panoply,
Nor Love, intrenched in his strong steely coat :
No little speck—no sail—no helper nigh,
No sign—no whispering—no plash of boat :—
The distant shores show dimly and remote,
Made of a deeper mist,—serene and grey,—
And slow and mute the cloudy shadows float
Over the gloomy wave, and pass away,
Chased by the silver beams that on their marges play.

And bright and silvery the willows sleep
Over the shady verge—no mad winds tease
Their hoary heads ; but quietly they weep
Their sprinkling leaves—half fountains and half trees :
There lilies be—and fairer than all these,

THE TWO SWANS

A solitary Swan her breast of snow
Launches against the wave that seems to freeze
Into a chaste reflection, still below,
Twin-shadow of herself wherever she may go.

And forth she paddles in the very noon
Of solemn midnight, like an elfin thing
Charmed into being by the argent moon—
Whose silver light for love of her fair wing
Goes with her in the shade, still worshipping
Her dainty plumage :—all around her grew
A radiant circlet, like a fairy ring ;
And all behind, a tiny little clue
Of light, to guide her back across the waters blue.

And sure she is no meaner than a fay
Redeemed from sleepy death, for beauty's sake,
By old ordainment :—silent as she lay,
Touched by a moonlight wand I saw her wake,
And cut her leafy slough and so forsake
The verdant prison of her lily peers,
That slept amidst the stars upon the lake—
A breathing shape—restored to human fears,
And new-born love and grief—self-conscious of her tears.

And now she clasps her wings around her heart,
And near that lonely isle begins to glide,
Pale as her fears, and oft-times with a start
Turns her impatient head from side to side
In universal terrors—all too wide
To watch ; and often to that marble keep
Upturns her pearly eyes, as if she spied
Some foe, and crouches in the shadows steep
That in the gloomy wave go diving fathoms deep.

And well she may, to spy that fearful thing
All down the dusky walls in circlets wound ;
Alas ! for what rare prize, with many a ring
Girding the marble casket round and round ?
His folded tail, lost in the gloom profound,

FAR

Terribly darkeneth the rocky base ;
But on the top his monstrous head is crowned
With prickly spears, and on his doubtful face
Gleam his unwearied eyes, red watchers of the place.

Alas ! of the hot fires that nightly fall,
No one will scorch him in those orbs of spite,
So he may never see beneath the wall
That timid little creature, all too bright,
That stretches her fair neck, slender and white,
Invoking the pale moon, and vainly tries
Her throbbing throat, as if to charm the night
With song—but, hush—it perishes in sighs,
And there will be no dirge sad-swelling, though she dies !

She droops—she sinks—she leans upon the lake,
Fainting again into a lifeless flower ;
But soon the chilly springs anoint and wake
Her spirit from its death, and with new power
She sheds her stifled sorrows in a shower
Of tender song, timed to her falling tears—
That wins the shady summit of that tower,
And, trembling all the sweeter for its fears,
Fills with imploring moan that cruel monster's ears.

And, lo ! the scaly beast is all deprest,
Subdued like Argus by the might of sound—
What time Apollo his sweet lute addrest
To magic converse with the air, and bound
The many monster eyes, all slumber-drowned :—
So on the turret-top that watchful Snake
Pillows his giant head, and lists profound,
As if his wrathful spite would never wake,
Charmed into sudden sleep for Love and Beauty's sake !

His prickly crest lies prone upon his crown,
And thirsty lip from lip disparted flies,
To drink that dainty flood of music down—
His scaly throat is big with pent-up sighs—
And whilst his hollow ear entrancèd lies,

THE TWO SWANS

His looks for envy of the charmèd sense
Are fain to listen, till his steadfast eyes,
Stung into pain by their own impotence,
Distil enormous tears into the lake immense.

Oh, tuneful Swan ! oh, melancholy bird !
Sweet was that midnight miracle of song,
Rich with ripe sorrow, needful of no word
To tell of pain, and love, and love's deep wrong—
Hinting a piteous tale—perchance how long
Thy unknown tears were mingled with the lake,
What time disguised thy leafy mates among—
And no eye knew what human love and ache
Dwelt in those dewy leaves, and heart so nigh to break.

Therefore no poet will ungently touch
The water-lily, on whose eyelids dew
Trembles like tears ; but ever hold it such
As human pain may wander through and through,
Turning the pale leaf paler in its hue—
Wherein life dwells, transfigured, not entombed,
By magic spells. Alas ! who ever knew
Sorrow in all its shades, leafy and plumed,
Or in gross husks of brutes eternally inhumed ?

And now the wingèd song has scaled the height
Of that dark dwelling, builded for despair,
And soon a little casement flashing bright
Widens self-opened into the cool air—
That music like a bird may enter there
And soothe the captive in his stony cage ;
For there is nought of grief, or painful care,
But plaintive song may happily engage
From sense of its own ill, and tenderly assuage.

And forth into the light, small and remote,
A creature, like the fair son of a king,
Draws to the lattice in his jewelled coat
Against the silver moonlight glistening,
And leans upon his white hand listening

To that sweet music that with tenderer tone
Salutes him, wondering what kindly thing
Is come to soothe him with so tuneful moan,
Singing beneath the walls as if for him alone !

And while he listens, the mysterious song,
Woven with timid particles of speech,
Twines into passionate words that grieve along
The melancholy notes, and softly teach
The secrets of true love,—that trembling reach
His earnest ear, and through the shadows dun
He missions like replies, and each to each
Their silver voices mingle into one,
Like blended streams that make one music as they run.

" Ah, Love ! my hope is swooning in my heart,—"
" Ay, sweet ! my cage is strong and hung full high—"
" Alas ! our lips are held so far apart,
Thy words come faint,—they have so far to fly !—"
" If I may only shun that serpent-eye !—"
" Ah me ! that serpent-eye doth never sleep ;—"
" Then nearer thee, Love's martyr, I will die !—"
" Alas, alas ! that word has made me weep !
For pity's sake remain safe in thy marble keep !"

" My marble keep ! it is my marble tomb—"
" Nay, sweet ! but thou hast there thy living breath—"
" Aye to expend in sighs for this hard doom ;—"
" But I will come to thee and sing beneath,
And nightly so beguile this serpent wreath ;—"
" Nay, I will find a path from these despairs."
" Ah ! needs then thou must tread the back of death,
Making his stony ribs thy stony stairs.—
Behold his ruby eye, how fearfully it glares !"

Full sudden at these words, the princely youth
Leaps on the scaly back that slumbers, still
Unconscious of his foot, yet not for ruth,
But numbed to dulness by the fairy skill
Of that sweet music (all more wild and shrill

THE TWO SWANS

For intense fear) that charmed him as he lay—
Meanwhile the lover nerves his desperate will,
Held some short throbs by natural dismay,
Then down the serpent-track begins his darksome way.

Now dimly seen—now toiling out of sight,
Eclipsed and covered by the envious wall ;
Now fair and spangled in the sudden light,
And clinging with wide arms for fear of fall :
Now dark and sheltered by a kindly pall
Of dusky shadow from his wakeful foe ;
Slowly he winds adown—dimly and small,
Watched by the gentle Swan that sings below,
Her hope increasing, still, the larger he doth grow.

But nine times nine the Serpent folds embrace
The marble walls about—which he must tread
Before his anxious foot may touch the base :
Long is the dreary path, and must be sped !
But Love, that holds the mastery of dread,
Braces his spirit, and with constant toil
He wins his way, and now, with arms outspread,
Impatient plunges from the last long coil :
So may all gentle Love ungentle Malice foil !

The song is hushed, the charm is all complete,
And two fair Swans are swimming on the lake :
But scarce their tender bills have time to meet,
When fiercely drops adown that cruel Snake—
His steely scales a fearful rustling make,
Like autumn leaves that tremble and foretell
The sable storm ;—the plumy lovers quake—
And feel the troubled waters pant and swell,
Heaved by the giant bulk of their pursuer fell.

His jaws, wide yawning like the gates of Death,
His horrible pursuit—his red eyes glare
The waters into blood—his eager breath
Grows hot upon their plumes :—now, minstrel fair !
She drops her ring into the waves, and there

FAR

It widens all around, a fairy ring
Wrought of the silver light—the fearful pair
Swim in the very midst, and pant and cling
The closer for their fears, and tremble wing to wing.

Bending their course over the pale grey lake,
Against the pallid East, wherein light played
In tender flushes, still the baffled Snake
Circled them round continually, and bayed
Hoarsely and loud, forbidden to invade
The sanctuary ring : his sable mail
Rolled darkly through the flood, and writhed and made
A shining track over the waters pale,
Lashed into boiling foam by his enormous tail.

And so they sailed into the distance dim,
Into the very distance—small and white,
Like snowy blossoms of the spring that swim
Over the brooklets—followed by the spite
Of that huge Serpent, that with wild affright
Worried them on their course, and sore annoy,
Till on the grassy marge I saw them 'light,
And change, anon, a gentle girl and boy,
Locked in embrace of sweet unutterable joy !

Then came the Morn, and with her pearly showers
Wept on them, like a mother, in whose eyes
Tears are no grief ; and from his rosy bowers
The Oriental sun began to rise,
Chasing the darksome shadows from the skies ;
Wherewith that sable Serpent far away
Fled, like a part of night—delicious sighs
From waking blossoms purified the day,
And little birds were singing sweetly from each spray.

Thomas Hood

324   THE EARL OF MAR'S DAUGHTER

It was intill a pleasant time,
    Upon a simmer's day,
The noble Earl of Mar's daughter
    Went forth to sport and play.

As thus she did amuse hersell,
    Below a green aik tree,
There she saw a sprightly doo [1]
    Set on a tower sae hie.

" O Cow-me-doo, my love sae true,
    If ye'll come down to me,
Ye'se hae a cage o' guid red gowd
    Instead o' simple tree :

" I'll put gowd hingers [2] roun' your cage,
    And siller roun' your wa' ;
I'll gar [3] ye shine as fair a bird
    As ony o' them a'."

But she hadnae these words well spoke,
    Nor yet these words well said,
Till Cow-me-doo flew frae the tower
    And lighted on her head.

Then she has brought this pretty bird
    Hame to her bowers and ha',
And made him shine as fair a bird
    As ony o' them a'.

When day was gane, and night was come,
    About the evening tide
This lady spied a sprightly youth
    Stand straight up by her side.

" From whence came ye, young man ?" she said ;
    " That does surprise me sair ;
My door was bolted right secure,
    What way hae ye come here ?"

[1] Dove   [2] Trappings   [3] Make

FAR

"O had[1] your tongue, ye lady fair,
  Lat a' your folly be ;
Mind ye not on your turtle-doo
  Last day ye brought wi' thee ?"

"O tell me mair, young man," she said,
  "This does surprise me now ;
What country hae ye come frae ?
  What pedigree are you ?"

"My mither lives on foreign isles,
  She has nae mair but me ;
She is a queen o' wealth and state,
  And birth and high degree.

"Likewise well skilled in magic spells,
  As ye may plainly see,
And she transformed me to yon shape,
  To charm such maids as thee.

"I am a doo the live-lang day,
  A sprightly youth at night ;
This aye gars me appear mair fair
  In a fair maiden's sight.

"And it was but this verra day
  That I came ower the sea ;
Your lovely face did me enchant ;
  I'll live and dee wi' thee."

"O Cow-me-doo, my luve sae true,
  Nae mair frae me ye'se gae ";
"That's never my intent, my luve,
  As ye said, it shall be sae. . . ."

[1] Hold

325 ### THE BROOMFIELD HILL

Brome, brome on hill,
The gentle brome on hill, hill,
Brome, brome on Hive hill,
The gentle brome on Hive hill,
The brome stands on Hive hill-a . . .

" O WHERE were ye, my milk-white steed,
    That I hae coft [1] sae dear,
That wadna' watch and waken me
    When there was maiden here ? "

" I stampèd wi' my foot, master,
    And gard my bridle ring,
But na kin thing wald waken ye,
    Till she was past and gane."

" And wae betide ye, my gay goss-hawk,
    That I did love sae dear,
That wadna' watch and waken me
    When there was maiden here."

" I clappèd wi' my wings, master,
    And aye my bells I rang,
And aye cryed, Waken, waken, master,
    Before the ladye gang."

" But haste and haste, my guide white steed,
    To come the maiden till,
Or a' the birds of gude green wood
    Of your flesh shall have their fill."

" Ye need no burst your gude white steed
    Wi' racing o'er the howm; [2]
Nae bird flies faster through the wood,
    Than she fled through the broom."

326 ### THE CHANGELING

TOLL no bell for me, dear Father, dear Mother,
    Waste no sighs ;
There are my sisters, there is my little brother
    Who plays in the place called Paradise,

[1] Bought   [2] The green margin of a river

309

FAR

Your children all, your children for ever ;
    But I, so wild,
Your disgrace, with the queer brown face, was never,
    Never, I know, but half your child !

In the garden at play, all day, last summer,
    Far and away I heard
The sweet " tweet-tweet " of a strange new-comer,
    The dearest, clearest call of a bird.
It lived down there in the deep green hollow,
    My own old home, and the fairies say
The word of a bird is a thing to follow,
    So I was away a night and a day.

One evening, too, by the nursery fire,
    We snuggled close and sat round so still,
When suddenly as the wind blew higher,
    Something scratched on the window-sill,
A pinched brown face peered in—I shivered ;
    No one listened or seemed to see ;
The arms of it waved and the wings of it quivered,
    Whoo—I knew it had come for me !
Some are as bad as bad can be !
All night long they danced in the rain,
Round and round in a dripping chain,
Threw their caps at the window-pane,
    Tried to make me scream and shout
    And fling the bedclothes all about :
I meant to stay in bed that night,
And if only you had left a light
    They would never have got me out !

    Sometimes I wouldn't speak, you see,
    Or answer when you spoke to me,
Because in the long, still dusks of Spring
You can hear the whole world whispering ;
    The shy green grasses making love,
    The feathers grow on the dear grey dove,
    The tiny heart of the redstart beat,
    The patter of the squirrel's feet,

THE CHANGELING

The pebbles pushing in the silver streams,
The rushes talking in their dreams,
   The swish-swish of the bat's black wings,
   The wild-wood bluebell's sweet ting-tings,
      Humming and hammering at your ear,
      Everything there is to hear
In the heart of hidden things.
   But not in the midst of the nursery riot,
   That's why I wanted to be quiet,
      Couldn't do my sums, or sing,
      Or settle down to anything.
And when, for that, I was sent upstairs
I *did* kneel down to say my prayers ;
But the King who sits on your high church steeple
Has nothing to do with us fairy people !

'Times I pleased you, dear Father, dear Mother,
   Learned all my lessons and liked to play,
And dearly I loved the little pale brother
   Whom some other bird must have called away.
Why did they bring me here to make me
   Not quite bad and not quite good,
Why, unless They're wicked, do They want, in spite, to
   take me
        Back to Their wet, wild wood ?
Now, every night I shall see the windows shining,
   The gold lamp's glow, and the fire's red gleam,
While the best of us are twining twigs and the rest of us
   are whining
        In the hollow by the stream.
Black and chill are Their nights on the wold ;
   And They live so long and They feel no pain :
I shall grow up, but never grow old,
I shall always, always be very cold,
      I shall never come back again !

                    CHARLOTTE MEW

THE HOST OF THE AIR

O'Driscoll drove with a song
The wild duck and the drake
From the tall and the tufted reeds
Of the drear Hart Lake.

And he saw how the reeds grew dark
At the coming of night tide,
And dreamed of the long dim hair
Of Bridget his bride.

He heard while he sang and dreamed
A piper piping away,
And never was piping so sad,
And never was piping so gay.

And he saw young men and young girls
Who danced on a level place
And Bridget his bride among them,
With a sad and a gay face.

The dancers crowded about him,
And many a sweet thing said,
And a young man brought him red wine
And a young girl white bread.

But Bridget drew him by the sleeve,
Away from the merry bands,
To old men playing at cards
With a twinkling of ancient hands.

The bread and the wine had a doom,
For these were the host of the air ;
He sat and played in a dream
Of her long dim hair.

He played with the merry old men
And thought not of evil chance,
Until one bore Bridget his bride
Away from the merry dance.

312

THE HOST OF THE AIR

He bore her away in his arms,
The handsomest young man there,
And his neck and his breast and his arms
Were drowned in her long dim hair.

O'Driscoll scattered the cards
And out of his dream awoke :
Old men and young men and young girls
Were gone like a drifting smoke ;

But he heard high up in the air
A piper piping away,
And never was piping so sad,
And never was piping so gay.

W. B. Yeats

328   THE LOVE-TALKER

I met the Love-Talker one eve in the glen,
He was handsomer than any of our handsome young men,
His eyes were blacker than the sloe, his voice sweeter far
Than the crooning of old Kevin's pipes beyond in Coolnagar.

I was bound for the milking with a heart fair and free—
My grief ! my grief ! that bitter hour drained the life from
    me ;
I thought him human lover, though his lips on mine were
    cold,
And the breath of death blew keen on me within his hold.

I know not what way he came, no shadow fell behind,
But all the sighing rushes swayed beneath a faery wind,
The thrush ceased its singing, a mist crept about,
We two clung together—with the world shut out.

Beyond the ghostly mist I could hear my cattle low,
The little cow from Ballina, clean as driven snow,
The dun cow from Kerry, the roan from Inisheer,
Oh, pitiful their calling—and his whispers in my ear !

His eyes were a fire ; his words were a snare ;
I cried my mother's name, but no help was there ;
I made the blessed Sign ; then he gave a dreary moan,
A wisp of cloud went floating by, and I stood alone.

Running ever through my head, is an old-time rune —
" Who meets the Love-Talker must weave her shroud soon."
My mother's face is furrowed with the salt tears that fall,
But the kind eyes of my father are the saddest sight of all.

I have spun the fleecy lint, and now my wheel is still,
The linen length is woven for my shroud fine and chill,
I shall stretch me on the bed where a happy maid I lay—
Pray for the soul of Mairé Og at dawning of the day !

ETHNA CARBERY

329   MARIANA

WITH blackest moss the flower-plots
    Were thickly crusted, one and all :
The rusted nails fell from the knots
    That held the pear to the garden-wall.
The broken sheds looked sad and strange :
    Unlifted was the clinking latch ;
    Weeded and worn the ancient thatch
Upon the lonely moated grange.
        She only said, " My life is dreary,
            He cometh not," she said ;
        She said, " I am aweary, aweary,
            I would that I were dead !"

Her tears fell with the dews at even ;
    Her tears fell ere the dews were dried ;
She could not look on the sweet heaven,
    Either at morn or eventide.
After the flitting of the bats,
    When thickest dark did trance the sky,
    She drew her casement-curtain by,
And glanced athwart the glooming flats.

314

MARIANA

She only said, " The night is dreary,
He cometh not," she said ;
She said, " I am aweary, aweary,
I would that I were dead !"

Upon the middle of the night,
  Waking she heard the night-fowl crow :
The cock sung out an hour ere light :
  From the dark fen the oxen's low
Came to her : without hope of change,
  In sleep she seemed to walk forlorn,
  Till cold winds woke the grey-eyed morn
About the lonely moated grange.
    She only said, " The day is dreary,
    He cometh not," she said ;
    She said, " I am aweary, aweary,
    I would that I were dead !"

About a stone-cast from the wall
  A sluice with blackened waters slept,
And o'er it many, round and small,
  The clustered marish-mosses crept.
Hard by a poplar shook alway,
  All silver-green with gnarlèd bark :
  For leagues no other tree did mark
The level waste, the rounding grey.
    She only said, " My life is dreary,
    He cometh not," she said ;
    She said, " I am aweary, aweary,
    I would that I were dead !"

And ever when the moon was low,
  And the shrill winds were up and away,
In the white curtain, to and fro,
  She saw the gusty shadow sway.
But when the moon was very low,
  And wild winds bound within their cell,
  The shadow of the poplar fell
Upon her bed, across her brow.

She only said, " The night is dreary,
He cometh not," she said ;
She said, " I am aweary, aweary,
I would that I were dead !"

All day within the dreamy house,
The doors upon their hinges creaked ;
The blue fly sung in the pane ; the mouse
Behind the mouldering wainscot shrieked,
Or from the crevice peered about.
Old faces glimmered thro' the doors,
Old footsteps trod the upper floors,
Old voices called her from without.
She only said, " My life is dreary,
He cometh not," she said ;
She said, " I am aweary, aweary,
I would that I were dead !"

The sparrow's chirrup on the roof,
The slow clock ticking, and the sound
Which to the wooing wind aloof
The poplar made, did all confound
Her sense ; but most she loathed the hour
When the thick-moted sunbeam lay
Athwart the chambers, and the day
Was sloping toward his western bower.
Then, said she, " I am very dreary,
He will not come," she said ;
She wept, " I am aweary, aweary,
Oh God, that I were dead !"

ALFRED, LORD TENNYSON

330   KEITH OF RAVELSTON

THE murmur of the mourning ghost
That keeps the shadowy kine,
" Oh, Keith of Ravelston,
The sorrows of thy line !"

KEITH OF RAVELSTON

Ravelston, Ravelston,
  The merry path that leads
Down the golden morning hill,
  And thro' the silver meads ;

Ravelston, Ravelston,
  The stile beneath the tree,
The maid that kept her mother's kine,
  The song that sang she !

She sang her song, she kept her kine,
  She sat beneath the thorn
When Andrew Keith of Ravelston
  Rode thro' the Monday morn.

His henchmen sing, his hawk-bells ring,
  His belted jewels shine !
Oh, Keith of Ravelston,
  The sorrows of thy line !

Year after year, where Andrew came,
  Comes evening down the glade,
And still there sits a moonshine ghost
  Where sat the sunshine maid.

Her misty hair is faint and fair,
  She keeps the shadowy kine ;
Oh, Keith of Ravelston,
  The sorrows of thy line !

I lay my hand upon the stile,
  The stile is lone and cold,
The burnie that goes babbling by
  Says naught that can be told.

Yet, stranger ! here, from year to year,
  She keeps her shadowy kine ;
Oh, Keith of Ravelston,
  The sorrows of thy line !

Step out three steps, where Andrew stood—
  Why blanch thy cheeks for fear ?

FAR

The ancient stile is not alone,
   'Tis not the burn I hear !

She makes her immemorial moan,
   She keeps her shadowy kine ;
 . Oh, Keith of Ravelston,
   The sorrows of thy line !

SYDNEY DOBELL

331   UNWELCOME

WE were young, we were merry, we were very very wise,
   And the door stood open at our feast,
When there passed us a woman with the West in her eyes,
   And a man with his back to the East.

O, still grew the hearts that were beating so fast,
   The loudest voice was still.
The jest died away on our lips as they passed,
   And the rays of July struck chill.

The cups of red wine turned pale on the board,
   The white bread black as soot.
The hound forgot the hand of her lord,
   She fell down at his foot.

Low let me lie, where the dead dog lies,
   Ere I sit me down again at a feast,
When there passes a woman with the West in her eyes,
   And a man with his back to the East.

MARY COLERIDGE

332   ON YES TOR

BENEATH our feet, the shuddering bogs
   Made earthquakes of their own,
For greenish-grizzled furtive frogs
   And lizards lithe and brown ;

318

And high to east and south and west,
  Girt round the feet with gorse,
Lay, summering, breast by giant breast,
  The titan brood of tors ;

Golden and phantom-pale they lay,
  Calm in the cloudless light,
Like gods that, slumbering, still survey
  The obsequious infinite.

Plod, plod, through herbage thin or dense ;
  Past chattering rills of quartz ;
Across brown bramble-coverts, whence
  The shy black ouzel darts ;

Through empty leagues of broad, bare lands,
  Beneath the empty skies,
Clutched in the grip of those vast hands,
  Cowed by those golden eyes,

We fled beneath their scornful stare,
  Like terror-hunted dogs,
More timid than the lizards were,
  And shyer than the frogs.

               EDMUND GOSSE

333   THE WITCHES' SONG

" I HAVE beene all day looking after
A raven feeding upon a quarter ;
And, soone as she turned her back to the south,
I snatched this morsell out of her mouth.". . .

" I last night lay all alone
O' the ground, to heare the madrake grone ;
And pluckt him up, though he grew full low :
And, as I had done, the cocke did crow.". . .

" And I ha' been plucking (plants among)
Hemlock, henbane, adders-tongue,

Night-shade, moone-wort, libbards-bane ;
And twise by the dogges was like to be tane.". . .

" Yes : I have brought, to helpe your vows,
Hornèd poppie, cypresse boughes,
The fig-tree wild, that grows on tombes,
And juice that from the larch-tree comes,
The basiliske's bloud, and the viper's skin ;
And now our orgies let's begin."

BEN JONSON

334   THE RAVEN

ONCE upon a midnight dreary, while I pondered, weak and
     weary,
Over many a quaint and curious volume of forgotten lore,—
While I nodded, nearly napping, suddenly there came a
     tapping,
As of some one gently rapping, rapping at my chamber door.
" 'Tis some visitor," I muttered, " tapping at my chamber
     door ;
   Only this and nothing more."

Ah, distinctly I remember it was in the bleak December,
And each separate dying ember wrought its ghost upon the
     floor.
Eagerly I wished the morrow ;—vainly I had sought to
     borrow
From my books surcease of sorrow—sorrow for the lost
     Lenore,
For the rare and radiant maiden whom the angels name
     Lenore :
   Nameless here for evermore.

And the silken sad uncertain rustling of each purple curtain
Thrilled me—filled me with fantastic terrors never felt before ;
So that now, to still the beating of my heart, I stood
     repeating,
" 'Tis some visitor entreating entrance at my chamber door—
Some late visitor entreating entrance at my chamber door ;
   This it is and nothing more."

THE RAVEN

Presently my soul grew stronger ; hesitating then no longer,
" Sir," said I, " or Madam, truly your forgiveness I implore ;
But the fact is I was napping, and so gently you came
    rapping,
And so faintly you came tapping, tapping at my chamber
    door,
That I scarce was sure I heard you "—here I opened wide
    the door :—
    Darkness there and nothing more.

Deep into that darkness peering, long I stood there wondering,
    fearing,
Doubting, dreaming dreams no mortals ever dared to dream
    before ;
But the silence was unbroken, and the stillness gave no
    token,
And the only word there spoken was the whispered word,
    " Lenore ? "
This I whispered, and an echo murmured back the word,
    " Lenore :"
    Merely this and nothing more.

Back into the chamber turning, all my soul within me
    burning,
Soon again I heard a tapping somewhat louder than before.
" Surely," said I, " surely that is something at my window
    lattice ;
Let me see, then, what thereat is, and this mystery explore :
Let my heart be still a moment and this mystery explore ;
    'Tis the wind and nothing more."

Open here I flung the shutter, when, with many a flirt and
    flutter,
In there stepped a stately Raven of the saintly days of yore.
Not the least obeisance made he ; not a minute stopped or
    stayed he ;
But, with mien of lord or lady, perched above my chamber
    door,
Perched upon a bust of Pallas just above my chamber door :
    Perched, and sat, and nothing more.

Then this ebony bird beguiling my sad fancy into smiling
By the grave and stern decorum of the countenance it wore,—
" Though thy crest be shorn and shaven, thou," I said, " art
    sure no craven,
Ghastly grim and ancient Raven wandering from the Nightly
    shore :
Tell me what thy lordly name is on the Night's Plutonian
    shore !"
    Quoth the Raven, " Nevermore."

Much I marvelled this ungainly fowl to hear discourse so
    plainly,
Though its answer little meaning—little relevancy bore ;
For we cannot help agreeing that no living human being
Ever yet was blessed with seeing bird above his chamber
    door—
Bird or beast upon the sculptured bust above his chamber
    door,
    With such name as " Nevermore."

But the Raven, sitting lonely on the placid bust, spoke only
That one word, as if his soul in that one word he did outpour.
Nothing further then he uttered, not a feather then he
    fluttered,
Till I scarcely more than muttered,—" Other friends have
    flown before ;
On the morrow *he* will leave me, as my Hopes have flown
    before."
    Then the bird said, " Nevermore."

Startled at the stillness broken by reply so aptly spoken,
" Doubtless," said I, " what it utters is its only stock and
    store,
Caught from some unhappy master whom unmerciful
    Disaster
Followed fast and followed faster till his songs one burden
    bore :
Till the dirges of his Hope that melancholy burden bore
    Of ' Never—nevermore.' "

But the Raven still beguiling all my sad soul into smiling,
Straight I wheeled a cushioned seat in front of bird and bust
    and door ;
Then, upon the velvet sinking, I betook myself to linking
Fancy unto fancy, thinking what this ominous bird of
    yore,
What this grim, ungainly, ghastly, gaunt, and ominous bird
    of yore
    Meant in croaking " Nevermore."

This I sat engaged in guessing, but no syllable expressing
To the fowl whose fiery eyes now burned into my bosom's
    core ;
This and more I sat divining, with my head at ease reclining
On the cushion's velvet lining that the lamplight gloated o'er,
But whose velvet violet lining with the lamplight gloating
    o'er
    She shall press, ah, nevermore !

Then, methought, the air grew denser, perfumed from an
    unseen censer
Swung by seraphim whose foot-falls tinkled on the tufted
    floor.
" Wretch," I cried, " thy God hath lent thee—by these
    angels he hath sent thee
Respite—respite and nepenthe from thy memories of Lenore !
Quaff, oh quaff this kind nepenthe, and forget this lost
    Lenore !"
    Quoth the Raven, " Nevermore."

" Prophet !" said I, " thing of evil ! prophet still, if bird
    or devil !
Whether Tempter sent or whether tempest tossed thee here
    ashore,
Desolate, yet all undaunted, on this desert land enchanted,
On this home by Horror haunted—tell me truly, I implore :
Is there—*is* there balm in Gilead ?—tell me—tell me, I
    implore !"
    Quoth the Raven, " Nevermore."

"Prophet!" said I, "thing of evil prophet still, if bird
    or devil!
By that Heaven that bends above us, by that God we both
    adore,
Tell this soul with sorrow laden if, within the distant Aidenn,
It shall clasp a sainted maiden whom the angels name Lenore:
Clasp a rare and radiant maiden whom the angels name
    Lenore!"
    Quoth the Raven, "Nevermore."

"Be that word our sign of parting, bird or fiend!" I
    shrieked, upstarting
"Get thee back into the tempest and the Night's Plutonian
    shore!
Leave no black plume as a token of that lie thy soul hath
    spoken!
Leave my loneliness unbroken! quit the bust above my
    door!
Take thy beak from out my heart, and take thy form from
    off my door!"
    Quoth the Raven, "Nevermore."

And the Raven, never flitting, still is sitting, still is sitting
On the pallid bust of Pallas just above my chamber door;
And his eyes have all the seeming of a demon's that is
    dreaming,
And the lamp-light o'er him streaming throws his shadow
    on the floor;
And my soul from out that shadow that lies floating on the
    floor
    Shall be lifted—nevermore!

                            EDGAR ALLAN POE

335   THE WITCH'S BALLAD

    O, I HAE come from far away,
      From a warm land far away,
    A southern land across the sea,
    With sailor-lads about the mast,
    Merry and canny, and kind to me.

THE WITCH'S BALLAD

And I hae been to yon town
   To try my luck in yon town ;
Nort, and Mysie, Elspie too.
Right braw we were to pass the gate,
Wi' gowden-clasps on girdles blue.

Mysie smiled wi' miminy mouth,
   Innocent mouth, miminy mouth ;
Elspie wore a scarlet gown.
Nort's grey eyes were unco' gleg.[1]
My Castile comb was like a crown.

We walk'd abreast all up the street,
   Into the market up the street ;
Our hair with marigolds was wound,
Our bodices with love-knots laced,
Our merchandise with tansy bound.

Nort had chickens, I had cocks ;
   Gamesome cocks, loud-crowing cocks ;
Mysie ducks, and Elspie drakes,—
For a wee groat or a pound
We lost nae time wi' gives and takes.

—Lost nae time for well we knew,
   In our sleeves full well we knew,
When the gloaming came that night,
Duck nor drake, nor hen nor cock
Would be found by candle-light.

And when our chaffering all was done,
   All was paid for, sold and done,
We drew a glove on ilka hand,
We sweetly curtsied, each to each,
And deftly danced a saraband.

The market-lassies looked and laughed,
   Left their gear, and looked and laughed ;
They made as they would join the game,
But soon their mithers, wild and wud,[2]
With whack and screech they stopped the same.

[1] Wild and lively   [2] Furious

325

FAR

Sae loud the tongues o' randies [1] grew,
  The flytin' [2] and the skirlin' grew,
At all the windows in the place,
Wi' spoons or knives, wi' needle or awl,
Was thrust out every hand and face.

And down each stair they thronged anon,
  Gentle, semple, thronged anon ;
Souter [3] and tailor, frowsy Nan,
The ancient widow young again,
Simpering behind her fan.

Without a choice, against their will,
  Doited, [4] dazed, against their will,
The market lassie and her mither,
The farmer and his husbandman,
Hand in hand dance a' thegither.

Slow at first, but faster soon,
  Still increasing, wild and fast,
Hoods and mantles, hats and hose,
Blindly doffed and cast away,
Left them naked, heads and toes.

They would have torn us limb from limb,
  Dainty limb from dainty limb ;
But never one of them could win
Across the line that I had drawn
With bleeding thumb a-widdershin.

But there was Jeff the provost's son,
  Jeff the provost's only son ;
There was Father Auld himsel',
The Lombard frae the hostelry,
And the lawyer Peter Fell.

All goodly men we singled out,
  Waled [5] them well, and singled out,
And drew them by the left hand in ;

[1] Carousers   [2] Brawling   [3] Cobbler
[4] Spellbound   [5] Chose

326

THE WITCH'S BALLAD

Mysie the priest, and Elspie won
The Lombard, Nort the lawyer carle,
I mysel' the provost's son.

Then, with cantrip [1] kisses seven,
    Three times round with kisses seven,
Warped and woven there spun we
Arms and legs and flaming hair,
Like a whirlwind on the sea.

Like a wind that sucks the sea,
    Over and in and on the sea,
Good sooth it was a mad delight ;
And every man of all the four
Shut his eyes and laughed outright.

Laughed as long as they had breath,
    Laughed while they had sense or breath ;
And close about us coiled a mist
Of gnats and midges, wasps and flies,
Like the whirlwind shaft it rist.

Drawn up I was right off my feet,
    Into the mist and off my feet ;
And, dancing on each chimney-top,
I saw a thousand darling imps
Keeping time with skip and hop.

And on the provost's brave ridge-tile,
    On the provost's grand ridge-tile,
The Blackamoor first to master me
I saw, I saw that winsome smile,
The mouth that did my heart beguile,
And spoke the great Word over me,
In the land beyond the sea.

I called his name, I called aloud,
    Alas ! I called on him aloud ;
And then he filled his hand with stour,[2]
And threw it towards me in the air ;
My mouse flew out, I lost my pow'r !

[1] Witching   [2] Dust : reek

327

FAR

My lusty strength, my power were gone;
  Power was gone, and all was gone.
He will not let me love him more!
Of bell and whip and horse's tail
He cares not if I find a store.

But I am proud if he is fierce!
  I am as proud as he is fierce;
I'll turn about and backward go,
If I meet again that Blackamoor,
And he'll help us then, for he shall know
I seek another paramour.

And we'll gang once more to yon town,
  Wi' better luck to yon town;
We'll walk in silk and cramoisie,
And I shall wed the provost's son
My lady of the town I'll be!

For I was born a crowned king's child,
  Born and nursed a king's child,
King o' a land ayont the sea,
Where the Blackamoor kissed me first,
And taught me art and glamourie.

Each one in her wame shall hide
  Her hairy mouse, her wary mouse,
Fed on madwort and agramie,—
Wear amber beads between her breasts,
And blind-worm's skin about her knee.

The Lombard shall be Elspie's man,
  Elspie's gowden husband-man;
Nort shall take the lawyer's hand;
The priest shall swear another vow;
We'll dance again the saraband!

WILLIAM BELL SCOTT

ANNAN WATER

Annan Water's wading deep,
  " And my Love Annie's wondrous bonny ;
And I am loath she should wet her feet,
  Because I love her best of ony."

He's loupen on his bonny gray,
  He rode the right gate [1] and the ready ; [2]
For all the storm he wadna stay,
  For seeking of his bonny lady.

And he has ridden o'er field and fell,
  Through moor, and moss, and many a mire ;
His spurs of steel were sair to bide,
  And from her four feet flew the fire.

" My bonny gray, now play your part !
  If ye be the steed that wins my dearie,
With corn and hay ye'll be fed for aye,
  And never spur shall make you wearie."

The gray was a mare, and a right gude mare ;
  But when she wan the Annan Water,
She should not have ridden the ford that night
  Had a thousand marks been wadded at her.

" O boatman, boatman, put off your boat,
  Put off your boat for golden money !"
But for all the gold in fair Scotland,
  He dared not take him through to Annie.

" O I was sworn so late yestreen,
  Not by a single oath, but mony !
I'll cross the drumly stream to-night,
  Or never could I face my honey."

The side was steep, and the bottom deep,
  From bank to brae the water pouring ;
The bonny gray mare she swat for fear,
  For she heard the Water-Kelpy roaring.

[1] Road　　[2] Nearest

FAR

He spurred her forth into the flood,
 I wot she swam both strong and steady;
But the stream was broad, and her strength did fail,
 And he never saw his bonny lady!

337　　　　　SONG

Ah! County Guy, the hour is nigh:
 The sun has left the lea,
The orange flower perfumes the bower,
 The breeze is on the sea,
The lark, his lay who thrilled all day,
 Sits hushed his partner nigh:
Breeze, bird, and flower, confess the hour,
 But where is County Guy?—

The village maid steals through the shade,
 Her shepherd's suit to hear;
To beauty shy, by lattice high,
 Sings high-born Cavalier;
The star of Love, all stars above,
 Now reigns o'er earth and sky,
And high and low the influence know—
 But where is County Guy?

Sir WALTER SCOTT

338　　　DEADMAN'S DIRGE

Prayer unsaid, and Mass unsung,
Deadman's dirge must still be rung:
 Dingle-dong, the dead-bells sound!
 Mermen chant his dirge around!

Wash him bloodless, smooth him fair,
Stretch his limbs, and sleek his hair:
 Dingle-dong, the dead-bells go!
 Mermen swing them to and fro!

DEADMAN'S DIRGE

In the wormless sand shall he
Feast for no foul glutton be :
  Dingle-dong, the dead-bells chime !
  Mermen keep the tone and time !

We must with a tombstone brave
Shut the shark out from his grave :
  Dingle-dong, the dead-bells toll !
  Mermen dirgers ring his knoll !

Such a slab will we lay o'er him,
All the dead shall rise before him :
  Dingle-dong, the dead-bells boom !
  Mermen lay him in his tomb !

GEORGE DARLEY

339 ## BOATS AT NIGHT

How lovely is the sound of oars at night
  And unknown voices, borne through windless air,
From shadowy vessels floating out of sight
  Beyond the harbour lantern's broken glare
To those piled rocks that make on the dark wave
  Only a darker stain. The splashing oars
Slide softly on as in an echoing cave
  And with the whisper of the unseen shores
Mingle their music, till the bell of night
  Murmurs reverberations low and deep
That droop towards the land in swooning flight
  Like whispers from the lazy lips of sleep.
The oars grow faint. Below the cloud-dim hill
The shadows fade and now the bay is still.

EDWARD SHANKS

340 ## A VOICE SINGS

HEAR, sweet spirit, hear the spell,
Lest a blacker charm compel !
So shall the midnight breezes swell
With thy deep long-lingering knell.

331

And at evening evermore,
In a chapel on the shore,
Shall the chaunters, sad and saintly,
Yellow tapers burning faintly,
Doleful masses chaunt for thee,
  Miserere Domine !

Hark, the cadence dies away
  On the quiet moonlight sea :
The boatmen rest their oars ; and say,
  Miserere Domine !

SAMUEL TAYLOR COLERIDGE

341   THE WANDERING SPECTRE

Wae's me, wae's me,
The acorn's not yet
Fallen from the tree
That's to grow the wood,
That's to make the cradle,
That's to rock the bairn,
That's to grow a man,
That's to lay me.

342   LUCIFER IN STARLIGHT

On a starred night Prince Lucifer uprose.
Tired of his dark dominion swung the fiend
Above the rolling ball in cloud part screened,
Where sinners hugged their spectre of repose.
Poor prey to his hot fit of pride were those.
And now upon his western wing he leaned,
Now his huge bulk o'er Afric's sands careened,
Now the black planet shadowed Arctic snows.
Soaring through wider zones that pricked his scars
With memory of the old revolt from Awe,
He reached a middle height, and at the stars,
Which are the brain of heaven, he looked, and sank.
Around the ancient track marched rank on rank,
The army of unalterable law.

GEORGE MEREDITH

332

343

THERE WAS A KNIGHT

THERE was a knicht riding frae the east,
Jennifer gentle an' rosemaree.
Who had been wooing at monie a place,
As the doo [1] flies owre the mulberry tree.

He cam' unto a widow's door,
And speird [2] whare her three dochters were.

" The auldest ane's to a washing gane,
The second's to a baking gane."

" The youngest ane's to a wedding gane,
And it will be nicht or [3] she be hame."

He sat him doun upon a stane,
Till thir three lasses cam' tripping hame.

The auldest ane she let him in,
And pinned the door wi' a siller pin.

The second ane she made his bed,
And laid saft pillows unto his head.

The youngest ane was bauld [4] and bricht,
And she tarried for words wi' this unco knicht.—

" Gin ye will answer me questions ten,
The morn ye sall me made my ain :—

" O what is higher nor [5] the tree ?
And what is deeper nor the sea ?

" Or what is heavier nor the lead ?
And what is better nor the bread ?

" Or what is whiter nor the milk ?
Or what is safter nor the silk ?

" Or what is sharper nor a thorn ?
Or what is louder nor a horn ?

[1] Dove   [2] Asked   [3] Ere   [4] Bold   [5] Than

" Or what is greener nor the grass ?
Or what is waur [1] nor a woman was ?"

" O heaven is higher nor the tree,
And hell is deeper nor the sea.

" O sin is heavier nor the lead,
The blessing's better nor the bread.

" The snaw is whiter nor the milk,
And the down is safter nor the silk.

" Hunger is sharper nor a thorn,
And shame is louder nor a horn.

" The pies are greener nor the grass,
And Clootie's waur nor a woman was."

As sune as she the fiend did name,
   Jennifer gentle an' rosemaree,
He flew awa' in a blazing flame,
   As the doo flies owre the mulberry tree.

344   THE FALSE KNIGHT UPON THE ROAD

" O WHARE are ye gaun ?"
   Quo' the fause knicht upon the road :
" I'm gaun to the scule."
   Quo' the wee boy, and still he stude.

" What is that upon your back ?"
   Quo' the fause knicht upon the road :
" Atweel [2] it is my bukes."
   Quo' the wee boy, and still he stude.

" What's that ye've got in your arm ?"
   Quo' the fause knicht upon the road :
" Atweel it is my peit." [3]
   Quo' the wee boy, and still he stude.

[1] Worse   [2] Why, sure   [3] Peat for school fire

" Wha's aucht [1] they sheep ?"
Quo' the fause knicht upon the road :
" They're mine and my mither's."
Quo' the wee boy, and still he stude.

" How monie o' them are mine ?"
Quo' the fause knicht upon the road :
" A' they that hae blue tails."
Quo' the wee boy, and still he stude.

" I wiss ye were on yon tree : "
Quo' the fause knicht upon the road :
" And a gude ladder under me."
Quo' the wee boy, and still he stude.

" And the ladder for to break : "
Quo' the fause knicht upon the road :
" And *you* for to fa' down."
Quo' the wee boy, and still he stude.

" I wiss ye were in yon sie : "
Quo' the fause knicht upon the road :
" And a gude bottom [2] under me."
Quo' the wee boy, and still he stude.

" And the bottom for to break : "
Quo' the fause knicht upon the road :
" And *ye* to be drowned."
Quo' the wee boy, and still he stude.

345   CHRISTABEL

'Tis the middle of night by the castle clock,
And the owls have awakened the crowing cock ;
Tu-whit!———Tu- whoo!
And hark, again ! the crowing cock,
How drowsily it crew.

Sir Leoline, the Baron rich,
Hath a toothless mastiff bitch ;

[1] Who owns   [2] Vessel, ship

FAR

From her kennel beneath the rock
She maketh answer to the clock,
Four for the quarters, and twelve for the hour ;
Ever and aye, by shine and shower,
Sixteen short howls, not over loud ;
Some say, she sees my lady's shroud.

Is the night chilly and dark ?
The night is chilly, but not dark.
The thin gray cloud is spread on high,
It covers but not hides the sky.
The moon is behind, and at the full ;
And yet she looks both small and dull.
The night is chill, the cloud is gray :
'Tis a month before the month of May,
And the Spring comes slowly up this way.

The lovely lady, Christabel,
Whom her father loves so well,
What makes her in the wood so late,
A furlong from the castle gate ?
She had dreams all yesternight
Of her own betrothèd knight ;
And she in the midnight wood will pray
For the weal of her lover that's far away.

She stole along, she nothing spoke,
The sighs she heaved were soft and low,
And naught was green upon the oak
But moss and rarest mistletoe :
She kneels beneath the huge oak tree,
And in silence prayeth she.

The lady sprang up suddenly,
The lovely lady, Christabel !
It moaned as near, as near can be,
But what it is she cannot tell.—
On the other side it seems to be,
Of the huge, broad-breasted, old oak tree.

CHRISTABEL

The night is chill ; the forest bare ;
Is it the wind that moaneth bleak ?
There is not wind enough in the air
To move away the ringlet curl
From the lovely lady's cheek—
There is not wind enough to twirl
The one red leaf, the last of its clan,
That dances as often as dance it can,
Hanging so light, and hanging so high,
On the topmost twig that looks up at the sky.

Hush, beating heart of Christabel !
Jesu, Maria, shield her well !
She folded her arms beneath her cloak,
And stole to the other side of the oak.
    What sees she there ?

There she sees a damsel bright,
Drest in a silken robe of white,
That shadowy in the moonlight shone :
The neck that made that white robe wan —
Her stately neck, and arms were bare ;
Her blue-veined feet unsandaled were,
And wildly glittered here and there
The gems entangled in her hair. . . .

SAMUEL TAYLOR COLERIDGE

346   THE FRUIT PLUCKER

ENCINCTURED with a twine of leaves,
That leafy twine his only dress,
A lovely Boy was plucking fruits,
By moonlight, in a wilderness.
The moon was bright, the air was free,
And fruits and flowers together grew
On many a shrub and many a tree :
And all put on a gentle hue,
Hanging in the shadowy air
Like a picture rich and rare.

FAR

It was a climate where, they say,
The night is more beloved than day.
But who that beauteous Boy beguiled,
That beauteous Boy to linger here?
Alone, by night, a little child,
In place so silent and so wild—
Has he no friend, no loving mother near?

SAMUEL TAYLOR COLERIDGE

THE HAUNTED PALACE

In the greenest of our valleys
    By good angels tenanted,
Once a fair and stately palace—
    Radiant palace—reared its head.
In the monarch Thought's dominion
        It stood there!
Never seraph spread a pinion
    Over fabric half so fair.

Banners yellow, glorious, golden,
    On its roof did float and flow,
(This—all this—was in the olden
        Time long ago),
And every gentle air that dallied
    In that sweet day,
Along the ramparts plumed and pallid
    A wingèd odour went away.

Wanderers, in that happy valley,
    Through two luminous windows saw
Spirits moving musically,
    To a lute's well-tunèd law,
Round about a throne, where sitting
        (Porphyrogene),
In state his glory well befitting,
    The ruler of the realm was seen.

338

THE HAUNTED PALACE

And all with pearl and ruby glowing
  Was the fair palace door,
Through which came flowing, flowing, flowing,
  And sparkling evermore,
A troop of Echoes, whose sweet duty
  Was but to sing,
In voices of surpassing beauty,
  The wit and wisdom of their king.

But evil things, in robes of sorrow,
  Assailed the monarch's high estate.
(Ah, let us mourn, for never morrow
  Shall dawn upon him desolate !)
And round about his home, the glory,
  That blushed and bloomed,
Is but a dim-remembered story
  Of the old time entombed.

And travellers, now, within that valley,
  Through the red-litten windows see
Vast forms, that move fantastically
  To a discordant melody ;
While, like a ghastly rapid river,
  Through the pale door
A hideous throng rush out for ever,
  And laugh—but smile no more.

EDGAR ALLAN POE

348   THE HOUSE OF RICHESSE

NEIGHBOURING THE GATE OF HELL INTO WHICH MAMMON LED THE ELFIN KNIGHT

. . . THAT houses forme within was rude and strong,
  Like an huge cave, hewne out of rocky clift,
From whose rough vaut the ragged breaches hong,
  Embost with massy gold of glorious gift,
  And with rich metall loaded every rift,

That heavy ruine they did seeme to threat ;
And over them *Arachne* high did lift
Her cunning web, and spred her subtile net,
Enwrappèd in fowle smoke and clouds more blacke then jet.

Both roofe, and floore, and wals were all of gold,
But overgrowne with dust and old decay,
And hid in darkenesse, that none could behold
The hew thereof : for vew of chearefull day
Did never in that house it selfe display,
But a faint shadow of uncertain light ;
Such as a lamp, whose life does fade away :
Or as the Noone cloathèd with clowdy night,
Does shew to him that walkes in feare and sad affright.

In all that rowme was nothing to be seene,
But huge great yron chests and coffers strong,
All bard with double bends,[1] that none could weene
Them to efforce by violence or wrong ;
On every side they placèd were along.
But all the ground with sculs was scatterèd,
And dead mens bones, which round about were flong,
Whose lives, it seemèd, whilome there were shed,
And their vile carcases now left unburièd. . . .

EDMUND SPENSER

349   THE OLD CITY

THOU hast come from the old city,
From the gate and the tower,
From King and priest and serving man
And burnished bower,
From beggar's whine and barking dogs,
From prison sealed—
Thou hast come from the old city
Into the field.

[1] Bands

THE OLD CITY

The gables in the old city
Are stooping awry,
They gloom upon the muddy lanes
And smother the sky,
And nightly through those mouldy lanes,
Moping and slow,
They who builded the old city
The cold ghosts go.

There is plague in the old city,
And the priests are sped
To graveyard and vault
To bury the dead ;
Brittle bones and dusty breath
To death must yield—
Fly, fly, from the old city
Into the field !

RUTH MANNING-SANDERS

350   THE TWO SPIRITS

First Spirit.   O THOU, who plumed with strong desire
                 Wouldst float above the earth, beware !
            A shadow tracks the flight of fire—
                 Night is coming !
            Bright are the regions of the air,
            And among the winds and beams
                 It were delight to wander there—
                 Night is coming !

Second Spirit. The deathless stars are bright above ;
                 If I would cross the shade of night,
            Within my heart is the lamp of love,
                 And that is day !
            And the moon will smile with gentle light
            On my golden plumes where'er they move ;
                 The meteors will linger round my flight ;
                 And make night day.

341

FAR

First Spirit. But if the whirlwinds of darkness waken
Hail, and lightning, and stormy rain ;
See, the bounds of the air are shaken—
Night is coming !
The red swift clouds of the hurricane
Yon declining sun have overtaken,
The clash of the hail sweeps over the plain—
Night is coming !

Second Spirit. I see the light, and I hear the sound ;
I'll sail on the flood of the tempests dark,
With the calm within and the light around
Which makes night day :
And then, when the gloom is deep and stark,
Look from thy dull earth, slumber-bound ;
My moon-like flight thou then may'st mark
On high, far away.

Some say there is a precipice
Where one vast pine is frozen to ruin
O'er piles of snow and chasms of ice
'Mid Alpine mountains ;
And that the languid storm pursuing
That wingèd shape, for ever flies
Round those hoar branches, aye renewing
Its aëry fountains.

Some say, when nights are dry and clear,
And the death-dews sleep on the morass,
Sweet whispers are heard by the traveller,
Which make night day ;
And a silver shape, like his early love, doth
pass
Up-borne by her wild and glittering hair,
And when he awakes on the fragrant grass,
He finds night day.

PERCY BYSSHE SHELLEY

"LILY BRIGHT AND SHINE-A"

SILLY SWEETHEART

SILLY Sweetheart, say not nay,
    Come away :
All I tell is sweet and merry ;
Soon rings evensong, and soon
Where was blossom hangs a berry ;
Where was darkness shines a moon.
Prythee, Sweetheart, then I say,
    Come, come away.

    O away,
    Come away :
Maids there are with cheeks like roses,
Thine are roses in the snow.
Fie, the lass whose dainty nose is
Tilted not as one I know.
Nought heeds she, Alackaday !
    My, Come, come away.

    O away,
    Come away :
Honeycomb by bees made sweet is ;
Dew on apple, bloom on plum ;
Hearken, my heart's lightest beat is
Drumming, drumming ; haste and come
    Say not nay, then ;
    Make no stay, then ;
Dance thy dainty foot and straying
    Come, come away !

352 HERE COMES A LUSTY WOOER

" HERE comes a lusty wooer,
My a dildin, my a daldin ;
Here comes a lusty wooer,
Lily bright and shine-a."

" Pray who do you woo ?
My a dildin, my a daldin ;
Pray who do you woo ?
Lily bright and shine-a."

" Woo ! Your fairest daughter !
My a dildin, my a daldin ;
Woo ! your fairest daughter !
Lily bright and shine-a."

" There ! there ! she is for you,
My a dildin, my a daldin ;
There ! there ! she is for you,
Lily bright and shine-a."

353 THREE KNIGHTS FROM SPAIN

WE are three Brethren come from Spain,
All in French garlands ;
We are come to court your daughter Jane,
And adieu to you, my darlings.

My daughter Jane !—she is too young,
All in French garlands ;
She cannot bide your flattering tongue,
And adieu to you, my darlings.

Be she young, or be she old,
All in French garlands ;
'Tis for a bride she must be sold,
And adieu to you, my darlings.

A bride, a bride, she shall not be
All in French garlands ;

THREE KNIGHTS FROM SPAIN

Till she go through this world with me,
And adieu to you, my darlings.

Then shall you keep your daughter Jane,
All in French garlands ;
Come once, we come not here again,
And adieu to you, my darlings.

Turn back, turn back, you Spanish Knights,
All in French garlands ;
Scour, scour your spurs, till they be bright,
And adieu to you, my darlings.

Sharp shine our spurs, all richly wrought,
All in French garlands ;
In towns afar our spurs were bought
And adieu to you, my darlings.

Smell my lilies, smell my roses,
All in French garlands ;
Which of my maidens do you choose ?
And adieu to you, my darlings.

Not she. Not she. Thy youngest, Jane !
All in French garlands ;
We ride—and ride not back again,
And adieu to you, my darlings.

In every pocket a thousand pound,
All in French garlands ;
On every finger a gay gold ring,
And adieu to you, my darlings.
And adieu to you, my darlings.

354 THE WHUMMIL BORE

Seven lang years I hae served the King,
Fa fa fa fa lilly :
And I never got a sight of his daughter but ane :
With my glimpy, glimpy, glimpy eedle,
Lillum too tee a ta too a tee a ta a tally.

LILY BRIGHT AND SHINE-A

I saw her thro' a whummil bore,
  Fa fa fa fa lilly :
And I ne'er got a sight of her no more.
  With my glimpy, glimpy, glimpy eedle,
  Lillum too tee a ta too a tee a ta a tally.

Twa was putting on her gown,
  Fa fa fa fa lilly :
And ten was putting pins therein.
  With my glimpy, glimpy, glimpy eedle.
  Lillum too tee a ta too a tee a ta a tally.

Twa was putting on her shoon,
  Fa fa fa fa lilly :
And twa was buckling them again.
  With my glimpy, glimpy, glimpy eedle.
  Lillum too tee a ta too a tee a ta a tally.

Five was combing down her hair,
  Fa fa fa fa lilly :
And I ne'er got a sight of her nae mair.
  With my glimpy, glimpy, glimpy eedle,
  Lillum too tee a ta too a tee a ta a tally.

Her neck and breast was like the snow,
  Fa fa fa fa lilly :
Then from the bore I was forced to go.
  With my glimpy, glimpy, glimpy eedle,
  Lillum too tee a ta too a tee a ta a tally.

355   HEY, WULLY WINE

Hey, Wully wine, and How, Wully wine,
  I hope for hame ye'll no' incline ;
Ye'll better light, and stay a' night,
  And I'll gie thee a lady fine.

I maun ride hame, I maun gang hame,
  And bide nae langer here ;
The road is lang, the mirk soon on,
  And howlets mak' me fear.

HEY, WULLY WINE

Light down, and bide wi' us a' night,
    We'll choose for ye a bonnie lass,
Ye'll get your wield and pick o' them a'
    And the time it soon awa' will pass.

Wha will ye gie, if I wi' ye bide,
To be my bonny bonny bride,
And lie down lovely by my side ?

I'll gie thee Kate o' Dinglebell,
A bonny body like yersell.

I'll stick her high in yon pear-tree
Sweet and meek, and sae is she :
I' lo'ed her ance, but she's no' for me,
Yet I thank ye for your courtesy.

I'll gie thee Rozie o' the Cleugh,
I'm sure she'll please thee weel eneugh.

Up wi' her on the bare bane dyke,
She'll be rotten or [1] I'll be ripe :
She's made for some ither, and no' me,
Yet I thank ye for your courtesy.

Then I'll gie ye Nell o' sweet Sprinkell,
Owre Galloway she bears the bell.

I'll set her up in my bed-head,
And feed her wi' new milk and bread ;
She's for nae ither, but just for me,
Sae I thank ye for your courtesy.

356   DOWN IN YONDER MEADOW

Down in yonder meadow where the green grass grows,
Pretty Pollie Pillicote bleaches her clothes.
She sang, she sang, she sang, oh, so sweet,
She sang, *Oh, come over !* across the street.

[1] Ere

LILY BRIGHT AND SHINE-A

He kissed her, he kissed her, he bought her a gown,
A gown of rich cramasie out of the town.
He bought her a gown and a guinea gold ring,
A guinea, a guinea, a guinea gold ring ;
Up street, and down, shine the windows made of glass,
Oh, isn't Pollie Pillicote a braw young lass ?
Cherries in her cheeks, and ringlets her hair,
Hear her singing *Handy, Dandy* up and down the stair.

357 · QUOTH JOHN TO JOAN

QUOTH John to Joan, will thou have me :
I prithee now, wilt ? and I'll marry thee,
My cow, my calf, my house, my rents,
And all my lands and tenements :
    Oh, say, my Joan, will not that do ?
    I cannot come every day to woo.

I've corn and hay in the barn hard-by,
And three fat hogs pent up in the sty,
I have a mare and she is coal black,
I ride on her tail to save my back.
    Then, say, my Joan, will not that do ?
    I cannot come every day to woo.

I have a cheese upon the shelf,
And I cannot eat it all myself ;
I've three good marks that lie in a rag,
In a nook of the chimney, instead of a bag.
    Then, say, my Joan, will not that do ?
    I cannot come every day to woo.

To marry I would have thy consent,
But faith I never could compliment ;
I can say nought but " Hoy, gee ho ! "
Words that belong to the cart and the plough.
    Oh, say, my Joan, will not that do ?
    I cannot come every day to woo.

358 MY MISTRESS IS AS FAIR AS FINE

My mistress is as fair as fine,
    Milk-white fingers, cherry nose.
Like twinkling day-stars look her eyne,
    Lightening all things where she goes.
Fair as Phoebe, though not so fickle,
Smooth as glass, though not so brickle.

My heart is like a ball of snow
    Melting at her lukewarm sight ;
Her fiery lips like night-worms glow,
    Shining clear as candle-light.
Neat she is, no feather lighter ;
Bright she is, no daisy whiter.

359 DIAPHENIA

DIAPHENIA, like the daffdowndilly,
White as the sun, fair as the lily,
    Heigh ho, how I do love thee !
I do love thee as my lambs
Are belovèd of their dams—
    How blest were I if thou wouldst prove me.

Diaphenia, like the spreading roses,
That in thy sweets all sweets encloses,
    Fair sweet, how I do love thee !
I do love thee as each flower
Loves the sun's life-giving power,
    For, dead, thy breath to life might move me.

Diaphenia, like to all things blessèd,
When all thy praises are expressèd,
    Dear joy, how I do love thee !
As the birds do love the Spring,
Or the bees their careful king.
    Then in requite, sweet virgin, love me !
                                HENRY CONSTABLE

360 AEGLAMOUR'S LAMENT

HERE she was wont to go, and here, and here!
Just where those daisies, pinks, and violets grow:
The world may find the spring by following her;
For other print her airy steps ne'er left:
Her treading would not bend a blade of grass,
Or shake the downy blow-ball from his stalk;
But like the soft west-wind she shot along;
And where she went, the flowers took thickest root
As she had sowed them with her odourous foot.
                                        BEN JONSON

361 MY TRUE-LOVE HATH MY HEART

MY true-love hath my heart, and I have his,
   By just exchange one for the other given;
I hold his dear, and mine he cannot miss;
   There never was a better bargain driven.

His heart in me keeps me and him in one,
   My heart in him his thoughts and senses guides;
He loves my heart, for once it was his own;
   I cherish his because in me it bides.

His heart his wound receivèd from my sight,
   My heart was wounded with his wounded heart;
For as from me on him his heart did light,
   So still methought in me his heart did smart.

Both equal hurt, in this change sought our bliss,
My true love hath my heart, and I have his.
                                        SIR PHILIP SIDNEY

362   A BIRTHDAY

MY heart is like a singing bird
   Whose nest is in a watered shoot;
My heart is like an apple-tree
   Whose boughs are bent with thickest fruit.

A BIRTHDAY

My heart is like a rainbow shell
   That paddles in a halcyon sea ;
My heart is gladder than all these
   Because my love is come to me.

Raise me a dais of silk and down ;
   Hang it with vair and purple dyes ;
Carve it in doves and pomegranates,
   And peacocks with a hundred eyes ;
Work it in gold and silver grapes,
   In leaves and silver fleurs-de-lys ;
Because the birthday of my life
   Is come, my love is come to me.

CHRISTINA ROSSETTI

363   LIFE OF LIFE

"VOICE IN THE AIR, SINGING"

LIFE of Life ! thy lips enkindle
   With their love the breath between them ;
And thy smiles before they dwindle
   Make the cold air fire ; then screen them
In those looks, where whoso gazes
Faints, entangled in their mazes.

Child of Light ! thy limbs are burning
   Through the vest which seeks to hide them ;
As the radiant lines of morning
   Through the clouds ere they divide them ;
And this atmosphere divinest
Shrouds thee wheresoe'er thou shinest.

Fair are others ; none beholds thee,
   But thy voice sounds low and tender
Like the fairest, for it folds thee
   From the sight, that liquid splendour,
And all feel, yet see thee never,
As I feel now, lost for ever !

LILY BRIGHT AND SHINE-A

Lamp of Earth ! where'er thou movest
  Its dim shapes are clad with brightness,
And the souls of whom thou lovest
  Walk upon the winds with lightness,
Till they fail, as I am failing,
Dizzy, lost, yet unbewailing !

PERCY BYSSHE SHELLEY

364   A SONNET OF THE MOON

Look how the pale Queen of the silent night
Doth cause the ocean to attend upon her,
And he, as long as she is in his sight,
With his full tide is ready her to honour :

But when the silver waggon of the Moon
Is mounted up so high he cannot follow,
The sea calls home his crystal waves to moan,
And with low ebb doth manifest his sorrow.

So you that are the sovereign of my heart,
Have all my joys attending on your will,
My joys low-ebbing when you do depart,
When you return, their tide my heart doth fill.

So as you come, and as you do depart,
Joys ebb and flow within my tender heart.

CHARLES BEST

365   THE OUTLAW OF LOCH LENE

O many a day have I made good ale in the glen,
That came not of stream or malt, like the brewing of men :
My bed was the ground ; my roof, the green-wood above ;
And the wealth that I sought, one far kind glance from my
    Love.

Alas, on that night when the horses I drove from the field
That I was not near from terror my angel to shield !

THE OUTLAW OF LOCH LENE

She stretched forth her arms ; her mantle she flung to the
    wind,
And swam o'er Loch Lene, her outlawed lover to find.

O would that a freezing sleet-winged tempest did sweep,
And I and my love were alone, far off on the deep ;
I'd ask not a ship, or a bark, or a pinnace, to save—
With her hand round my waist, I'd fear not the wind or the
    wave.

'Tis down by the lake where the wild tree fringes its sides,
The maid of my heart, my fair one of Heaven resides :
I think, as at eve she wanders its mazes among,
The birds go to sleep by the sweet wild twist of her song.

JEREMIAH JOHN CALLANAN

366   O WHAT IF THE FOWLER

O WHAT if the fowler my blackbird has taken ?
  The roses of dawn blossom over the sea ;
Awaken, my blackbird, awaken, awaken,
  And sing to me out of my red fuchsia tree !

O what if the fowler my blackbird has taken ?
  The sun lifts his head from the lip of the sea—
Awaken, my blackbird, awaken, awaken,
  And sing to me out of my red fuchsia tree !

O what if the fowler my blackbird has taken ?
  The mountain grows white with the birds of the sea ;
But down in my garden forsaken, forsaken,
  I'll weep all the day by my red fuchsia tree !

CHARLES DALMON

367   WHITHER AWAY ?

" WHERE are you going, Master mine ? "
" Mistress of mine, farewell !
Pledge me a cup of golden wine !
Light shall be dark and darkness shine
    Before I tell ! "

355

LILY BRIGHT AND SHINE-A

" O go you by the firwoods blue ?
  And by the Fairies' Trysting Tree ?"
" No, for the path is grown with rue
And nightshade's purple fruit, since you
    Walked there with me !"

" O go you by the pastures high—
  A grassy road and daisies fair ?"
" No, for I saw them fade and die
On the bright evening, love, that I
    Sat with you there."

MARY COLERIDGE

368   BONNY BARBARA ALLAN

It was in and about the Martinmas time,
  When the green leaves were a falling,
That Sir John Graeme, in the West Country,
  Fell in love with Barbara Allan.

He sent his man down through the town,
  To the place where she was dwelling :
" O haste and come to my master dear,
  Gin ye be Barbara Allan."

O hooly, hooly ¹ rose she up,
  To the place where he was lying,
And when she drew the curtain by ;—
  " Young man, I think you're dying."

" O it's I'm sick, and very, very sick,
  And 't is a' for Barbara Allan."—
" O the better for me ye's never be,
  Tho your heart's blood were a spilling.

" O dinna ye mind, young man," said she,
  " When ye was in the tavern a-drinking,
That ye made the healths gae round and round,
  And slighted Barbara Allan ?"

¹ Slowly, softly

BARBARA ALLAN

He turned his face unto the wall,
  And death was with him dealing :
" Adieu, adieu, my dear friends all,
  And be kind to Barbara Allan."

She had not gane a mile but twa,
  When she heard the dead-bell ringing,
And every jow that the dead-bell gied,
  It cryed, *Woe to Barbara Allan !*

" O mother, mother, make my bed !
  O make it saft and narrow !
Since my love died for me to-day,
  I'll die for him to-morrow."

369   # PROUD MAISIE

PROUD Maisie is in the wood,
  Walking so early ;
Sweet Robin sits on the bush,
  Singing so rarely.

" Tell me, thou bonny bird,
  When shall I marry me ?"
" When six braw gentlemen
  Kirkward shall carry ye."

" Who makes the bridal bed,
  Birdie, say truly ?"
" The grey-headed sexton
  That delves the grave duly."

" The glowworm o'er grave and stone
  Shall light thee steady ;
The owl from the steeple sing
  Welcome, proud lady."
SIR WALTER SCOTT

370 A LEAVE TAKING

Let us go hence, my songs ; she will not hear.
Let us go hence together without fear ;
Keep silence now, for singing-time is over,
And over all old things and all things dear.
She loves not you nor me as all we love her.
Yea, though we sang as angels in her ear,
　　　She would not hear.

Let us rise up and part ; she will not know.
Let us go seaward as the great winds go,
Full of blown sand and foam ; what help is here ?
There is no help, for all these things are so,
And all the world is bitter as a tear.
And how these things are, though ye strove to show,
　　　She would not know.

Let us go home and hence ; she will not weep.
We gave love many dreams and days to keep,
Flowers without scent, and fruits that would not grow,
Saying, " If thou wilt, thrust in thy sickle and reap."
All is reaped now ; no grass is left to mow ;
And we that sowed, though all we fell on sleep,
　　　She would not weep.

Let us go hence and rest ; she will not love.
She shall not hear us if we sing hereof,
Nor see love's ways, how sore they are and steep.
Come hence, let be, lie still ; it is enough.
Love is a barren sea, bitter and deep ;
And though she saw all heaven in flower above,
　　　She would not love.

Let us give up, go down ; she will not care.
Though all the stars made gold of all the air,
And the sea moving saw before it move
One moon-flower making all the foam-flowers fair ;
Though all those waves went over us, and drove
Deep down the stifling lips and drowning hair,
　　　She would not care.
358

A LEAVE TAKING

Let us go hence, go hence ; she will not see.
Sing all once more together ; surely she,
She, too, remembering days and words that were,
Will turn a little toward us, sighing ; but we,
We are hence, we are gone, as though we had not been there.
Nay, and though all men seeing had pity on me,
      She would not see.
          ALGERNON CHARLES SWINBURNE

371   THE UNQUIET GRAVE

   " THE wind doth blow to-day, my love,
     And a few small drops of rain ;
  I never had but one true love,
     In cold grave she was lain.

   " I'll do as much for my true love
     As any young man may ;
  I'll sit and mourn all at her grave
     For a twelvemonth and a day."

  The twelvemonth and a day being up,
     The dead began to speak :
  " Oh who sits weeping on my grave,
     And will not let me sleep ? "

  " 'T is I, my love, sits on your grave,
     And will not let you sleep ;
  For I crave one kiss of your clay-cold lips,
     And that is all I seek."

  " You crave one kiss of my clay-cold lips ;
     But my breath smells earthy strong ;
  If you have one kiss of my clay-cold lips,
     Your time will not be long.

  " 'Tis down in yonder garden green,
     Love, where we used to walk,
  The finest flower that ere was seen
     Is withered to a stalk.

" The stalk is withered dry, my love,
   So will our hearts decay ;
So make yourself content, my love,
   Till God calls you away."

372   A LAMENT : 1547

" Departe, departe, departe—
   Allace ! I most departe
From hir that hes my hart,
   With hairt full soir ;
Aganis my will in deid,
And can find no remeid :
I wait the pains of deid—
   Can do no moir. . . .

" Adew, my ain sueit thing,
My joy and comforting,
My mirth and sollesing
   Of erdly gloir :
Fair weill, my lady bricht,
And my remembrance rycht ;
Fair weill and haif gud nycht :
   I say no moir."

                         ALEXANDER SCOTT

373   I DIED TRUE

Lay a garland on my hearse
   Of the dismal yew ;
Maidens, willow branches bear ;
   Say I died true.

My love was false, but I was firm
   From my hour of birth.
Upon my buried body lie
   Lightly, gentle earth !

                         JOHN FLETCHER

374

SONG

How should I your true love know
   From another one ?
By his Cockle hat and staffe,
   And his Sandal shoone.

He is dead and gone Lady,
   He is dead and done,—
At his head a grasse-greene Turfe,
   At his heeles a stone.

White his Shrowd as the Mountain Snow,
   Larded with sweet flowers :
Which bewept to the grave did not go,
   With true-love showres.

            WILLIAM SHAKESPEARE

375   IT WAS THE TIME OF ROSES

IT was not in the winter
Our loving lot was cast :
It was the time of roses—
We plucked them as we passed !

That churlish season never frowned
On early lovers yet !
O, no—the world was newly crowned
With flowers, when first we met.

'Twas twilight, and I bade you go,
But still you held me fast :
It was the time of roses—
We plucked them as we passed.". . .

            THOMAS HOOD

AULD ROBIN GRAY

WHEN the sheep are in the fauld, and the kye [1] at hame,
And a' the warld to rest are gane,
The waes o' my heart fa' in showers frae my e'e,
While my gudeman [2] lies sound by me.

Young Jamie lo'ed me weel, and sought me for his bride,
But saving a croun he had naething else beside :
To make the croun a pund, young Jamie gaed to sea,
And the croun and the pund were baith for me.

He hadna been awa a week but only twa,
When my father brak his arm, and the cow was stown awa ;
My mother she fell sick, and my Jamie at the sea—
And auld Robin Gray came a-courtin' me.

My father couldna work, and my mother couldna spin ;
I toiled day and night, but their bread I couldna win ;
Auld Rob maintained them baith, and wi' tears in his e'e
Said :—" Jennie, for their sakes, O, marry me !"

My heart it said nay ; I look'd for Jamie back ;
But the wind it blew high, and the ship it was a wrack ;
His ship it was a wrack. . . . Why didna Jamie dee ?
Or why do I live to cry, Wae's me ?

My father urgit sair : my mother didna speak,
But she looked in my face till my heart was like to break :
They gi'ed him my hand, but my heart was at the sea,
Sae auld Robin Gray he was gudeman to me.

I hadna been a wife a week but only four,
When, mournfu' as I sat on the stane at the door,
I saw my Jamie's wraith, for I couldna think it he—
Till he said :—" I'm come hame to marry thee."

O, sair, sair did we greet,[3] and muckle [4] did we say ;
We took but ae kiss, and I bad him gang away ;
I wish that I were dead, but I'm no like to dee,
And why was I born to say, Wae's me !

    [1] Cows   [2] Husband   [3] Weep   [4] Much

AULD ROBIN GRAY

I gang like a ghaist, and I carena to spin ;
I daurna think on Jamie, for that wad be a sin ;
But I'll do my best a gude wife ay to be,
For auld Robin Gray, he is kind unto me.

LADY ANNE LINDSAY

377   THE LAWLANDS O' HOLLAND

" THE love that I hae chosen,
    I'll therewith be content ;
The saut sea sall be frozen
    Before that I repent. .
Repent it sall I never
    Until the day I dee ;
But the Lawlands o' Holland
    Hae twinned my love and me.

" My love he built a bonny ship,
    And set her to the main,
Wi' twenty-four brave mariners
    To sail her out and hame.
But the weary wind began to rise,
    The sea began to rout,
And my love and his bonny ship
    Turned withershins about.

" There sall nae mantle cross my back,
    No kaim gae in my hair,
Neither sall coal nor candle-light
    Shine in my bower mair ;
Nor sall I choose anither love,
    Until the day I dee,
Sin' the Lawlands o' Holland,
    Hae twinned my love and me."

" Noo haud your tongue, my daughter dear,
    Be still, and bide content ;
There's ither lads in Galloway ;
    Ye needna sair lament."

LILY BRIGHT AND SHINE-A

" O there is nane in Galloway,
    There's nane at a' for me.
I never lo'ed a lad but ane,
    And he's drowned in the sea."

378   THE CHURCHYARD ON THE SANDS

My love lies in the gates of foam,
    The last dear wreck of shore ;
The naked sea-marsh binds her home,
    The sand her chamber door.

The gray gull flaps the written stones,
    The ox-birds chase the tide ;
And near that narrow field of bones
    Great ships at anchor ride.

Black piers with crust of dripping green,
    One foreland, like a hand,
O'er intervals of grass between
    Dim lonely dunes of sand.

A church of silent weathered looks,
    A breezy reddish tower,
A yard whose wounded resting-nooks
    Are tinged with sorrel flower.

In peace the swallow's eggs are laid
    Along the belfry walls ;
The tempest does not reach her shade,
    The rain her silent halls.

But sails are sweet in summer sky,
    The lark throws down a lay ;
The long salt levels steam and dry,
    The cloud-heart melts away.

And patches of the sea-pink shine,
    The pied crows poise and come ;
The mallow hangs, the bind-weeds twine,
    Where her sweet lips are dumb.

The passion of the wave is mute ;
No sound or ocean shock ;
No music save the thrilling flute
That marks the curlew flock. . . .

LORD DE TABLEY

379 ROSE AYLMER

AH, what avails the sceptred race,
Ah, what the form divine !
What every virtue, every grace !
Rose Aylmer, all were thine.
Rose Aylmer, whom these wakeful eyes
May weep, but never see,
A night of memories and sighs
I consecrate to thee.

WALTER SAVAGE LANDOR

380 TO HELEN

HELEN, thy beauty is to me
Like those Nicæan barks of yore,
That gently, o'er a perfumed sea,
The weary, wayworn wanderer bore
To his own native shore.

On desperate seas long wont to roam,
Thy hyacinth hair, thy classic face,
Thy Naiad air, have brought me home
To the glory that was Greece
And the grandeur that was Rome.

Lo ! in yon brilliant window-niche
How statue-like I see thee stand,
The agate lamp within thy hand !
Ah, Psyche, from the regions which
Are Holy Land !

EDGAR ALLAN POE

LILY BRIGHT AND SHINE-A

381   "THERE IS A LADY SWEET AND KIND"

     THERE is a Lady sweet and kind,
     Was never face so pleased my mind;
     I did but see her passing by,
     And yet I love her till I die.

     Her gesture, motion, and her smiles,
     Her wit, her voice, my heart beguiles,
     Beguiles my heart, I know not why,
     And yet I love her till I die. . . .

     Cupid is wingèd and doth range,
     Her country so my love doth change:
     But change she earth, or change she sky,
     Yet will I love her till I die.

                    THOMAS FORD

382   "LOVE NOT ME FOR COMELY GRACE"

     LOVE not me for comely grace,
     For my pleasing eye or face,
     Nor for any outward part:
     No, nor for my constant heart!
       For these may fail or turn to ill:
       So thou and I shall sever:
     Keep therefore a true woman's eye,
     And love me still, but know not why!
       So hast thou the same reason still
       To doat upon me ever.

383   NOW WOLDE

     Now wolde I faine some merthès [1] make,
     All only for my lady sake,
       When her I see;
     But now I am so far fro her
       It will not be.

[1] Praises

NOW WOLDE

Though I be far out of her sight
I am her man both day and night
   And so will be.
Therefore wolde ; as I love her,
   She lovèd me.

When she is mery, then I am glad ;
When she is sory, then I am sad ;
   And causè why,[1]
For he liveth not that loveth her
   As well as I.

She saith that she hath seen it written
That " seldom seen is soon forgotten " ;
   It is not so.
For in good feith, save only her,
   I love no mo.[2]

384   EGYPT'S MIGHT IS TUMBLED DOWN

Egypt's might is tumbled down
   Down a-down the deeps of thought ;
Greece is fallen and Troy town,
Glorious Rome hath lost her crown,
   Venice' pride is nought.

But the dreams their children dreamed
   Fleeting, unsubstantial, vain,
Shadowy as the shadows seemed,
Airy nothing, as they deemed,
   These remain.
                    MARY COLERIDGE

[1] Good reason why   [2] More

367

LILY BRIGHT AND SHINE-A

DREAM LOVE

Young Love lies sleeping
  In May-time of the year.
Among the lilies,
  Lapped in the tender light :
White lambs come grazing,
  White doves come building there ;
And round about him
  The May-bushes are white.

Soft moss the pillow
  For oh, a softer cheek ;
Broad leaves cast shadow
  Upon the heavy eyes :
There winds and waters
  Grow lulled and scarcely speak ;
There twilight lingers
  The longest in the skies.

Young Love lies dreaming ;
  But who shall tell the dream ?
A perfect sunlight
  On rustling forest tips ;
Or perfect moonlight
  Upon a rippling stream ;
Or perfect silence,
  Or song of cherished lips.

Burn odours round him
  To fill the drowsy air ;
Weave silent dances
  Around him to and fro ;
For oh, in waking
  The sights are not so fair,
And song and silence
  Are not like these below.

Young Love lies dreaming
  Till summer days are gone,—

DREAM LOVE

Dreaming and drowsing
    Away to perfect sleep :
He sees the beauty
    Sun hath not looked upon,
And tastes the fountain
    Unutterably deep.

Him perfect music
    Doth hush unto his rest,
And through the pauses
    The perfect silence calms.
Oh, poor the voices
    Of earth from east to west,
And poor earth's stillness
    Between her stately palms.

Young Love lies drowsing
    Away to poppied death ;
Cool shadows deepen
    Across the sleeping face :
So fails the summer
    With warm, delicious breath ;
And what hath autumn
    To give us in its place ?

Draw close the curtains
    Of branched evergreen ;
Change cannot touch them
    With fading fingers sere :
Here the first violets
    Perhaps will bud unseen,
And a dove, may be,
    Return to nestle here.

CHRISTINA ROSSETTI

386   AT COMMON DAWN

At common dawn there is a voice of bird
So sweet, 'tis kin to pain ;
For love of earthly life it needs be heard,
And lets not sleep again.

LILY BRIGHT AND SHINE-A

This bird I did one time at midnight hear
In wet November wood
Say to himself his lyric faint and clear
As one at daybreak should.

He ceased ; the covert breathed no other sound,
Nor moody answer made ;
But all the world at beauty's worship found,
Was waking in the glade.

Vivian Locke Ellis

"ECHO THEN SHALL AGAIN
TELL HER I FOLLOW."

GLYCINE'S SONG

A sunny shaft did I behold,
From sky to earth it slanted :
And poised therein a bird so bold—
Sweet bird, thou wert enchanted !

He sank, he rose, he twinkled, he trolled
Within that shaft of sunny mist ;
His eyes of fire, his beak of gold,
All else of amethyst !

And thus he sang : " Adieu ! adieu !
Love's dreams prove seldom true.
The blossoms, they make no delay :
The sparkling dew-drops will not stay.
Sweet month of May,
We must away ;
Far, far away !
To-day ! to-day !"

SAMUEL TAYLOR COLERIDGE

388   THE CRYSTAL CABINET

The Maiden caught me in the wild,
Where I was dancing merrily ;
She put me into her Cabinet,
And locked me up with a golden key.

This Cabinet is formed of Gold
And Pearl and Crystal shining bright,

373

"TELL HER I FOLLOW"

And within it opens into a World
And a little lovely Moony Night.

Another England there I saw
Another London with its Tower,
Another Thames and other Hills,
And another pleasant Surrey Bower.

Another Maiden like herself,
Translucent, lovely, shining clear,
Threefold each in the other closed—
O, what a pleasant trembling fear !

O, what a smile ! a Threefold Smile
Filled me, that like a flame I burned ;
I bent to kiss the lovely Maid,
And found a Threefold Kiss returned.

I strove to seize the inmost form
With ardour fierce and hands of flame,
But burst the Crystal Cabinet,
And like a Weeping Babe became—

A Weeping Babe upon the wild,
And Weeping Woman pale reclined,
And in the outward air again
I filled with woes the passing wind.

WILLIAM BLAKE

389   THE CHASE

Art thou gone in haste ?
    I'll not forsake thee ;
Runn'st thou ne'er so fast ?
    I'll overtake thee :
O'er the dales, o'er the downs,
    Through the green meadows,
From the fields through the towns,
    To the dim shadows.

374

THE CHASE

All along the plain,
   To the low fountains,
Up and down again
   From the high mountains ;
Echo then shall again
   Tell her I follow,
And the floods to the woods
   Carry my holla !
      Holla !
   Ce ! la ! ho ! ho ! hu !
                    WILLIAM ROWLEY

390   TONY O !

OVER the bleak and barren snow
A voice there came a-calling ;
" Where are you going to, Tony O !
Where are you going this morning ? "

" I am going where there are rivers of wine,
The mountains bread and honey ;
There Kings and Queens do mind the swine,
And the poor have all the money."
                    COLIN FRANCIS

391   ROMANCE

WHEN I was but thirteen or so
   I went into a golden land,
Chimborazo, Cotopaxi
   Took me by the hand.

My father died, my brother too,
   They passed like fleeting dreams.
I stood where Popocatapetl
   In the sunlight gleams.

I dimly heard the master's voice
   And boys far-off at play,
Chimborazo, Cotopaxi
   Had stolen me away.

375

"TELL HER I FOLLOW"

I walked in a great golden dream
    To and fro from school—
Shining Popocatapetl
    The dusty streets did rule.

I walked home with a gold dark boy,
    And never a word I'd say,
Chimborazo, Cotopaxi
    Had taken my speech away:

I gazed entranced upon his face
    Fairer than any flower—
O shining Popocatapetl
    It was thy magic hour:

The houses, people, traffic seemed
    Thin fading dreams by day,
Chimborazo, Cotopaxi
    They had stolen my soul away!

                        WALTER J. TURNER

392   HALLO MY FANCY

        IN melancholic fancy,
            Out of myself,
        In the vulcan dancy,
            All the world surveying,
            Nowhere staying,
    Just like a fairy elf;
Out o'er the tops of highest mountains skipping,
Out o'er the hill, the trees and valleys tripping,
Out o'er the ocean seas, without an oar or shipping,—
    Hallo my fancy, whither wilt thou go?

        Amidst the misty vapours
        Fain would I know
        What doth cause the tapers;
        Why the clouds benight us
        And affright us.
    While we travel here below;

HALLO MY FANCY

Fain would I know what makes the roaring thunder,
And what these lightnings be that rend the clouds asunder,
And what these comets are on which we gaze and wonder—
Hallo my fancy, whither wilt thou go?

> Fain would I know the reason,
> Why the little ant,
> All the summer season,
> Layeth up provision
> On condition
> To know no winter's want.

And how housewives, that are so good and painful,
Do unto their husbands prove so good and gainful;
And why the lazy drones to them do prove disdainful—
Hallo my fancy, whither wilt thou go? . . .

> Amidst the foamy ocean,
> Fain would I know
> What doth cause the motion,
> And returning
> In its journeying,
> And doth so seldom swerve?

And how the little fishes that swim beneath salt waters,
Do never blind their eye; methinks it is a matter
An inch above the reach of old Erra Pater!—
Hallo my fancy, whither wilt thou go?

> Fain would I be resolvèd
> How things are done;
> And where the bull was calvèd
> Of bloody Phalaris,
> And where the tailor is
> That works to the man i' the moon!

Fain would I know how Cupid aims so rightly;
And how the little fairies do dance and leap so lightly,
And where fair Cynthia makes her ambles nightly—
Hallo my fancy, whither wilt thou go?

> In conceit like Phaeton
> I'll mount Phoebus' chair

377

"TELL HER I FOLLOW"

Having ne'er a hat on,
All my hair a-burning
In my journeying ;
Hurrying through the air.
Fain would I hear his fiery horses neighing
And see how they on foamy bits are playing,
All the stars and planets I will be surveying !—
Hallo my fancy, whither wilt thou go ?

O from what ground of nature
Doth the pelican,
That self devouring creature
Prove so froward
And untoward,
Her vitals for to strain !
And why the subtle fox, while in death's wounds a-lying,
Do not lament his pangs by howling and by crying,
And why the milk-swan doth sing when she's a-dying—
Hallo my fancy, whither wilt thou go ?

Fain would I conclude this,
At least make essay ;
What similitude is :
Why fowls of a feather
Flock and fly together,
And lambs know beasts of prey ;
How Nature's alchemists, these small laborious creatures,
Acknowledge still a prince in ordering their matters,
And suffer none to live who slothing lose their features—
Hallo my fancy, whither wilt thou go ? . . .

To know this world's centre
Height, depth, breadth and length,
Fain would I adventure
To search the hid attractions
Of magnetic actions
And adamantine strength.
Fain would I know, if in some lofty mountain,
Where the moon sojourns, if there be tree or fountain ;

HALLO MY FANCY

If there be beasts of prey, or yet be fields to hunt in—
Hallo my fancy, whither wilt thou go ? . . .

Hallo my fancy, hallo,
Stay, stay at home with me,
I can no longer follow,
For thou hast betrayed me,
And bewrayed me ;
It is too much for thee.
Stay, stay at home with me, leave off thy lofty soaring ;
Stay then at home with me, and on thy books be poring ;
For he that goes abroad, lays little up in storing—
Thou'rt welcome my fancy, welcome home to me.

WILLIAM CLELAND

393 SONNET

THERE was an Indian, who had known no change,
Who strayed content along a sunlit beach
Gathering shells.   He heard a sudden strange
Commingled noise : looked up ; and gasped for speech.
For in the bay, where nothing was before,
Moved on the sea, by magic, huge canoes,
With bellying clothes on poles, and not one oar,
And fluttering coloured signs and clambering crews.

And he, in fear, this naked man alone,
His fallen hands forgetting all their shells,
His lips gone pale, knelt low behind a stone,
And stared, and saw, and did not understand,
Columbus's doom-burdened caravels
Slant to the shore, and all their seamen land.

J. C. SQUIRE

394   ON FIRST LOOKING INTO CHAPMAN'S
HOMER

Much have I travelled in the realms of gold,
    And many goodly states and kingdoms seen :
    Round many western islands have I been
Which bards in fealty to Apollo hold.

Oft of one wide expanse had I been told
    That deep-browed Homer ruled as his demesne ;
    Yet did I never breathe its pure serene
Till I heard Chapman speak out loud and bold :

Then felt I like some watcher of the skies
    When a new planet swims into his ken ;
Or like stout Cortez, when with eagle eyes

He stared at the Pacific—and all his men
    Looked at each other with a wild surmise—
Silent, upon a peak in Darien.
                                    JOHN KEATS

395   " TO SEA "

To sea, to sea ! The calm is o'er ;
The wanton water leaps in sport,
And rattles down the pebbly shore ;
The dolphin wheels, the sea-cows snort,
And unseen Mermaids' pearly song
Comes bubbling up, the weeds among.
    Fling broad the sail, dip deep the oar :
To sea, to sea ! the calm is o'er.

To sea, to sea ! our wide-winged bark
Shall billowy cleave its sunny way,
And with its shadow, fleet and dark,
Break the caved Tritons' azure day,
Like mighty eagle soaring light
O'er antelopes on Alpine height.
    The anchor heaves, the ship swings free,
The sails swell full : To sea, to sea !
                    THOMAS LOVELL BEDDOES

BERMUDAS

WHERE the remote Bermudas ride,
In the Ocean's bosom unespied,
From a small boat, that rowed along,
The listening winds received this song :   .

" What should we do but sing His praise,
That led us through the watery maze,
Unto an isle so long unknown,
And yet far kinder than our own ?
Where He the huge sea-monsters wracks
That lift the deep upon their backs,
He lands us on a grassy stage,
Safe from the storms' and prelates' rage :
He gave us this eternal Spring
Which here enamels everything,
And sends the fowls to us in care
On daily visits through the air :
He hangs in shades the orange bright,
Like golden lamps in a green night,
And does in the pomegranates close
Jewels more rich than Ormus shows ;
He makes the figs our mouths to meet,
And throws the melons at our feet ;
But apples plants of such a price
No tree could ever bear them twice.
With cedars, chosen by His hand
From Lebanon, He stores the land,
And makes the hollow seas, that roar,
Proclaim the ambergris on shore.
He cast (of which we rather boast)
The Gospel's pearl upon our coast ;
And in these rocks for us did frame
A temple where to sound His name.
Oh ! let our voice His praise exalt,
Till it arrive at Heaven's vault,
Which, thence (perhaps) rebounding, may
Echo beyond the Mexique bay."

Thus sung they, in the English boat,
A holy and a cheerful note ;
And all the way, to guide their chime,
With falling oars they kept the time.

ANDREW MARVELL

THE OLD SHIPS

I HAVE seen old ships sail like swans asleep
Beyond the village which men still call Tyre,
With leaden age o'ercargoed, dipping deep
For Famagusta and the hidden sun
That rings black Cyprus with a lake of fire ;
And all those ships were certainly so old—
Who knows how oft with squat and noisy gun
Questing brown slaves or Syrian oranges,
The pirate Genoese
Hell-raked them till they rolled
Blood, water, fruit and corpses up the hold.
But now through friendly seas they softly run,
Painted the mid-sea blue or shore-sea green,
Still patterned with the vine and grapes in gold.

But I have seen
Pointing her shapely shadows from the dawn
And image tumbled on a rose-swept bay
A drowsy ship of some yet older day ;
And, wonder's breath indrawn,
Thought I—who knows—who knows—but in that
    same
(Fished up beyond Aeaea, patched up new
—Stern painted brighter blue—)
That talkative, bald-headed seaman came
(Twelve patient comrades sweating at the oar)
From Troy's doom-crimson shore,
And with great lies about his wooden horse
Set the crew laughing, and forgot his course.

THE OLD SHIPS

It was so old a ship—who knows, who knows ?
—And yet so beautiful, I watched in vain
To see the mast burst open with a rose,
And the whole deck put on its leaves again.

JAMES ELROY FLECKER

398 THE RIME OF THE ANCIENT MARINER

IN SEVEN PARTS

ARGUMENT : *How a Ship having passed the Line is driven by storms to the cold Country towards the South Pole ; and how from thence she made her course to the Tropical Latitude of the great Pacific Ocean ; and of the strange things that befell ; and in what manner the Ancient Mariner came back to his own Country.*

PART I

IT is an ancient Mariner,
And he stoppeth one of three.
" By thy long grey beard and glittering eye,
Now wherefore stopp'st thou me ?

The Bridegroom's doors are opened wide,
And I am next of kin ;
The guests are met, the feast is set :
May'st hear the merry din."

He holds him with his skinny hand,
" There was a ship," quoth he.
" Hold off ! unhand me, grey-beard loon !"
Eftsoons his hand dropt he.

He holds him with his glittering eye—
The Wedding-Guest stood still,
And listens like a three years' child :
The Mariner hath his will.

The Wedding-Guest sat on a stone :
He cannot choose but hear ;
And thus spake on that ancient man,
The bright-eyed Mariner.

383

"TELL HER I FOLLOW"

" The ship was cheered, the harbour cleared,
Merrily did we drop
Below the kirk, below the hill,
Below the lighthouse top.

The Sun came up upon the left,
Out of the sea came he !
And he shone bright, and on the right
Went down into the sea.

Higher and higher every day,
Till over the mast at noon—"
The Wedding-Guest here beat his breast,
For he heard the loud bassoon.

The bride hath paced into the hall,
Red as a rose is she ;
Nodding their heads before her goes
The merry minstrelsy.

The Wedding-Guest he beat his breast,
Yet he cannot choose but hear ;
And thus spake on that ancient man,
The bright-eyed Mariner.

" And now the STORM-BLAST came, and he
Was tyrannous and strong :
He struck with his o'ertaking wings,
And chased us south along.

With sloping masts and dipping prow,
As who pursued with yell and blow
Still treads the shadow of his foe,
And forward bends his head,
The ship drove fast, loud roared the blast,
And southward aye we fled.

And now there came both mist and snow,
And it grew wondrous cold :
And ice, mast-high, came floating by,
As green as emerald.

And through the drifts the snowy clifts
Did send a dismal sheen :
Nor shapes of men nor beasts we ken—
The ice was all between.

The ice was here, the ice was there,
The ice was all around :
It cracked and growled, and roared and howled,
Like noises in a swound !

At length did cross an Albatross,
Thorough the fog it came ;
As if it had been a Christian soul,
We hailed it in God's name.

It ate the food it ne'er had eat,
And round and round it flew.
The ice did split with a thunder-fit ;
The helmsman steered us through !

And a good south wind sprung up behind ;
The Albatross did follow,
And every day, for food or play,
Came to the mariner's hollo !

In mist or cloud, on mast or shroud,
It perched for vespers nine ;
Whiles all the night, through fog-smoke white,
Glimmered the white Moon-shine."

" God save thee, ancient Mariner !
From the fiends, that plague thee thus !—
Why look'st thou so ? "
                    —" With my cross-bow
I shot the ALBATROSS."

PART II

The Sun now rose upon the right :
Out of the sea came he,
Still hid in mist, and on the left
Went down into the sea.

" TELL HER I FOLLOW "

And the good south wind still blew behind,
But no sweet bird did follow,
Nor any day for food or play
Came to the mariners' hollo !

And I had done a hellish thing,
And it would work 'em woe :
For all averred, I had killed the bird
That made the breeze to blow.
Ah wretch ! said they, the bird to slay,
That made the breeze to blow !

Nor dim nor red, like God's own head,
The glorious Sun uprist :
Then all averred, I had killed the bird
That brought the fog and mist.
'Twas right, said they, such birds to slay,
That bring the fog and mist.

The fair breeze blew, the white foam flew.
The furrow followed free ;
We were the first that ever burst
Into that silent sea.

Down dropt the breeze, the sails dropt down,
'Twas sad as sad could be ;
And we did speak only to break
The silence of the sea !

All in a hot and copper sky,
The bloody Sun, at noon,
Right up above the mast did stand,
No bigger than the Moon.

Day after day, day after day,
We stuck, nor breath nor motion ;
As idle as a painted ship
Upon a painted ocean.

Water, water, every where,
And all the boards did shrink ;

Water, water, every where,
Nor any drop to drink.

The very deep did rot : O Christ !
That ever this should be !
Yea, slimy things did crawl with legs
Upon the slimy sea.

About, about, in reel and rout
The death-fires danced at night ;
The water, like a witch's oils,
Burnt green, and blue, and white.

And some in dreams assurèd were
Of the Spirit that plagued us so ;
Nine fathom deep he had followed us
From the land of mist and snow.

And every tongue, through utter drought,
Was withered at the root ;
We could not speak, no more than if
We had been choked with soot.

Ah ! well a-day ! what evil looks
Had I from old and young !
Instead of the cross, the Albatross
About my neck was hung.

Part III

" There passed a weary time.   Each throat
Was parched, and glazed each eye.
A weary time ! a weary time !
How glazed each weary eye,
When looking westward, I beheld
A something in the sky.

At first it seemed a little speck,
And then it seemed a mist ;
It moved and moved, and took at last
A certain shape, I wist.

"TELL HER I FOLLOW"

A speck, a mist, a shape, I wist !
And still it neared and neared :
As if it dodged a water-sprite,
It plunged and tacked and veered.

With throats unslaked, with black lips baked,
We could nor laugh nor wail ;
Through utter drought all dumb we stood !
I bit my arm, I sucked the blood,
And cried, A sail ! a sail !

With throats unslaked, with black lips baked,
Agape they heard me call :
Gramercy ! they for joy did grin,
And all at once their breath drew in,
As they were drinking all.

See ! see ! (I cried) she tacks no more !
Hither to work us weal ;
Without a breeze, without a tide,
She steadies with upright keel !

The western wave was all a-flame,
The day was well nigh done !
Almost upon the western wave
Rested the broad bright Sun ;
When that strange shape drove suddenly
Betwixt us and the Sun.

And straight the Sun was flecked with bars,
(Heaven's Mother send us grace !)
As if through a dungeon-grate he peered
With broad and burning face.

Alas ! (thought I, and my heart beat loud)
How fast she nears and nears !
Are those *her* sails that glance in the Sun,
Like restless gossameres ?

Are those *her* ribs through which the Sun
Did peer, as through a grate ?

388

THE RIME OF THE ANCIENT MARINER

And is that Woman all her crew ?
Is that a DEATH ? and are there two ?
Is DEATH that woman's mate ?

Her lips were red, *her* looks were free,
Her locks were yellow as gold :
Her skin was as white as leprosy,
The Night-mare LIFE-IN-DEATH was she,
Who thicks man's blood with cold.

The naked hulk alongside came,
And the twain were casting dice ;
" The game is done ! I've won ! I've won !"
Quoth she, and whistles thrice.

The Sun's rim dips : the stars rush out :
At one stride comes the dark ;
With far-heard whisper, o'er the sea,
Off shot the spectre-bark.

We listened and looked sideways up !
Fear at my heart, as at a cup,
My life-blood seemed to sip !
The stars were dim, and thick the night,
The steersman's face by his lamp gleamed white ;
From the sails the dew did drip—
Till clomb above the eastern bar
The hornèd Moon, with one bright star
Within the nether tip.

One after one, by the star-dogged Moon,
Too quick for groan or sigh,
Each turned his face with a ghastly pang,
And cursed me with his eye.

Four times fifty living men,
(And I heard nor sigh nor groan)
With heavy thump, a lifeless lump,
They dropped down one by one.

"TELL HER I FOLLOW"

The souls did from their bodies fly,—
They fled to bliss or woe !
And every soul, it passed me by,
Like the whizz of my cross-bow !"

PART IV

" I fear thee, ancient Mariner !
I fear thy skinny hand !
And thou art long, and lank, and brown,
As is the ribbed sea-sand.

I fear thee and thy glittering eye,
And thy skinny hand, so brown."
" Fear not, fear not, thou Wedding-Guest !
This body dropt not down.

Alone, alone, all, all alone,
Alone on a wide wide sea !
And never a saint took pity on
My soul in agony.

The many men, so beautiful !
And they all dead did lie :
And a thousand thousand slimy things
Lived on ; and so did I.

I looked upon the rotting sea,
And drew my eyes away ;
I looked upon the rotting deck,
And there the dead men lay.

I looked to heaven, and tried to pray ;
But or ever a prayer had gusht,
A wicked whisper came, and made
My heart as dry as dust.

I closed my lids, and kept them close,
And the balls like pulses beat ;
For the sky and the sea, and the sea and the sky
Lay like a load on my weary eye,
And the dead were at my feet.

390

THE RIME OF THE ANCIENT MARINER

The cold sweat melted from their limbs,
Nor rot nor reek did they :
The look with which they looked on me
Had never passed away.

An orphan's curse would drag to hell
A spirit from on high ;
But oh ! more horrible than that
Is the curse in a dead man's eye !
Seven days, seven nights, I saw that curse,
And yet I could not die.

The moving Moon went up the sky,
And no where did abide :
Softly she was going up,
And a star or two beside—

Her beams bemocked the sultry main,
Like April hoar-frost spread ;
But where the ship's huge shadow lay,
The charmèd water burnt alway
A still and awful red.

Beyond the shadow of the ship,
I watched the water-snakes :
They moved in tracks of shining white,
And when they reared, the elfish light
Fell off in hoary flakes.

Within the shadow of the ship
I watched their rich attire :
Blue, glossy green, and velvet black,
They coiled and swam ; and every track
Was a flash of golden fire.

O happy living things ! no tongue
Their beauty might declare :
A spring of love gushed from my heart,
And I blessed them unaware :
Sure my kind saint took pity on me,
And I blessed them unaware.

"TELL HER I FOLLOW"

The self-same moment I could pray;
And from my neck so free
The Albatross fell off, and sank
Like lead into the sea.

PART V

Oh sleep! it is a gentle thing,
Beloved from pole to pole!
To Mary Queen the praise be given!
She sent the gentle sleep from Heaven,
That slid into my soul.

The silly buckets on the deck,
That had so long remained,
I dreamt that they were filled with dew;
And when I awoke, it rained.

My lips were wet, my throat was cold,
My garments all were dank;
Sure I had drunken in my dreams,
And still my body drank.

I moved, and could not feel my limbs:
I was so light—almost
I thought that I had died in sleep,
And was a blessèd ghost.

And soon I heard a roaring wind:
It did not come anear;
But with its sound it shook the sails,
That were so thin and sere.

The upper air burst into life!
And a hundred fire-flags sheen,
To and fro they were hurried about!
And to and fro, and in and out,
The wan stars danced between.

And the coming wind did roar more loud,
And the sails did sigh like sedge;

THE RIME OF THE ANCIENT MARINER

And the rain poured down from one black cloud ;
The Moon was at its edge.

The thick black cloud was cleft, and still
The Moon was at its side :
Like waters shot from some high crag,
The lightning fell with never a jag,
A river steep and wide.

The loud wind never reached the ship,
Yet now the ship moved on !
Beneath the lightning and the Moon
The dead men gave a groan.

They groaned, they stirred, they all uprose,
Nor spake, nor moved their eyes ;
It had been strange, even in a dream,
To have seen those dead men rise.

The helmsman steered, the ship moved on ;
Yet never a breeze up-blew ;
The mariners all 'gan work the ropes,
Where they were wont to do ;
They raised their limbs like lifeless tools—
We were a ghastly crew.

The body of my brother's son
Stood by me, knee to knee :
The body and I pulled at one rope,
But he said nought to me."—

" I fear thee, ancient Mariner !"—
" Be calm, thou Wedding-Guest !
'Twas not those souls that fled in pain,
Which to their corses came again,
But a troop of spirits blest :

For when it dawned—they dropped their arms,
And clustered round the mast ;
Sweet sounds rose slowly through their mouths,
And from their bodies passed.

393

"TELL HER I FOLLOW"

Around, around, flew each sweet sound,
Then darted to the Sun ;
Slowly the sounds came back again,
Now mixed, now one by one.

Sometimes a-dropping from the sky
I heard the sky-lark sing ;
Sometimes all little birds that are,
How they seemed to fill the sea and air
With their sweet jargoning !

And now 'twas like all instruments,
Now like a lonely flute ;
And now it is an angel's song,
That makes the heavens be mute.

It ceased ; yet still the sails made on
A pleasant noise till noon,
A noise like of a hidden brook
In the leafy month of June,
That to the sleeping woods all night
Singeth a quiet tune.

Till noon we silently sailed on,
Yet never a breeze did breathe :
Slowly and smoothly went the ship,
Moved onward from beneath.

Under the keel nine fathom deep,
From the land of mist and snow,
The spirit slid : and it was he
That made the ship to go.
The sails at noon left off their tune,
And the ship stood still also.

The Sun, right up above the mast,
Had fixed her to the ocean ;
But in a minute she 'gan stir,
With a short uneasy motion—
Backwards and forwards half her length
With a short uneasy motion.

Then like a pawing horse let go,
She made a sudden bound :
It flung the blood into my head,
And I fell down in a swound.

How long in that same fit I lay,
I have not to declare ;
But ere my living life returned,
I heard and in my soul discerned
Two voices in the air.

" Is it he ? " quoth one, " Is this the man ?
By him who died on cross,
With his cruel bow he laid full low
The harmless Albatross.

The spirit who bideth by himself
In the land of mist and snow,
He loved the bird that loved the man
Who shot him with his bow."

The other was a softer voice,
As soft as honey-dew :
Quoth he, " The man hath penance done,
And penance more will do."

Part VI

First Voice. " But tell me, tell me ! speak again,
Thy soft response renewing—
What makes that ship drive on so fast ?
What is the ocean doing ? "

Second Voice. " Still as a slave before his lord,
The ocean hath no blast ;
His great bright eye most silently
Up to the Moon is cast—

If he may know which way to go ;
For she guides him smooth or grim.

" TELL HER I FOLLOW "

See, brother, see ! how graciously
She looketh down on him."

First Voice. " But why drives on that ship so fast,
Withouten wave or wind ?"

Second Voice. " The air is cut away before,
And closes from behind.

Fly, brother, fly ! more high, more high !
Or we shall be belated :
For slow and slow that ship will go, ·
When the Mariner's trance is abated."—

I woke, and we were sailing on
As in a gentle weather :
'Twas night, calm night, the moon was high ;
The dead men stood together.

All stood together on the deck,
For a charnel-dungeon fitter :
All fixed on me their stony eyes,
That in the Moon did glitter.

The pang, the curse, with which they died,
Had never passed away :
I could not draw my eyes from theirs,
Nor turn them up to pray.

And now this spell was snapt : once more
I viewed the ocean green,
And looked far forth, yet little saw
Of what had else been seen—

Like one, that on a lonesome road
Doth walk in fear and dread,
And having once turned round walks on,
And turns no more his head ;
Because he knows, a frightful fiend
Doth close behind him tread.

But soon there breathed a wind on me,
Nor sound nor motion made :
Its path was not upon the sea,
In ripple or in shade.

It raised my hair, it fanned my cheek
Like a meadow-gale of spring—
It mingled strangely with my fears,
Yet it felt like a welcoming.

Swiftly, swiftly flew the ship,
Yet she sailed softly too :
Sweetly, sweetly blew the breeze—
On me alone it blew.

Oh ! dream of joy ! is this indeed
The light-house top I see ?
Is this the hill ? is this the kirk ?
Is this mine own countree ?

We drifted o'er the harbour-bar,
And I with sobs did pray—
O let me be awake, my God !
Or let me sleep alway.

The harbour-bay was clear as glass,
So smoothly it was strewn !
And on the bay the moonlight lay,
And the shadow of the Moon.

The rock shone bright, the kirk no less,
That stands above the rock :
The moonlight steeped in silentness
The steady weathercock.

And the bay was white with silent light,
Till rising from the same,
Full many shapes, that shadows were,
In crimson colours came.

"TELL HER I FOLLOW"

A little distance from the prow
Those crimson shadows were :
I turned my eyes upon the deck—
Oh, Christ ! what saw I there !

Each corse lay flat, lifeless and flat,
And, by the holy rood !
A man all light, a seraph-man,
On every corse there stood.

This seraph-band, each waved his hand :
It was a heavenly sight !
They stood as signals to the land,
Each one a lovely light ;

This seraph-band, each waved his hand,
No voice did they impart—
No voice ; but oh ! the silence sank
Like music on my heart.

But soon I heard the dash of oars,
I heard the Pilot's cheer ;
My head was turned perforce away,
And I saw a boat appear.

The Pilot and the Pilot's boy,
I heard them coming fast :
Dear Lord in Heaven ! it was a joy
The dead men could not blast.

I saw a third—I heard his voice :
It is the Hermit good !
He singeth loud his godly hymns
That he makes in the wood.
He'll shrieve my soul, he'll wash away
The Albatross's blood.

THE RIME OF THE ANCIENT MARINER

Part VII

This Hermit good lives in that wood
Which slopes down to the sea.
How loudly his sweet voice he rears !
He loves to talk with marineres
That come from a far countree.

He kneels at morn, and noon, and eve—
He hath a cushion plump :
It is the moss that wholly hides
The rotted old oak-stump.

The skiff-boat neared : I heard them talk,
" Why, this is strange, I trow !
Where are those lights so many and fair,
That signal made but now ?"

" Strange, by my faith !" the Hermit said—
" And they answered not our cheer !
The planks looked warped ! and see those sails,
How thin they are and sere !
I never saw aught like to them,
Unless perchance it were

Brown skeletons of leaves that lag
My forest-brook along ;
When the ivy-tod is heavy with snow,
And the owlet whoops to the wolf below,
That eats the she-wolf's young."

" Dear Lord ! it hath a fiendish look—
(The Pilot made reply)
I am a-feared "—" Push on, push on !"
Said the Hermit cheerily.

The boat came closer to the ship,
But I nor spake nor stirred ;
The boat came close beneath the ship,
And straight a sound was heard.

"TELL HER I FOLLOW"

Under the water it rumbled on,
Still louder and more dread :
It reached the ship, it split the bay ;
The ship went down like lead.

Stunned by that loud and dreadful sound,
Which sky and ocean smote,
Like one that hath been seven days drowned
My body lay afloat ;
But swift as dreams, myself I found
Within the Pilot's boat.

Upon the whirl, where sank the ship,
The boat spun round and round ;
And all was still, save that the hill
Was telling of the sound.

I moved my lips—the Pilot shrieked
And fell down in a fit ;
The holy Hermit raised his eyes,
And prayed where he did sit.

I took the oars : the Pilot's boy,
Who now doth crazy go,
Laughed loud and long, and all the while
His eyes went to and fro.
" Ha ! ha !" quoth he, " full plain I see,
The Devil knows how to row."

And now, all in my own countree,
I stood on the firm land !
The Hermit stepped forth from the boat,
And scarcely he could stand.

" O shrieve me, shrieve me, holy man !"
The Hermit crossed his brow.
" Say quick," quoth he, " I bid thee say—
What manner of man art thou ?"

Forthwith this frame of mine was wrenched
With a woful agony,
Which forced me to begin my tale ;
And then it left me free.

Since then, at an uncertain hour,
That agony returns :
And till my ghastly tale is told,
This heart within me burns.

I pass, like night, from land to land ;
I have strange power of speech ;
That moment that his face I see,
I know the man that must hear me :
To him my tale I teach.

What loud uproar bursts from that door !
The wedding-guests are there :
But in the garden-bower the bride
And bride-maids singing are :
And hark the little vesper bell,
Which biddeth me to prayer !

O Wedding-Guest ! this soul hath been
Alone on a wide wide sea :
So lonely 'twas, that God himself
Scarce seemèd there to be.

O sweeter than the marriage-feast,
'Tis sweeter far to me,
To walk together to the kirk
With a goodly company !—

To walk together to the kirk,
And all together pray,
While each to his great Father bends,
Old men, and babes, and loving friends
And youths and maidens gay !

Farewell, farewell ! but this I tell
To thee, thou Wedding-Guest !

"TELL HER I FOLLOW"

He prayeth well, who loveth well
Both man and bird and beast.

He prayeth best, who loveth best
All things both great and small ;
For the dear God who loveth us,
He made and loveth all." —

The Mariner, whose eye is bright,
Whose beard with age is hoar,
Is gone : and now the Wedding-Guest
Turned from the bridegroom's door.

He went like one that hath been stunned,
And is of sense forlorn :
A sadder and a wiser man,
He rose the morrow morn.

SAMUEL TAYLOR COLERIDGE

399 THE CHILD AND THE MARINER

This sailor knows of wondrous lands afar,
More rich than Spain, when the Phoenicians shipped
Silver for common ballast, and they saw
Horses at silver mangers eating grain ;
This man has seen the wind blow up a mermaid's hair
Which, like a golden serpent, reared and stretched
To feel the air away beyond her head. . . .
He many a tale of wonder told : of where,
At Argostoli, Cephalonia's sea
Ran over the earth's lip in heavy floods ;
And then again of how the strange Chinese
Conversed much as our homely Blackbirds sing.
He told us how he sailed in one old ship
Near that volcano Martinique, whose power
Shook like dry leaves the whole Caribbean seas ;
And made the sun set in a sea of fire
Which only half was his ; and dust was thick
On deck, and stones were pelted at the mast. . . .

402

THE CHILD AND THE MARINER

He told how isles sprang up and sank again,
Between short voyages, to his amaze ;
How they did come and go, and cheated charts ;
Told how a crew was cursed when one man killed
A bird that perched upon a moving barque ;
And how the sea's sharp needles, firm and strong,
Ripped open the bellies of big, iron ships ;
Of mighty icebergs in the Northern seas,
That haunt the far horizon like white ghosts.
He told of waves that lift a ship so high.
That birds could pass from starboard unto port
Under her dripping keel.
                              Oh, it was sweet
To hear that seaman tell such wondrous tales. . . .
                                    WILLIAM H. DAVIES

THE PARROTS

SOMEWHERE, somewhen I've seen, ·
But where or when I'll never know,
Parrots of shrilly green
With crests of shriller scarlet flying
Out of black cedars as the sun was dying
Against cold peaks of snow.

From what forgotten life
Of other worlds I cannot tell
Flashes that screeching strife :
Yet the shrill colour and shrill crying
Sing through my blood and set my heart replying
And jangling like a bell.
                                    WILFRID GIBSON

401   OZYMANDIAS OF EGYPT

I MET a traveller from an antique land
Who said : Two vast and trunkless legs of stone
Stand in the desart.   Near them, on the sand,
Half sunk, a shattered visage lies, whose frown
And wrinkled lip, and sneer of cold command
Tell that its sculptor well those passions read
Which yet survive, stamped on these lifeless things,
The hand that mocked them, and the heart that fed :
And on the pedestal these words appear :
" My name is Ozymandias, king of kings :
Look on my works, ye Mighty, and despair !"
Nothing beside remains.   Round the decay
Of that colossal wreck, boundless and bare
The lone and level sands stretch far away.
                              PERCY BYSSHE SHELLEY

402   ST. ANTHONY'S TOWNSHIP

THE trees of the elder lands,
Give ear to the march of Time,
To his steps that are heavy and slow
In the streets of ruined cities
That were great awhile ago—
Skeletons bare to the skies
Or mummies hid in the sands,
Wasting to rubble and lime.
Ancient are they and wise ;

But the gum-trees down by the creek,
Gnarled, archaic and grey,
Are even as wise as they.
They have learned in a score of years
The lore that their brethren know ;
For they saw a town arise,
Arise and pass.

404

ST. ANTHONY'S TOWNSHIP

There are pits by the dry, dead river,
Whence the diggers won their gold,
A circle traced in the grass,
A hearthstone long a-cold,
A path none come to seek—
The trail of the pioneers—
Where the sheep wind to and fro ;
And the rest is a tale that is told
By voices quavering and weak
Of men grown old.

GILBERT SHELDON

403   SILENCE

THERE is a silence where hath been no sound,
    There is a silence where no sound may be,
    In the cold grave—under the deep—deep sea,
Or in wide desert where no life is found,
Which hath been mute, and still must sleep profound ;
    No voice is hushed—no life treads silently,
    But clouds and cloudy shadows wander free,
That never spoke, over the idle ground :
But in green ruins, in the desolate walls
    Of antique palaces, where Man hath been,
Though the dun fox, or wild hyaena, calls,
    And owls, that flit continually between,
Shriek to the echo, and the low winds moan,
There the true Silence is, self-conscious and alone.

THOMAS HOOD

404   KUBLA KHAN

IN Xanadu did Kubla Khan
A stately pleasure-dome decree :
Where Alph, the sacred river, ran
Through caverns measureless to man
    Down to a sunless sea.
So twice five miles of fertile ground
With walls and towers were girdled round :

405

"TELL HER I FOLLOW"

And here were gardens bright with sinuous rills
Where blossomed many an incense-bearing tree ;
And here were forests ancient as the hills,
Enfolding sunny spots of greenery.

But oh ! that deep romantic chasm which slanted
Down the green hill athwart a cedarn cover !
A savage place ! as holy and enchanted
As e'er beneath a waning moon was haunted
By woman wailing for her demon-lover !
And from this chasm, with ceaseless turmoil seething,
As if this earth in fast thick pants were breathing,
A mighty fountain momently was forced :
Amid whose swift half-intermitted burst
Huge fragments vaulted like rebounding hail,
Or chaffy grain beneath the thresher's flail :
And 'mid these dancing rocks at once and ever
It flung up momently the sacred river.
Five miles meandering with a mazy motion
Through wood and dale the sacred river ran,
Then reached the caverns measureless to man,
And sank in tumult to a lifeless ocean :
And 'mid this tumult Kubla heard from far
Ancestral voices prophesying war !
    The shadow of the dome of pleasure
    Floated midway on the waves ;
    Where was heard the mingled measure
    From the fountain and the caves.
  It was a miracle of rare device,
  A sunny pleasure-dome with caves of ice !

    A damsel with a dulcimer
    In a vision once I saw :
    It was an Abyssinian maid,
    And on her dulcimer she played,
    Singing of Mount Abora.
    Could I revive within me
    Her symphony and song,
  To such a deep delight 'twould win me,
  That with music loud and long
406

KUBLA KHAN

I would build that dome in air,
That sunny dome ! those caves of ice !
And all who heard should see them there,
And all should cry, Beware ! Beware !
His flashing eyes, his floating hair !
Weave a circle round him thrice,
And close your eyes with holy dread,
For he on honey-dew hath fed,
And drunk the milk of Paradise. . .

SAMUEL TAYLOR COLERIDGE

405

LOST LOVE

His eyes are quickened so with grief,
He can watch a grass or leaf
Every instant grow ; he can
Clearly through a flint wall see,
Or watch the startled spirit flee
From the throat of a dead man.
   Across two counties he can hear,
And catch your words before you speak.
The woodlouse, or the maggot's weak
Clamour rings in his sad ear ;
And noise so slight it would surpass
Credence :—drinking sound of grass,
Worm talk, clashing jaws of moth
Chumbling holes in cloth :
The groan of ants who undertake
Gigantic loads for honour's sake,
Their sinews creak, their breath comes thin :
Whir of spiders when they spin,
And minute whispering, mumbling, sighs
Of idle grubs and flies.
   This man is quickened so with grief,
He wanders god-like or like thief
Inside and out, below, above,
Without relief seeking lost love.

ROBERT GRAVES

400　　　　　　　　　ECSTASY

I saw a frieze on whitest marble drawn
Of boys who sought for shells along the shore,
Their white feet shedding pallor in the sea,
The shallow sea, the spring-time sea of green
That faintly creamed against the cold, smooth pebbles. . . .

One held a shell unto his shell-like ear
And there was music carven in his face,
His eyes half-closed, his lips just breaking open
To catch the lulling, mazy, coralline roar
Of numberless caverns filled with singing seas.

And all of them were hearkening as to singing
Of far-off voices thin and delicate,
Voices too fine for any mortal wind
To blow into the whorls of mortal ears—
And yet those sounds flowed from their grave, sweet faces.

And as I looked I heard that delicate music,
And I became as grave, as calm, as still
As those carved boys. I stood upon that shore,
I felt the cool sea dream around my feet,
My eyes were staring at the far horizon. . . .

WALTER J. TURNER

407　　　　　　THE SEA OF DEATH

. . . AND there were spring-faced cherubs that did sleep
Like water-lilies on that motionless deep,
How beautiful ! with bright unruffled hair
On sleek unfretted brows, and eyes that were
Buried in marble tombs, a pale eclipse !
And smile-bedimpled cheeks, and pleasant lips,
Meekly apart, as if the soul intense
Spake out in dreams of its own innocence. . . .

408

THE SEA OF DEATH

So lay they garmented in torpid light,
Under the pall of a transparent night,
Like solemn apparitions lulled sublime
To everlasting rest,—and with them Time
Slept, as he sleeps upon the silent face
Of a dark dial in a sunless place.

THE FROZEN OCEAN

THE sea would flow no longer,
    It wearied after change,
It called its tides and breakers in,
    From where they might range.

It sent an icy message
    To every wave and rill ;
They lagged, they paused, they stiffened,
    They froze, and were still.

It summoned in its currents,
    They reached not where they led ;
It bound its foaming whirlpools.
    " Not the old life," it said,

" Not fishes for the fishermen,
    Not bold ships as before,
Not beating loud for ever
    Upon the seashore,

" But cold white foxes stepping
    On to my hard proud breast,
And a bird coming sweetly
    And building a nest.

" My icebergs shall be mountains,
    My silent fields of snow
Unmarked shall join the lands' snowfields—
    Where,   no man shall know."
                              VIOLA MEYNELL

THE END OF THE WORLD

The snow had fallen many nights and days ;
The sky was come upon the earth at last,
Sifting thinly down as endlessly
As though within the system of blind planets
Something had been forgot or overdriven.
The dawn now seemed neglected in the grey
Where mountains were unbuilt and shadowless trees
Rootlessly paused or hung upon the air.
There was no wind, but now and then a sigh
Crossed that dry falling dust and rifted it
Through crevices of slate and door and casement.
Perhaps the new moon's time was even past.
Outside, the first white twilights were too void
Until a sheep called once, as to a lamb,
And tenderness crept everywhere from it ;
But now the flock must have strayed far away.
The lights across the valley must be veiled,
The smoke lost in the greyness or the dusk.
For more than three days now the snow had thatched
That cow-house roof where it had ever melted
With yellow stains from the beasts' breath inside ;
But yet a dog howled there, though not quite lately.
Someone passed down the valley swift and singing,
Yes, with locks spreaded like a son of morning ;
But if he seemed too tall to be a man
It was that men had been so long unseen,
Or shapes loom larger through a moving snow.
And he was gone and food had not been given him.
When snow slid from an overweighted leaf,
Shaking the tree, it might have been a bird
Slipping in sleep or shelter, whirring wings ;
Yet never bird fell out, save once a dead one—
And in two days the snow had covered it.
The dog had howled again—or thus it seemed
Until a lean fox passed and cried no more.
All was so safe indoors where life went on

THE END OF THE WORLD

Glad of the close enfolding snow—O glad
To be so safe and secret at its heart,
Watching the strangeness of familiar things.
They knew not what dim hours went on, went by,
For while they slept the clock stopt newly wound
As the cold hardened.   Once they watched the road,
Thinking to be remembered.   Once they doubted
If they had kept the sequence of the days,
Because they heard not any sound of bells.
A butterfly, that hid until the Spring
Under a ceiling's shadow, dropt, was dead.
The coldness seemed more nigh, the coldness deepened
As a sound deepens into silences ;
It was of earth and came not by the air ;
The earth was cooling and drew down the sky.
The air was crumbling.   There was no more sky.
Rails of a broken bed charred in the grate,
And when he touched the bars he thought the sting
Came from their heat—he could not feel such cold . . .
She said, " O do not sleep,
Heart, heart of mine, keep near me.   No, no ; sleep.
I will not lift his fallen, quiet eyelids,
Although I know he would awaken then—
He closed them thus but now of his own will.
He can stay with me while I do not lift them."

GORDON BOTTOMLEY

OLD TALES AND ⊗
BALLADRY ⊗ ⊗ ⊗

" Though three men dwell on Flannan Isle
To keep the lamp alight,
As we steered under the lee, we caught
No glimmer through the night."—

A passing ship at dawn had brought
The news ; and quickly we set sail,
To find out what strange thing might ail
The keepers of the deep-sea light.

The Winter day broke blue and bright,
With glancing sun and glancing spray,
While o'er the swell our boat made way,
As gallant as a gull in flight.

But as we neared the lonely Isle,
And looked up at the naked height,
And saw the lighthouse towering white,
With blinded lantern, that all night
Had never shot a spark
Of comfort through the dark,
So ghostly in the cold sunlight
It seemed, that we were struck the while
With wonder all too dread for words.

And as into the tiny creek
We stole beneath the hanging crag,
We saw three queer, black, ugly birds—
Too big, by far, in my belief,
For cormorant or shag—

OLD TALES AND BALLADRY

Like seamen sitting bolt-upright
Upon a half-tide reef :
But, as we neared, they plunged from sight,
Without a sound, or spurt of white.

And still too mazed to speak,
We landed ; and made fast the boat ;
And climbed the track in single file,
Each wishing he were safe afloat,
On any sea, however far,
So it be far from Flannan Isle :
And still we seemed to climb, and climb,
As though we'd lost all count of time,
And so must climb for evermore.
Yet, all too soon, we reached the door
The black, sun-blistered lighthouse-door,
That gaped for us ajar.

As, on the threshold, for a spell,
We paused, we seemed to breathe the smell
Of limewash and of tar,
Familiar as our daily breath,
As though 'twere some strange scent of death :
And so, yet wondering, side by side,
We stood a moment, still tongue-tied :
And each with black foreboding eyed
The door, ere we should fling it wide,
To leave the sunlight for the gloom :
Till, plucking courage up, at last,
Hard on each other's heels we passed,
Into the living-room.

Yet, as we crowded through the door,
We only saw a table, spread
For dinner, meat and cheese and bread ;
But, all untouched ; and no one there :
As though, when they sat down to eat,
Ere they could even taste,
Alarm had come ; and they in haste
Had risen and left the bread and meat :

456

FLANNAN ISLE

For at the table-head a chair
Lay tumbled on the floor.

We listened ; but we only heard
The feeble cheeping of a bird
That starved upon its perch :
And, listening still, without a word,
We set about our hopeless search.

We hunted high, we hunted low ;
And soon ransacked the empty house ;
Then o'er the Island, to and fro,
We ranged, to listen and to look
In every cranny, cleft or nook
That might have hid a bird or mouse :
But, though we searched from shore to shore
We found no sign in any place :
And soon again stood face to face
Before the gaping door :
And stole into the room once more
As frightened children steal.
Ay : though we hunted high and low,
And hunted everywhere,
Of the three men's fate we found no trace
Of any kind in any place,
But a door ajar, and an untouched meal,
And an overtoppled chair.

And as we listened in the gloom
Of that forsaken living-room—
A chill clutch on our breath—
We thought how ill-chance came to all
Who kept the Flannan Light :
And how the rock had been the death
Of many a likely lad :
How six had come to a sudden end,
And three had gone stark mad :
And one whom we'd all known as friend
Had leapt from the lantern one still night,
And fallen dead by the lighthouse wall :

And long we thought
On the three we sought,
And of what might yet befall.

Like curs a glance has brought to heel,
We listened, flinching there :
And looked, and looked, on the untouched meal,
And the overtoppled chair.

We seemed to stand for an endless while,
Though still no word was said,
Three men alive on Flannan Isle,
Who thought on three men dead.

WILFRID GIBSON

411   THE GOLDEN VANITY

THERE was a gallant ship, and a gallant ship was she,
  Eck iddle du, and the Lowlands low ;
And she was called The Goulden Vanitie.
  As she sailed to the Lowlands low.

She had not sailed a league, a league but only three,
When she came up with a French gallee.
  As she sailed to the Lowlands low.

Out spoke the little cabin-boy, out spoke he ;
" What will you give me if I sink that French gallee ?
  As ye sail to the Lowlands low."

" I'll give thee gold, and I'll give thee fee,
And my eldest daughter thy wife shall be
  If you sink her off the Lowlands low."

" Then row me up ticht in a black bull's skin,
And throw me oer deck-buird, sink I or swim.
  As ye sail to the Lowlands low."

So they've rowed him up ticht in a black bull's skin,
And have thrown him oer deck-buird, sink he or swim.
  As they sail to the Lowlands low.

418

THE GOLDEN VANITY

About, and about, and about went he,
Until he cam up with the French gallee.
   As they sailed to the Lowlands low.

O some were playing cards, and some were playing dice,
The boy he had an auger bored holes two at twice ;
He let the water in, and it dazzled in their eyes,
   As they sailed to the Lowlands low.

Then some they ran with cloaks, and some they ran with
     caps,
To try if they could stap the saut-water draps.
   As they sailed to the Lowlands low.

About, and about, and about went he,
Until he cam back to The Goulden Vanitie.
   As they sailed to the Lowlands low.

" Now throw me oer a rope and pu me up on buird,
And prove unto me as guid as your word.
   As ye sail to the Lowlands low."

" We'll no throw ye oer a rope, nor pu you up on buird,
Nor prove unto you as guid as our word.
   As we sail to the Lowlands low."

" You promised me gold, and you promised me fee,
Your eldest daughter my wife she should be.
   As ye sail to the Lowlands low."

" You shall have gold, and you shall have fee,
But my eldest daughter your wife shall never be.
   As we sail to the Lowlands low."

Out spoke the little cabin-boy, out spoke he ;
" Then hang me, I'll sink ye as I sunk the French gallee.
   As ye sail to the Lowlands low."

The boy he swam round all by the starboard side,
When they pu'd him up on buird it's there he soon died ;
They threw him o'er deck-buird to go down with the tide,
   And sink off the Lowlands low.

BROWN ROBYN

It fell upon a Wodensday
Brown Robyn's men went to sea,
But they saw neither moon nor sun,
Nor starlight with their ee.

" We'll cast kevels us amang,
See wha the unhappy man may be : "
The kevel fell on Brown Robyn,
The master-man was hee.

" It is nae wonder," said Brown Robyn,
" Altho I dinna thrive ;
[For if the deidly sins be seven,
Befallen me hae five.]

" But tie me to a plank o wude,
And throw me in the sea ;
And if I sink, ye may bid me sink,
But if I swim, lat me bee."

They've tyed him to a plank o wude,
And thrown him in the sea ;
He didna sink, tho they bade him sink ;
He swimd, and they lat him be.—

He hadna been into the sea
An hour but barely three,
Till by and came Our Blessed Lady,
Her dear young son her wi.

" Will ye gang to your men again ?
Or will ye gang wi me ?
Will ye gang to the high heavens,
Wi my dear son and me ?"

" I winna gang to my men again,
For they woud be feared at mee ;
But I woud gang to the high heavens,
Wi thy dear son and thee."

BROWN ROBYN

" It's for nae honour ye did to me, Brown Robyn,
   It's for nae guid ye did to mee ;
But a' is for your fair confession
   You've made upon the sea."

ONE FRIDAY MORN

ONE Friday morn when we set sail,
   Not very far from land,
We there did espy a fair pretty maid
   With a comb and a glass in her hand, her hand, her
     hand,
   With a comb and a glass in her hand.
     While the raging seas did roar,
      And the stormy winds did blow,
     While we jolly sailor-boys were up into the top,
      And the land-lubbers lying down below, below, below,
      And the land-lubbers lying down below.

Then up starts the captain of our gallant ship,
   And a brave young man was he :
" I've a wife and a child in fair Bristol town,
   But a widow I fear she will be."
     And the raging seas did roar,
     And the stormy winds did blow.

Then up starts the mate of our gallant ship,
   And a bold young man was he :
" Oh ! I have a wife in fair Portsmouth town,
   But a widow I fear she will be."
     And the raging seas did roar,
     And the stormy winds did blow.

Then up starts the cook of our gallant ship,
   And a gruff old soul was he :
" Oh ! I have a wife in fair Plymouth town,
   But a widow I fear she will be."
     And the raging seas did roar,
     And the stormy winds did blow.

OLD TALES AND BALLADRY

And then up spoke the little cabin-boy,
  And a pretty little boy was he ;
" Oh ! I am more grieved for my daddy and my mammy
  Than you for your wives all three."
    And the raging seas did roar,
      And the stormy winds did blow.

Then three times round went our gallant ship,
  And three times round went she ;
And three times round went our gallant ship,
  And she sank to the bottom of the sea. . . .

    And the raging seas did roar,
      And the stormy winds did blow.
    While we jolly sailor-boys were up into the top,
      And the land-lubbers lying down below, below, below,
      And the land-lubbers lying down below.

THE SHIP

THERE was no song nor shout of joy
  Nor beam of moon or sun,
When she came back from the voyage
  Long ago begun ;
But twilight on the waters
  Was quiet and grey,
And she glided steady, steady and pensive,
  Over the open bay.

Her sails were brown and ragged,
  And her crew hollow-eyed,
But their silent lips spoke content
  And their shoulders pride ;
Though she had no captives on her deck,
  And in her hold
There were no heaps of corn or timber
  Or silks or gold.

                    J. C. SQUIRE

414

422

415

THE MOON-CHILD

A LITTLE lonely child am I
That have not any soul :
God made me as the homeless wave,
That has no goal.

A seal my father was, a seal
That once was man ;
My mother loved him tho' he was
'Neath mortal ban.

He took a wave and drownèd her,
She took a wave and lifted him :
And I was born where shadows are
In sea-depths dim.

All through the sunny blue-sweet hours
I swim and glide in waters green :
Never by day the mournful shores
By me are seen.

But when the gloom is on the wave
A shell unto the shore I bring :
And then upon the rocks I sit
And plaintive sing.

I have no playmate but the tide
The seaweed loves with dark brown eyes :
The night-waves have the stars for play,
For me but sighs.

"FIONA MACLEOD" (WILLIAM SHARP)

416   THE MERMAID

To yon fause stream that, by the sea,
Hides mony an elf and plum,[1]
And rives wi' fearful din the stanes,
A witless knicht did come.

[1] Pool

OLD TALES AND BALLADRY

The day shines clear. Far in he's gane,
    Whar shells are silver bright ;
Fishes war loupin'[1] a' aroun'
    An' sparklin' to the light.

When, as he laved, sounds came sae sweet
    Frae ilka rock ajee ;[2]
The brief[3] was out ; 'twas him it doomed
    The mermaid's face to see.

Frae 'neath a rock sune, sune she rose,
    An' stately on she swam,
Stopped i' the midst, and becked and sang
    For him to stretch his han' ;

Gowden glist the yellow links
    That roun' her neck she'd twine ;
Her een war o' the skyie blue,
    Her lips did mock the wine.

The smile upon her bonnie cheek
    Was sweeter than the bee ;
Her voice excelled the birdie's sang
    Upon the birchen tree.

Sae couthie, couthie did she look,
    And meikle had she fleeched ;[4]
Out shot his hand—alas ! alas !
    Fast in the swirl he screeched.

The mermaid leuched ;[5] her brief was dane ;
    The kelpie's blast was blawin' ;
Fu' low she dived, ne'er cam' again ;
    For deep, deep was the fawin'.

Aboon the stream his wraith was seen :
    Warlocks tirled lang at gloamin' :
That e'en was coarse ;[6] the blast blew hoarse
    Ere lang the waves war foamin'.

[1] Leaping   [2] Crooked, awry   [3] Spell
[4] Charmed and cozened   [5] Laughed   [6] Foul

424

QUO' THE TWEED

Quo' the Tweed to the Till,
  "What gars ye gang sae still?"
Quo' the Till to the Tweed,
  "Though ye rin wi' speed,
And I rin slaw,
For ilka ane that ye droon,
    I droon twa."

SIR PATRICK SPENCE

THE king sits in Dumferling toune,
  Drinking the blude-reid wine :
" O whar will I get ae guid sailor,
  To sail this schip of mine ?"

Up and spak an eldern knicht,
  Sat at the king's richt kne ;
" Sir Patrick Spence is the best sailor
  That sails upon the se."

The king has written a braid letter,
  And signd it wi his hand,
And sent it to Sir Patrick Spence,
  Was walking on the sand.

The first line that Sir Patrick red,
  A loud lauch lauched he ;
The next line that Sir Patrick red,
  The teir blinded his ee.

" O wha is this has done this deid,
  This ill deid don to me,
To send me out this time o' the yeir,
  To sail upon the se !

" Mak haste, mak haste, my mirry men all,
    Our guid schip sails the morne."
" O say na sae, my master deir,
    Fir I feir a deadlie storme.

" Late, late yestreen I saw the new moone
    Wi' the auld moone in hir arme,
And I feir, I feir, my deir master,
    That we will cum to harme."

O our Scots nobles wer richt laith [1]
    To weet [2] their cork-heil'd schoone ;
Bot lang owre [3] a' the play wer playd,
    Thair hats they swam aboone.

O lang, lang may their ladies sit
    Wi' thair fans into their hand
Or eir they se Sir Patrick Spence
    Cum sailing to the land.

O lang, lang may the ladies stand,
    Wi' thair gold kems in their hair,
Waiting for thair ain deir lords,
    For they'll se thame no mair.

Haf owre, haf owre to Aberdour,
    It's fiftie fadom deip,
And thair lies guid Sir Patrick Spence,
    Wi' the Scots lords at his feit.

ALLISON GROSS

419

O Allison Gross, that lives in yon towr,
    The ugliest witch i the north country,
Has trysted me ae day up till her bowr,
    An monny fair speech she made to me.

She stroaked my head, an she kembed my hair,
    An she set me down saftly on her knee ;
Says, Gin [4] ye will be my luver so true,
    Sae monny braw things as I woud you gi'e.

[1] Right loth   [2] Wet   [3] But long ere   [4] If

ALLISON GROSS

She showd me a mantle o red scarlet,
    Wi gouden flowrs an fringes fine ;
Says, Gin ye will be my luver so true,
    This goodly gift it sal be thine.

" Awa, awa, ye ugly witch,
    Haud far awa, an lat me be ;
I never will be your luver sae true,
    An I wish I were out o your company."

She neist brought a sark o the saftest silk,
    Well wrought wi pearles about the ban ;
Says, Gin you will be my ain true love,
    This goodly gift you sal comman.

She showd me a cup of the good red gold,
    Well set wi jewls sae fair to see ;
Says, Gin you will be my luver sae true,
    This goodly gift I will you gi'e.

" Awa, awa, ye ugly witch,
    Haud far awa, and lat me be ;
For I woudna ance kiss your ugly mouth
    For a' the gifts that ye could gi'e."

She's turnd her right and roun about,
    An thrice she blaw on a grass-green horn,
An she sware by the moon and the stars aboon,
    That she'd gar me rue the day I was born.

Then out has she taen a silver wand,
    An she's turnd her three times roun an roun ;
She's mutterd sich words till my strength it faild,
    An I fell down senceless upon the groun.

She's turnd me into an ugly worm,
    And gard me writhle about the tree ;
An ay, on ilka Saturdays night,
    My sister Maisry came to me,

427

Wi silver bason an silver kemb,
  To kemb my heady upon her knee ;
But or I had kissd her ugly mouth,
  I'd rather a writhled about the tree.

But as it fell out on last Hallow-even,
  When the seely court was ridin by,
The queen lighted down on a gowany bank,
  Nae far frae the tree where I wont to lye.

She took me up in her milk-white han,
  An she's stroakd me three times oer her knee ;
She chang'd me again to my ain proper shape,
  An I nae mair maun writhle about the tree.

420   SIR HUGH, OR, THE JEW'S DAUGHTER

Four and twenty bonny boys
  Were playing at the ba',
And by it came him sweet Sir Hugh,
  And he playd o'er them a'.

He kicked the ba' with his right foot,
  And catchd it wi' his knee,
And throuch-and-thro the Jew's window
  He gard the bonny ba' flee.

He's doen him to the Jew's castell,
  And walkd it round about ;
And there he saw the Jew's daughter,
  At the window looking out.

" Throw down the ba', ye Jew's daughter,
  Throw down the ba' to me !"
" Never a bit," says the Jew's daughter,
  " Till up to me come ye."

" How will I come up ?   How can I come up ?
  How can I come to thee ?
For as ye did to my auld father
  The same ye'll do to me."

SIR HUGH, OR, THE JEW'S DAUGHTER

She's gane till her father's garden,
    And pu'd an apple red and green ;
'T was a' to wyle him—sweet Sir Hugh,
    And to entice him in.

She's led him in through ae dark door,
    And sae has she thro nine ;
She's laid him on a dressing-table,
    And stickit him like a swine.

And first came out the thick, thick blood,
    And syne came out the thin,
And syne came out the bonny heart's blood ;
    There was nae mair within.

She's rowd him in a cake o' lead,
    Bade him lie still and sleep ;
She's thrown him in Our Lady's draw-well,
    Was fifty fathom deep.

When bells were rung, and mass was sung,
    And a' the bairns came hame,
When every lady gat hame her son,
    The Lady Maisry gat nane.

She's ta'en her mantle her about,
    Her coffer [1] by the hand,
And she's gane out to seek her son,
    And wanderd o'er the land.

She's doen her to the Jew's castell,
    Where a' were fast asleep :
" Gin ye be there, my sweet Sir Hugh,
    I pray you to me speak."

She's doen her to the Jew's garden,
    Thought he had been gathering fruit :
" Gin ye be there, my sweet Sir Hugh,
    I pray you to me speak !

[1] Hand-bag

She neard Our Lady's deep draw-well,
  Was fifty fathom deep :
" Whareer ye be, my sweet Sir Hugh,
  I pray you to me speak."

" Gae hame, gae hame, my mither dear,
  Prepare my winding sheet,
And at the birks [1] o' merry Lincoln
  The morn I will you meet."

Now Lady Maisry is gane hame,
  Made him a winding sheet,
And at the birks o' merry Lincoln
  The dead corpse did her meet.

And a' the bells o' merry Lincoln
  Without men's hands were rung,
And a' the books o' merry Lincoln
  Were read without man's tongue,

When bells war rung, and mass was sung
  And a' men bound for bed,
Every mither had her son,
  But sweet Sir Hugh was dead.

421   EDWARD

" Why does your brand so drop wi' blood,
                    Edward, Edward,
Why does your brand so drop wi' blood,
  And why so sad go ye O ?"
" O I have killed my hawk so good,
                    Mother, mother,
O I have killed my hawk so good,
  And I had no more but he O."

" Your hawk's blood was never so red,
                    Edward, Edward,
Your hawk's blood was never so red,
  My dear son I tell thee O."

[1] Birch-wood

430

EDWARD

" O I have killed my red-roan steed,
        Mother, mother,
O I have killed my red-roan steed,
    That erst was so fair and free O."

" Your steed was old, and ye have got more,
        Edward, Edward,
Your steed was old, and ye have got more,
    Some other grief you bear O."
" O I have killed my father dear,
        Mother, mother,
O I have killed my father dear,
    Alas, and woe is me O !"

" And what penance will ye do for that,
        Edward, Edward ?
And what penance will ye do for that ?
    My dear son, now tell me O."
" I'll set my foot in yonder boat,
        Mother, mother,
I'll set my foot in yonder boat,
    And I'll fare over the sea O."

" And what will ye do wi' your towers and your hall,
        Edward, Edward ?
And what will ye do wi' your towers and your hall,
    That were so fair to see O ?"
" I'll let them stand till they down fall,
        Mother, mother,
I'll let them stand till they down fall,
    For here never more may I be O."

" And what will ye leave to your bairns and your wife,
        Edward, Edward ?
And what will ye leave to your bairns and your wife,
    When ye go over the sea O ?"
" The world's wide, let them beg their life,
        Mother, mother,
The world's wide, let them beg their life,
    For them never more will I see O."

" And what will ye leave to your own mother dear,
    Edward, Edward ?
And what will ye leave to your own mother dear ?
 My dear son, now tell me O."
" The curse of hell from me shall ye bear,
    Mother, mother,
The curse of hell from me shall ye bear,
 Such counsels ye gave to me O."

422   THE LAIRD O' LOGIE

I will sing, if ye will hearken,
 If ye will hearken unto me ;
The King has ta'en a poor prisoner,
 The wanton laird of Young Logie.

Young Logie's laid in Edinburgh chapel,
 Carmichael's the keeper o' the key ;
I heard a may [1] lamenting sair
 A' for the laird of Young Logie.

" Lament, lament na, May Margaret,
 And o' your weeping let me be ;
For ye maun to the king your sell,
 And ask the life of Young Logie.

May Margaret has kilted her green cleiding,[2]
 And she's currlld back her yellow hair ;
" If I canna get young Logie's life,
 Farewell to Scotland for ever mair !"

When she came before the king,
 She knelit low doon on her knee :
" It's what's your will wi' me, May Margaret,
 And what needs a' this courtesie ?"

" A boon, a boon, my noble liege,
 A boon, a boon, I beg o' thee !

[1] The young wife   [2] Skirts of bright green

THE LAIRD O' LOGIE

And the first boon that I come to crave,
    It's to grant me the life o' Young Logie."

" O na, O na, May Margaret,
    Na, in sooth it mauna [1] be ;
For the [2] morn, ere I taste meat or drink,
    Hee [3] hangèd shall Young Logie be."

She has stolen the king's redding-kaim, [4]
    Likewise the queen her wedding-knife ;
And sent the tokens to Carmichael,
    To cause Young Logie get [5] his life.

She sent him a purse o' the red gowd,
    Another o' the white monie ;
And sent him a pistol into each hand,
    And bade him shoot when he gat free.

When he came to the Tolbooth stair,
    There he let his volley flee,
It made the king in his chamber start,
    E'en in the bed where he might be.

" Gae out, gae out, my merrie men a',
    And gar Carmichael come speak wi' me,
For I'll lay my life the pledge o' that,
    That yon's the volley of Young Logie."

When Carmichael came before the king,
    He fell low down upon his knee ;
The very first word that the king spake,
    Was, " Where's the laird o' Young Logie ?"

Carmichael turn'd him round about,
    I wat the salt tear blinded his ee,
" There came a token frae your grace,
    Has ta'en the laird awa frae me."

[1] Must not   [2] This   [3] High   [4] Hair-comb
[5] Save

" Hast thou played me that Carmichael ?—
Hast thou played me that ?" quoth he ;
" The morn the Justice Court's to stand,
And Logie's place ye maun supplie."

Carmichael's awa to May Margaret's bower,
Even as fast as he may dree ;
" O if Young Logie be within,
Tell him to come and speak with me."

May Margaret's turn'd her round about,
I wat a loud laughter gae she :
" The egg is chipp'd, the bird is flown,
Ye'll see nae mair o' Young Logie."

Tane[1] is shipped at the pier o' Leith,
T'other at the Queen's Ferrie,
And she's gotten a father to her bairn,
The wanton laird of Young Logie.

FAIR ANNIE

THE reivers[2] they stole Fair Annie,
As she walked by the sea ;
But a noble knight was her ransom soon,
Wi' gowd and white monie.[3]

She bided in strangers' land wi' him,
And none knew whence she cam ;
She lived in the castle wi' her love,
But never told her name.—

" It's narrow, narrow, mak your bed,
And learn to lie your lane ; [4]
For I'm gaun owre the sea, Fair Annie,
A braw Bride to bring hame.
Wi' her I will get gowd and gear,
Wi' you I ne'er gat nane.

[1] The one   [2] Raiders   [3] Gold and silver
[4] Alone

FAIR ANNIE

" But wha will bake my bridal bread,
  Or brew my bridal ale ?
And wha will welcome my bright Bride,
  That I bring owre the dale ? "

" It's I will bake your bridal bread,
  And brew your bridal ale ;
And I will welcome your bright Bride,
  That you bring owre the dale."

" But she that welcomes my bright Bride
  Maun gang like maiden fair ;
She maun lace on her robe sae jimp,
  And comely braid her hair.

" Bind up, bind up your yellow hair,
  And tie it on your neck ;
And see you look as maiden-like
  As the day that first we met."

" O how can I gang maiden-like,
  When maiden I am nane ?
Have I not borne six sons to thee,
  And am wi' child again ? "

" I'll put cooks into my kitchen,
  And stewards in my hall,
And I'll have bakers for my bread,
  And brewers for my ale ;
But you're to welcome my bright Bride,
  That I bring owre the dale."

Three months and a day were gane and past,
  Fair Annie she gat word
That her love's ship was come at last,
  Wi' his bright young Bride aboard.

She's ta'en her young son in her arms,
  Anither in her hand ;
And she's gane up to the highest tower,
  Looks over sea and land.

" Come doun, come doun, my mother dear,
Come aff the castle wa' !
I fear if langer ye stand there,
Ye'll let yoursell doun fa'."

She's ta'en a cake o' the best bread,
A stoup o' the best wine,
And a' the keys upon her arm,
And to the yett is gane.[1]

" O ye're welcome hame, my ain gude lord,
To your castles and your towers ;
Ye're welcome hame, my ain gude lord,
To your ha's,[2] but and your bowers.
And welcome to your hame, fair lady !
For a' that's here is yours."

" O whatna lady's that, my lord,
That welcomes you and me ?
Gin [3] I be lang about this place,
Her friend I mean to be."—

Fair Annie served the lang tables
Wi' the white bread and the wine ;
But ay she drank the wan water
To keep her colour fine.

And she gaed by the first table,
And smiled upon them a' ;
But ere she reached the second table,
The tears began to fa'.

She took a napkin lang and white,
And hung it on a pin ;
It was to wipe away the tears,
As she gaed out and in.

When bells were rung and mass was sung,
And a' men bound for bed,
The bridegroom and the bonny Bride
In ae [4] chamber were laid.—

[1] To the gate is gone   [2] Halls   [3] If   [4] One

FAIR ANNIE

Fair Annie's ta'en a harp in her hand,
 To harp thir twa [1] asleep ;
But ay, as she harpit and she sang,
 Fu' sairly did she weep.

" O gin my sons were seven rats,
 Rinnin' on the castle wa',
And I mysell a grey grey cat,
 I soon wad worry them a' !

" O gin my sons were seven hares,
 Rinnin' owre yon lily lea,
And I mysell a good greyhound,
 Soon worried they a' should be !"—

Then out and spak the bonny young Bride,
 In bride-bed where she lay :
" That's like my sister Annie," she says ;
 " Wha is it doth sing and play ?

" I'll put on my gown," said the new-come Bride
 " And my shoes upon my feet ;
I will see wha doth sae sadly sing,
 And what is it gars her greet. [2]

" What ails you, what ails you, my housekeeper,
 That ye mak sic a mane ? [3]
Has ony wine-barrel cast its girds,
 Or is a' your white bread gane ? "

" It isna because my wine is spilt,
 Or that my white bread's gane ;
But because I've lost my true love's love,
 And he's wed to anither ane."

" Noo tell me wha was your father ?" she says,
 " Noo tell me wha was your mother ?
And had ye ony sister ?" she says,
 " And had ye ever a brother ? "

[1] The twain [2] Makes her weep [3] Such lament

OLD TALES AND BALLADRY

" The Earl of Wemyss was my father,
  The Countess of Wemyss my mother,
Young Elinor she was my sister dear,
  And Lord John he was my brother."

" If the Earl of Wemyss was your father,
  I wot sae was he mine ;
And it's O my sister Annie !
  Your love ye sallna tyne.[1]

" Tak your husband, my sister dear ;
  You ne'er were wrangd for me,
Beyond a kiss o' his merry mouth
  As we cam owre the sea.

" Seven ships, loaded weel,
  Cam owre the sea wi' me ;
Ane o' them will tak me hame,
  And six I'll gie to thee."

HELEN OF KIRCONNELL.

. . . I wish I were where Helen lies,
Night and day on me she cries ;
O that I were where Helen lies
  On fair Kirconnell lea !

Curst be the heart that thought the thought,
And curst the hand that fired the shot,
When in my arms burd Helen dropt,
  And died for sake o' me !

O think na but my heart was sair
When my love dropt down and spak nae mair :
I laid her down wi' meikle care
  On fair Kirconnell lea.

As I went down the water-side,
None but my foe to be my guide,

[1] Shall not lose

HELEN OF KIRCONNELL

None but my foe to be my guide,
　　On fair Kirconnell lea ;

I lighted down, my sword to draw,
I hackèd him in pieces sma',
I hackèd him in pieces sma',
　　For her that died for me.

O Helen fair, beyond compare,
I'll make a garland of thy hair
Shall bind my heart for evermair,
　　Until the day I die.

O that I were where Helen lies,
Night and day on me she cries ;
Out of my bed she bids me rise,
　　Says, " Haste and come to me !"

O Helen fair ! O Helen chaste !
If I were with thee, I were blest,
Where thou lies low and takes thy rest
　　On fair Kirconnell lea.

I wish my grave were growing green,
A winding-sheet drawn ower my een,
And I in Helen's arms lying,
　　On fair Kirconnell lea.

I wish I were where Helen lies,
Night and day on me she cries ;
And I am weary of the skies,
　　Since my love died for me.

THE BONNIE BOWER

The Lament of the Border Widow

My love he built me a bonnie bower,
And clad it a' wi' lily flower ;
A brawer bower ye ne'er did see,
Than my true-love he built for me.

425

OLD TALES AND BALLADRY

There came a man, by middle day,
He spied his sport, and went away ;
And brought the king that very night,
Who brake my bower, and slew my knight.

He slew my knight, to me sae dear ;
He slew my knight, and poin'd his gear : [1]
My servants all for life did flee,
And left me in extremitie.

I sewed his sheet, making my mane ;
I watched the corpse, mysel alane ;
I watched his body night and day ;
No living creature came that way.

I took his body on my back,
And whiles I gaed, and whiles I sat ;
I digged a grave, and laid him in,
And happed him with the sod sae green.

But think na' ye my heart was sair,
When I laid the moul' on his yellow hair ?
O, think na' ye my heart was wae,
When I turned about, away to gae ?

Nae living man I'll love again,
Since that my lovely knight is slain ;
Wi' ae lock o' his yellow hair
I'll chain my heart for evermair.

WEEP NO MORE

Weep no more, nor sigh nor groan,
Sorrow calls no time that's gone :
Violets plucked, the sweetest rain
Makes not fresh nor grow again ;

[1] Seized his all

WEEP NO MORE

Trim thy locks, look chearfully,
Fate's hidden ends eyes cannot sèe.
Joys as wingèd dreams fly fast,
Why should sadness longer last ?
Grief is but a wound to woe ;
Gentlest fair, mourn, mourn no moe.[1]

JOHN FLETCHER

427   THE TWA SISTERS

THERE were twa sisters sat in a bowr ;
    Binnorie, O Binnorie :
There came a knight to be their wooer
    By the bonny mill-dams of Binnorie.

He courted the eldest wi' glove an ring,
But he lov'd the youngest above a' thing.[2]

He courted the eldest wi' brotch an knife,
But lov'd the youngest as his life.

The eldest she was vexèd sair,
An' much envi'd her sister fair.

Into [3] her bow'r she could not rest,
Wi' grief an spite she almos brast.

Upon a morning fair an' clear,
She cried upon her sister dear :—

" O sister, come to yon sea stran,
An see our father's ships come to lan."

She's ta'en her by the milk-white han,
An led her down to yon sea stran.

The youngest stood upon a stane,
The eldest came an threw her in.

[1] More   [2] Everything   [3] Within

441

OLD TALES AND BALLADRY

She tooke her by the middle sma,'
An dashed her bonny back to the jaw.[1]

" O sister, sister, tak my han,
And Ise mack[2] you heir to a' my lan.

" O sister, sister, tak my middle,
An yes get[3] my goud and my gouden girdle.

" O sister, sister, save my life,
An I swear Ise never be nae man's wife."

" Foul fa' the han that I should tacke,
It twin'd me an my wardles make.[4]

" Your cherry cheeks an yallow hair
Gars me gae maiden for evermair."

Sometimes she sank, an sometimes she swam,
Till she came down yon bonny mill-dam.

O out it came the miller's son,
An' saw the fair maid swimmin in.

" O father, father, draw your dam,
Here's either a mermaid or a swan."

The miller quickly drew the dam,
An there he found a drown'd woman.

You coudna see her yallow hair
For gold and pearle that were so rare.

You coudna see her middle sma'
For gouden girdle that was sae braw.

You coudna see her fingers white,
For gouden rings that was sae gryte.[5]

An by there came a harper fine,
That harpèd to the king at dine.

[1] And dashed her backwards into the waves
[2] And I'll make   [3] You shall have
[4] It parted me and my world's mate   [5] Great

THE TWA SISTERS

When he did look that lady upon,
He sigh'd and made a heavy moan.

He's taen three locks o' her yallow hair,
An wi' them strung his harp sae fair.

The first tune he did play and sing,
Was, " Farewell to my father the king."

The nextin tune that he play'd syne,
Was, " Farewell to my mother the queen."

The lastin tune that he play'd then,
Was, " Wae to my sister, fair Ellen."

428   SWEET WILLIAM AND MAY MARGARET

THERE came a ghost to Margret's door,
   With many a grievous groan ;
And aye he tirlèd at the pin,
   But answer made she none. . . .

" Is that my father Philip ?
   Or is't my brother John ?
Or is't my true-love Willie,
   From Scotland new come home ?"

'Tis not thy father Philip,
   Nor yet thy brother John,
But 'tis thy true-love Willie,
   From Scotland new come home.

" O sweet Margret, O dear Margret,
   I pray thee speak to me ;
Give me my faith and troth, Margret,
   As I gave it to thee."

" Thy faith and troth thou's never get,
   Nor yet will I thee lend,
Till that thou come within my bower
   And kiss me cheek and chin."

443

" If I shou'd come within thy bower,
    I am no earthly man ;
And shou'd I kiss thy ruby lips,
    Thy days would not be lang.

" O sweet Margret, O dear Margret,
    I pray thee speak to me :
Give me my faith and troth, Margret,
    As I gave it to thee."

" Thy faith and troth thou's never get,
    Nor yet will I thee lend,
Till thou take me to yon kirk-yard,
    And wed me with a ring."

" My bones are buried in yon kirk-yard
    Afar beyond the sea ;
And it is but my spirit, Margret,
    That's now speaking to thee."

She stretched out her lily-white hand,
    And, for to do her best :
" Hae, there's your faith and troth, Willie ;
    God send your soul good rest." . . .

Now she has kilted her robes o' green
    A piece below her knee,
And a' the live-lang winter night
    The dead corp followed she.

" Is there any room at your head, Willie,
    Or any room at your feet ?
Or any room at your side, Willie,
    Wherein that I may creep ?"

" There's nae room at my head, Margret,
    There's nae room at my feet ;
There's nae room at my side, Margret,
    My coffin's made so meet."

Then up and crew the red, red cock,
    And up and crew the grey ;
" 'Tis time, 'tis time, my dear Margret,
    That you were gane awa'."

429   THE WIFE OF USHER'S WELL

THERE lived a wife at Usher's Well
    And a wealthy wife was she ;
She had three stout and stalwart sons,
    And sent them o'er the sea.

They hadna been a week from her,
    A week but barely ane,
Whan word came to the carline wife
    That her three sons were gane.

They hadna been a week from her,
    A week but barely three,
Whan word came to the carline wife
    That her sons she'd never see.

" I wish the wind may never cease,
    Nor fashes in the flood,
Till my three sons come hame to me,
    In earthly flesh and blood."—

It fell about the Martinmass,
    When nights are lang and mirk,
The carline wife's three sons came hame,
    And their hats were o the birk.

It neither grew in syke nor ditch,
    Nor yet in ony sheugh ;
But at the gates o' Paradise
    That birk grew fair eneugh. . . .

" Blow up the fire, my maidens,
    Bring water from the well ;
For a' my house shall feast this night
    Since my three sons are well."

OLD TALES AND BALLADRY

And she has made to them a bed,
  She's made it large and wide ;
And she's ta'en her mantle her about,
  Sat down at the bedside.

" Lie still, lie still but a little wee while,
  Lie still but if we may ;
Gin my mother should miss us when she wakes
  She'll go mad ere it be day.

" Our mother has nae mair but us ;
  See where she leans asleep ;
The mantle that was on herself,
  She has happ'd it round our feet."

Up then crew the red, red cock,
  And up and crew the grey ;
The eldest to the youngest said,
  " 'Tis time we were away !"

The cock he hadna crawed but once,
  And clapped his wings at a',
When the youngest to the eldest said,
  " Brother, we must awa'.

" The cock doth craw, the day doth daw,
  The channerin worm doth chide ;
Gin we be mist out o' our place,
  A sair pain we maun bide.

* Fare ye weel, my mother dear !
  Fareweel to barn and byre !
And fare ye weel, the bonny lass
  That kindles my mother's fire !"

EVENING AND DREAM

DREAM-PEDLARY

If there were dreams to sell,
    What would you buy ?
Some cost a passing bell ;
    Some a light sigh,
That shakes from Life's fresh crown
Only a rose-leaf down.
If there were dreams to sell,
Merry and sad to tell,
And the crier rang the bell,
    What would you buy ?

A cottage lone and still,
    With bowers nigh,
Shadowy, my woes to still,
    Until I die.
Such peace from Life's fresh crown
Fain would I shake me down.
Were dreams to have at will,
This would best heal my ill,
    This would I buy.

THOMAS LOVELL BEDDOES

THE EVENING SUN

The evening sun was sinking down
    On low green hills and clustered trees ;
It was a scene as fair and lone
    As ever felt the soothing breeze

EVENING AND DREAM

That cools the grass when day is gone,
  And gives the waves a brighter blue,
And makes the soft white clouds sail on—
  Like spirits of ethereal dew

Which all the morn had hovered o'er
  The azure flowers, where they were nursed,
And now return to Heaven once more,
  Where their bright glories shone at first.

EMILY BRONTË

432   TO THE EVENING STAR

Thou Fair-haired Angel of the Evening,
Now, whilst the sun rests on the mountains, light
Thy bright torch of love ; thy radiant crown
Put on, and smile upon our evening bed !
Smile on our loves ; and while thou drawest the
Blue curtains of the sky, scatter thy silver dew
On every flower that shuts its sweet eyes
In timely sleep. Let thy West Wind sleep on
The lake ; speak silence with thy glimmering eyes,
And wash the dusk with silver. Soon, full soon,
Dost thou withdraw ; then the wolf rages wide,
And the lion glares through the dun forest :
The fleeces of the flocks are covered with
Thy sacred dew : protect them with thine influence.

WILLIAM BLAKE

433   TO DAISIES, NOT TO SHUT SO SOON

Shut not so soon ; the dull-eyed night
  Hath not as yet begun
To make a seisure on the light,
  Or to seale up the Sun.

TO DAISIES, NOT TO SHUT SO SOON

No Marigolds yet closèd are ;
No shadowes great appeare :
Nor doth the early Shepheard's Starre
Shine like a spangle here.

Stay but till my *Julia* close
Her life-begetting eye ;
And let the whole world then dispose
It selfe to live or dye.

ROBERT HERRICK

434 OF THE GOING DOWN OF THE SUN

WHAT, hast thou run thy Race ? Art going down ?
Thou seemest angry, why dost on us frown ?
Yea wrap thy head with Clouds, and hide thy face,
As threatning to withdraw from us thy Grace ?
Oh leave us not ! When once thou hid'st thy head,
Our Hórizon with darkness will be spread.
Tell's, who hath thee offended ? Turn again :
Alas ! too late—Entreaties are in vain !. . .

JOHN BUNYAN

435   VIRTUE

SWEET day, so cool, so calm, so bright
 The bridal of the earth and skie :
The dew shall weep thy fall to-night,
    For thou must die.

Sweet rose, whose hue angry and brave
 Bids the rash gazer wipe his eye,
Thy root is ever in its grave,
    And thou must die.

Sweet spring, full of sweet days and roses,
 A box where sweets compacted lie,
My music shows ye have your closes,
    And all must die.

451

EVENING AND DREAM

Only a sweet and vertuous soul,
    Like seasoned timber, never gives ;
But though the whole world turn to coal,
        Then chiefly lives.

NIGHT

The sun descending in the west,
The evening star does shine ;
The birds are silent in their nest,
And I must seek for mine.
    The moon, like a flower,
    In heaven's high bower,
    With silent delight
    Sits and smiles on the night.

Farewell green fields and happy groves,
Where flocks have took delight.
Where lambs have nibbled, silent moves
The feet of angels bright ;
    Unseen they pour blessing,
    And joy without ceasing,
    On each bud and blossom,
    And each sleeping bosom.

They look in every thoughtless nest,
Where birds are covered warm ;
They visit caves of every beast,
To keep them all from harm.
    If they see any weeping,
    That should have been sleeping,
    They pour sleep on their head,
    And sit down by their bed.

When wolves and tygers howl for prey,
They pitying stand and weep ;
Seeking to drive their thirst away,
And keep them from the sheep.

452

But if they rush dreadful,
The angels, most heedful,
Receive each mild spirit,
New worlds to inherit.

And there the lion's ruddy eyes
Shall flow with tears of gold,
And pitying the tender cries,
And walking round the fold,
 Saying, " Wrath, by his meekness,
 And, by his health, sickness
 Is driven away
 From our immortal day.

" And now beside thee, bleating lamb,
I can lie down and sleep ;
Or think on Him who bore thy name,
Graze after thee and weep.
 For, washed in life's river,
 My bright mane for ever
 Shall shine like the gold,
 As I guard o'er the fold."

WILLIAM BLAKE

437   NURSE'S SONG

WHEN the voices of children are heard on the green,
And laughing is heard on the hill,
My heart is at rest within my breast,
And everything else is still.

" Then come home, my children, the sun is gone down,
And the dews of night arise ;
Come, come, leave off play, and let us away
Till the morning appears in the skies."

" No, no, let us play, for it is yet day,
And we cannot go to sleep ;
Besides, in the sky the little birds fly,
And the hills are all covered with sheep."

EVENING AND DREAM

" Well, well, go and play till the light fades away,
And then go home to bed."
The little ones leapèd and shouted and laughed
And all the hills echoèd.

WILLIAM BLAKE

438   THE EVENING PRIMROSE

WHEN once the sun sinks in the west,
And dew-drops pearl the evening's breast ;
Almost as pale as moonbeams are,
Or its companionable star,
The evening primrose opes anew
Its delicate blossoms to the dew ;
And, shunning hermit of the light,
Wastes its fair bloom upon the night ;
Who, blindfold to its fond caresses,
Knows not the beauty he possesses.
Thus it blooms on till night is bye
And day looks out with open eye,
Abashed at the gaze it cannot shun,
It faints and withers, and is done.

EMILY BRONTË

439   " TIME, YOU OLD GIPSY MAN "

TIME, you old gipsy man,
Will you not stay,
Put up your caravan
Just for one day ?

All things I'll give you
Will you be my guest,
Bells for your jennet
Of silver the best,
Goldsmiths shall beat you
A great golden ring
Peacocks shall bow to you,
Little boys sing,

454

" TIME, YOU OLD GIPSY MAN "

Oh, and sweet girls will
Festoon you with may.
Time, you old gipsy,
Why hasten away ?

Last week in Babylon,
Last night in Rome,
Morning, and in the crush
Under Paul's dome ;
Under Paul's dial
You tighten your rein—
Only a moment,
And off once again ;
Off to some city
Now blind in the womb,
Off to another
Ere that's in the tomb.

Time, you old gipsy man,
Will you not stay,
Put up your caravan
Just for one day ?

RALPH HODGSON

440   AFTERWARDS

WHEN the Present has latched its postern behind my
     tremulous stay,
And the May month flaps its glad green leaves like wings,
Delicate-filmed as new-spun silk, will the neighbours say,
     " He was a man who used to notice such things " ?

If it be in the dusk when, like an eyelid's soundless blink,
     The dewfall-hawk comes crossing the shades to alight
Upon the wind-warped upland thorn, a gazer may think,
     " To him this must have been a familiar sight."

If I pass during some nocturnal blackness, mothy and warm,
     When the hedgehog travels furtively over the lawn,

455

EVENING AND DREAM

One may say, " He strove that such innocent creatures
    should come to no harm,
But he could do little for them ; and now he is gone."

If, when hearing that I have been stilled at last, they stand
    at the door,
    Watching the full-starred heavens that winter sees,
Will this thought rise on those who will meet my face no
    more,
    " He was one who had an eye for such mysteries " ?

And will any say when my bell of quittance is heard in the
    gloom,
    And a crossing breeze cuts a pause in its outrollings,
Till they rise again, as they were a new bell's boom,
    " He hears it not now, but used to notice such things " ?

THOMAS HARDY

441   STEPPING WESTWARD

" What, you are stepping westward ?"—" Yea."
  —'Twould be a wildish destiny,
If we, who thus together roam
In a strange land, and far from home,
Were in this place the guests of chance ;
Yet who would stop, or fear to advance,
Though home or shelter he had none,
With such a sky to lead him on ?"

The dewy ground was dark and cold ;
Behind, all gloomy to behold ;
And stepping westward seemed to be
A kind of heavenly destiny ;
I liked the greeting ; 'twas a sound
Of something without place or bound ;
And seemed to give me spiritual right
To travel through that region bright.

STEPPING WESTWARD

The voice was soft, and she who spake
Was walking by her native lake ;
The salutation had to me
The very sound of courtesy ;
Its power was felt ; and while my eye
Was fixed upon the glowing sky,
The echo of the voice enwrought
A human sweetness with the thought
Of travelling through the world that lay
Before me in my endless way.

WILLIAM WORDSWORTH

FOLDING THE FLOCKS

SHEPHERDS all, and Maidens fair,
Fold your Flocks up ; for the Air
'Gins to thicken, and the Sun
Already his great course hath run.
See the Dew-drops how they kiss
Every little Flower that is :
Hanging on their Velvet Heads,
Like a Rope of Cristal Beads.
See the heavy Clouds low falling,
And bright *Hesperus* down calling
The dead Night from under Ground,
At whose rising, Mists unsound,
Damps and Vapours fly apace,
Hov'ring o'er the smiling Face
Of these Pastures, where they come,
Striking dead both Bud and Bloom ;
Therefore, from such Danger, lock
Ev'ry one of his lovèd Flock ;
And let your Dogs lie loose without,
Lest the Wolf come as a scout
From the Mountain, and, ere day,
Bear a Lamb or Kid away ;
Or the crafty, thievish Fox
Break upon your simple Flocks :

EVENING AND DREAM

To secure yourself from these
Be not too secure in ease :
Let one Eye his watches keep,
While the other Eye doth sleep ;
So shall you good Shepherds prove,
And deserve your Master's love.
Now, good night ! may Sweetest Slumbers
And soft Silence fall in numbers
On your Eye-lids : So, farewell ;
Thus I end my Evening knell.

JOHN FLETCHER

443   ## TO THE NIGHT

SWIFTLY walk o'er the western wave,
        Spirit of Night !
Out of the misty eastern cave,
Where, all the long and lone daylight,
Thou wovest dreams of joy and fear,
Which make thee terrible and dear,—
        Swift be thy flight !

Wrap thy form in a mantle grey
        Star-inwrought ;
Blind with thine hair the eyes of Day,
Kiss her until she be wearied out :
Then wander o'er city and sea and land,
Touching all with thine opiate wand —
        Come, long-sought !

When I arose and saw the dawn
        I sighed for thee ;
When light rode high, and the dew was gone,
And noon lay heavy on flower and tree,
And the weary Day turned to his rest,
Lingering like an unloved guest,
        I sighed for thee.

TO THE NIGHT

Thy brother Death came, and cried
  Wouldst thou me ?
Thy sweet child Sleep, the filmy-eyed,
Murmured like a noon-tide bee,
Shall I nestle near thy side ?
  Wouldst thou me ?—And I replied
   No, not thee !

Death will come when thou art dead,
  Soon, too soon—
Sleep will come when thou art fled ;
Of neither would I ask the boon
I ask of thee, belovèd Night—
Swift be thine approaching flight,
  Come soon, soon !
     PERCY BYSSHE SHELLEY

444 LIGHT THE LAMPS UP, LAMPLIGHTER !

(FOR A LAMPLIGHTER, A GRANDMOTHER, THE ANGEL
GABRIEL, AND ANY NUMBER OF OTHERS)

LIGHT the lamps up, Lamplighter,
The people are in the street—
  Without a light
  They have no sight,
And where will they plant their feet ?
Some will tread in the gutter,
And some in the mud—oh dear !
Light the lamps up, Lamplighter,
Because the night is here.

Light the candles, Grandmother,
The children are going to bed—
  Without a wick
  They'll stumble and stick,
And where will they lay their head ?

459

EVENING AND DREAM

Some will lie on the staircase,
And some in the hearth—oh dear!
Light the candles, Grandmother,
Because the night is here.

Light the stars up, Gabriel,
The cherubs are out to fly—
    If heaven is blind
    How will they find
Their way across the sky?
Some will splash in the Milky Way,
Or bump on the moon—oh dear!
Light the stars up, Gabriel,
Because the night is here.

ELEANOR FARJEON

445   WILL YOU COME?

WILL you come?
Will you come?
Will you ride
So late
At my side?
O, will you come?

Will you come?
Will you come
If the night
Has a moon,
Full and bright?
O, will you come?

Would you come?
Would you come
If the noon
Gave light,
Not the moon?
Beautiful, would you come?

460

WILL YOU COME?

Would you have come?
Would you have come
Without scorning,
Had it been
Still morning?
Beloved, would you have come?

If you come
Haste and come.
Owls have cried;
It grows dark
To ride.
Beloved, beautiful, come!

EDWARD THOMAS

COME!

Wull ye come in eärly Spring,
Come at Easter, or in Mäy?
Or when Whitsuntide mid bring
Longer light to show your wäy?
Wull ye come, if you be true,
Vor to quicken love anew?
Wull ye call in Spring or Fall?
Come now soon by zun or moon?
　　　Wull ye come?

Come wi' väice to väice the while
All their words be sweet to hear;
Come that feäce to feäce mid smile,
While their smiles do seem so dear;
Come within the year to seek
Woone you have sought woonce a week?
Come while flow'rs be on the bow'rs,
And the bird o' songs a-heärd.
　　　Wull ye come?

Ees come *to* ye, an' come *vor* ye, is my word,
　　　I wull come.

WILLIAM BARNES

EVENING AND DREAM

HYMN TO DIANA

Queen and huntress, chaste and fair,
  Now the sun is laid to sleep,
Seated in thy silver chair,
  State in wonted manner keep ;
    Hesperus entreats thy light,
    Goddess excellently bright.

Earth, let not thy envious shade
  Dare itself to interpose ;
Cynthia's shining orb was made
  Heaven to clear when day did close :
    Bless us then with wishèd sight,
    Goddess excellently bright.

Lay thy bow of pearl apart,
  And thy crystal shining quiver ;
Give unto the flying hart
  Space to breathe, how short soever :
    Thou that mak'st a day of night,
    Goddess excellently bright.

                          BEN JONSON

THE CLOUDS HAVE LEFT THE SKY

The clouds have left the sky,
The wind hath left the sea,
The half-moon up on high
Shrinketh her face of dree.

She lightens on the comb
Of leaden waves, that roar
And thrust their hurried foam
Up on the dusky shore.

Behind the western bars
The shrouded day retreats,
And unperceived the stars
Steal to their sovran seats.

THE CLOUDS HAVE LEFT THE SKY

And whiter grows the foam,
The small moon lightens more ;
And as I turn me home,
My shadow walks before.

Robert Bridges

WITH HOW SAD STEPS

With how sad steps, O Moon, thou climb'st the skies !
How silently, and with how wan a face !
What ! may it be that even in heavenly place
That busy archer his sharp arrows tries ?
Sure, if that long-with-love-acquainted eyes
Can judge of love, thou feel'st a lover's case :
I read it in thy looks ; thy languished grace
To me, that feel the like, thy state descries.

Then, even of fellowship, O Moon, tell me,
Is constant love deemed there but want of wit ?
Are beauties there as proud as here they be ?
Do they above love to be loved, and yet
Those lovers scorn whom that love doth possess ?
Do they call virtue there ungratefulness ?

Sir Philip Sidney

IN DISPRAISE OF THE MOON

I would not be the Moon, the sickly thing,
To summon owls and bats upon the wing ;
For when the noble Sun is gone away,
She turns his night into a pallid day.

She hath no air, no radiance of her own,
That world unmusical of earth and stone.
She wakes her dim, uncoloured, voiceless hosts,
Ghost of the Sun, herself the sun of ghosts.

463

EVENING AND DREAM

The mortal eyes that gaze too long on her
Of Reason's piercing ray defrauded are.
Light in itself doth feed the living brain ;
That light, reflected, but makes darkness plain.

MARY COLERIDGE

451   ## THE WANING MOON

AND like a dying lady, lean and pale,
Who totters forth, wrapt in a gauzy veil,
Out of her chamber, led by the insane
And feeble wanderings of her fading brain,
The moon arose up in the murky east,
A white and shapeless mass.

PERCY BYSSHE SHELLEY

452   ## WE'LL GO NO MORE A-ROVING

So, we'll go no more a-roving
    So late into the night,
Though the heart be still as loving,
    And the moon be still as bright.

For the sword outwears its sheath,
    And the soul wears out the breast,
And the heart must pause to breathe,
    And love itself have rest.

Though the night was made for loving,
    And the day returns too soon,
Yet we'll go no more a-roving
    By the light of the moon.

GEORGE GORDON, LORD BYRON

453   ## SONG OF THE NIGHT AT DAYBREAK

ALL my stars forsake me,
And the dawn-winds shake me.
Where shall I betake me ?

SONG OF THE NIGHT AT DAYBREAK

Whither shall I run
Till the set of sun,
Till the day be done ?

To the mountain-mine,
To the boughs o' the pine,
To the blind man's eyne,

To a brow that is
Bowed upon the knees,
Sick with memories.

ALICE MEYNELL

454   THE NIGHT WILL NEVER STAY

THE night will never stay,
The night will still go by,
Though with a million stars
You pin it to the sky ;
Though you bind it with the blowing wind
And buckle it with the moon,
The night will slip away
Like sorrow or a tune.

ELEANOR FARJEON

455   LINES FOR A BED AT KELMSCOTT MANOR

" THE wind's on the wold
And the night is a-cold,
And Thames runs chill
Twixt mead and hill,
But kind and dear
Is the old house here,
And my heart is warm
Midst winter's harm.
Rest then and rest,
And think of the best
Twixt summer and spring
When all birds sing

EVENING AND DREAM

In the town of the tree,
And ye lie in me
And scarce dare move
Lest earth and its love
Should fade away
Ere the full of the day.

I am old and have seen
Many things that have been,
Both grief and peace,
And wane and increase.
No tale I tell
Of ill or well,
But this I say,
Night treadeth on day,
And for worst and best
Right good is rest."

WILLIAM MORRIS

456 ROCK, BALL, FIDDLE

He that lies at the stock,
Shall have the gold rock ;
He that lies at the wall,
Shall have the gold ball ;
He that lies in the middle,
Shall have the gold fiddle.

457 BEFORE SLEEPING

MATTHEW, Mark, Luke, and John,
Bless the bed that I lie on.
Before I lay me down to sleep
I give my soul to Christ to keep.
Four corners to my bed,
Four angels there aspread,
Two to foot, and two to head,
And four to carry me when I'm dead.

466

BEFORE SLEEPING

I go by sea, I go by land,
The Lord made me with His right hand.
If any danger come to me,
Sweet Jesus Christ deliver me.
He's the branch and I'm the flower,
Pray God send me a happy hour,
And if I die before I wake,
I pray that Christ my soul will take.

458   ON A QUIET CONSCIENCE

CLOSE thine eyes, and sleep secure ;
Thy soul is safe, thy body sure.
He that guards thee, he that keeps,
Never slumbers, never sleeps.
A quiet conscience in the breast
Has only peace, has only rest.
The wisest and the mirth of kings
Are out of tune unless she sings :
Then close thine eyes in peace and sleep secure,
No sleep so sweet as thine, no rest so sure.
                                    CHARLES I.

459   SONG

WHILE Morpheus thus does gently lay
    His powerful charge upon each part
Making thy spirits even obey
    The silver charms of his dull art ;

I, thy Good Angel, from thy side,—
    As smoke doth from the altar rise,
Making no noise as it doth glide,—
    Will leave thee in this soft surprise ;

And from the clouds will fetch thee down
    A holy vision, to express
Thy right unto an earthly crown ;
    No power can make this kingdom less.

EVENING AND DREAM

But gently, gently, lest I bring
A start in sleep by sudden flight,
Playing aloof, and hovering,
Till I am lost unto the sight.

This is a motion still and soft ;
So free from noise and cry,
That Jove himself, who hears a thought,
Knows not when we pass by.

HENRY KILLIGREW

THE EVE OF SAINT MARK

Upon a Sabbath-day it fell ;
Twice holy was the Sabbath-bell,
That called the folk to evening prayer ;
The city streets were clean and fair
From wholesome drench of April rains ;
And, on the western window panes,
The chilly sunset faintly told
Of unmatured green vallies cold,
Of the green thorny bloomless hedge,
Of rivers new with spring-tide sedge,
Of primroses by sheltered rills,
And daisies on the aguish hills.
Twice holy was the Sabbath-bell :
The silent streets were crowded well
With staid and pious companies,
Warm from their fire-side oratories ;
And moving, with demurest air,
To even-song, and vesper-prayer.
Each archèd porch, and entry low,
Was filled with patient folk and slow,
With whispers hush, and shuffling feet,
While played the organ loud and sweet.
The bells had ceased, the prayers begun,
And Bertha had not yet half done

THE EVE OF ST. MARK

A curious volume, patched and torn,
That all day long, from earliest morn,
Had taken captive her two eyes,
Among its golden broideries ;
Perplexed her with a thousand things,—
The stars of Heaven, and angels' wings,
Martyrs in a fiery blaze,
Azure saints in silver rays,
Moses' breastplate, and the seven
Candlesticks John saw in Heaven,
The winged Lion of Saint Mark,
And the Covenantal Ark,
With its many mysteries,
Cherubim and golden mice.

Bertha was a maiden fair,
Dwelling in the old Minster-square ;
From her fire-side she could see,
Sidelong, its rich antiquity,
Far as the Bishop's garden-wall ;
Where sycamores and elm-trees tall,
Full-leaved, the forest had outstript,
By no sharp north-wind ever nipt,
So sheltered by the mighty pile,
Bertha arose, and read awhile,
With forehead 'gainst the window-pane,
Again she tryed, and then again,
Until the dusk eve left her dark
Upon the legend of St. Mark.
From plaited lawn-frill, fine and thin,
She lifted up her soft warm chin,
With aching neck and swimming eyes,
And dazed with saintly imageries.

All was gloom, and silent all,
Save now and then the still foot-fall
Of one returning homewards late,
Past the echoing minster-gate.

EVENING AND DREAM

The clamorous daws, that all the day
Above tree-tops and towers play,
Pair by pair had gone to rest,
Each in its ancient belfry-nest,
Where asleep they fall betimes,
To music of the drowsy chimes.

All was silent, all was gloom,
Abroad and in the homely room :
Down she sat, poor cheated soul !
And struck a lamp from the dismal coal ;
Leaned forward, with bright drooping hair
And slant book, full against the glare.
Her shadow, in uneasy guise,
Hovered about, a giant size,
On ceiling-beam and old oak chair,
The parrot's cage, and panel square ;
And the warm angled winter screen,
On which were many monsters seen,
Called doves of Siam, Lima mice,
And legless birds of Paradise,
Macaw, and tender Avadavat,
And silken-furred Angora cat.
Untired she read, her shadow still
Glowered about, as it would fill
The room with wildest forms and shades,
As though some ghostly queen of spades
Had come to mock behind her back,
And dance, and ruffle her garments black.
Untired she read the legend page,
Of holy Mark, from youth to age,
On land, on sea, in pagan chains,
Rejoicing for his many pains.
Sometimes the learned eremite,
With golden star, or dagger bright,
Referred to pious poesies
Written in smallest crow-quill size
Beneath the text ; and thus the rhyme
Was parcelled out from time to time :—

THE EVE OF ST. MARK

" 'Gif ye wol stonden [1] hardie wight—
Amiddès of the blackè night—
Righte in the churchè porch, pardie
Ye wol behold a companie
Approchen thee full dolourouse :
For sooth to sain from everich house
Be it in city or villàge
Wol come the Phantom and imàge
Of ilka [2] gent and ilka carle
Whom coldè Deathè hath in parle
And wol some day that very year
Touchen with foulè venime spear
And sadly do them all to die.—
Hem all shalt thou see verilie—
And everichon shall by thee pass
All who must die that year, Alas.'

" Als [3] writith he of swevenis, [4]
Men han beforne they wake in bliss,
Whanne that hir friendès thinke hem bound
In crimpèd shroude farre under grounde ;
And how a litling child mote be
A saint er its nativitie,
Gif that the modre—God her blesse !—
Kepen in solitarinesse,
And kissen devoute the holy croce—
Of Goddès love, and Sathan's force,—
He writith ; and thinges many mo,
Of swichè thinges I may not show.
Bot I must tellen verilie
Somdel of Saintè Cicilie,
And chieflie what he auctoriethe
Of Saintè Markis life and dethe : "

At length her constant eyelids come
Upon the fervent martyrdom ;
Then lastly to his holy shrine,
Exalt amid the tapers' shine
At Venice. . . .   JOHN KEATS

[1] If you will stand   [2] Every   [3] Likewise   [4] Visions
471

EVENING AND DREAM

461   LAID IN MY QUIET BED

Laid in my quiet bed, in study as I were,
I saw within my troubled head a heap of thoughts appear ;
And every thought did shew so lively in mine eyes,
That now I sighed, and then I smiled, as cause of thought
      did rise.
I saw the little boy in thought how oft that he
Did wish of God, to scape the rod, a tall young man to be.
The young man eke that feels his bones with pains opprest,
How he would be a rich old man, to live and lie at rest.
The rich old man that sees his end draw on so sore,
How he would be a boy again, to live so much the more.
Whereat full oft I smiled, to see how all these three,
From boy to man, from man to boy, would chop and change
      degree. . . .

                    HENRY HOWARD, EARL OF SURREY

462   AT NIGHT

Home, home from the horizon far and clear,
    Hither the soft wings sweep ;
Flocks of the memories of the day draw near
    The dovecote doors of sleep.

Oh, which are they that come through sweetest light
    Of all these homing birds ?
Which with the straightest and the swiftest flight ?
    Your words to me, your words !

                    ALICE MEYNELL

463   ECHO

Come to me in the silence of the night ;
    Come in the speaking silence of a dream ;
Come with soft rounded cheeks and eyes as bright
    As sunlight on a stream ;
        Come back in tears,
O memory, hope, love of finished years.

ECHO

O dream how sweet, too sweet, too bitter sweet,
  Whose wakening should have been in Paradise,
Where souls brimfull of love abide and meet ;
  Where thirsting longing eyes
    Watch the slow door
That opening, letting in, lets out no more.

Yet come to me in dreams, that I may live
  My very life again though cold in death :
Come back to me in dreams, that I may give
  Pulse for pulse, breath for breath :
    Speak low, lean low,
As long ago, my love, how long ago.

Christina Rossetti

464   THE SHADOW OF NIGHT

How strange it is to wake
  And watch while others sleep,
Till sight and hearing ache
  For objects that may keep
The awful inner sense
  Unroused, lest it should mark
The life that haunts the emptiness
  And horror of the dark.

How strange the distant bay
  Of dogs ; how wild the note
Of cocks that scream for day,
  In homesteads far remote ;
How strange and wild to hear
  The old and crumbling tower,
Amidst the darkness, suddenly
  Take life and speak the hour. . . .

The nightingale is gay,
  For she can vanquish night ;
Dreaming, she sings of day,
  Notes that make darkness bright :

473

EVENING AND DREAM

But when the refluent gloom
  Saddens the gaps of song,
We charge on her the dolefulness,
  And call her crazed with wrong.
                    COVENTRY PATMORE

465

OUT IN THE DARK

Out in the dark over the snow
The fallow fawns invisible go
With the fallow doe;
And the winds blow
Fast as the stars are slow.

Stealthily the dark haunts round
And, when the lamp goes, without sound
At a swifter bound
Than the swiftest hound,
Arrives, and all else is drowned;

And I and star and wind and deer,
Are in the dark together,—near,
Yet far,—and fear
Drums on my ear
In that sage company drear.

How weak and little is the light,
All the universe of sight,
Love and delight,
Before the might,
If you love it not, of night.
                    EDWARD THOMAS

466

NOCTURNE

THE red flame flowers bloom and die,
  The embers puff a golden spark.
Now and again a horse's eye
  Shines like a topaz in the dark.

474

NOCTURNE

A prowling jackal jars the hush,
  The drowsy oxen chump and sigh—
The ghost moon lifts above the bush
  And creeps across the starry sky.

Low in the south the " Cross " is bright,
  And sleep comes dreamless, undefiled,
Here in the blue and silver night,
  In the star-chamber of the Wild.

CROSBIE GARSTIN

467   THE ANGEL

I DREAMT a Dream ! what can it mean ?
And that I was a maiden Queen
Guarded by an Angel mild :
Witless woe was ne'er beguiled !

And I wept both night and day,
And he wiped my tears away ;
And I wept both day and night,
And hid from him my heart's delight.

So he took his wings and fled ;
Then the morn blushed rosy red ;
I dried my tears, and armed my fears
With ten thousand shields and spears.

Soon my Angel came again ;
I was armed, he came in vain ;
For the time of youth was fled,
And grey hairs were on my head.

WILLIAM BLAKE

468   " ANGEL SPIRITS OF SLEEP "

    ANGEL spirits of sleep,
    White-robed, with silver hair,
    In your meadows fair,
    Where the willows weep,

475

EVENING AND DREAM

And the sad moonbeam
On the gliding stream
Writes her scattered dream :

Angel spirits of sleep,
Dancing to the weir
In the hollow roar
Of its waters deep ;
Know ye how men say
That ye haunt no more
Isle and grassy shore
With your moonlit play ;
That ye dance not here,
White-robed spirits of sleep,
All the summer night
Threading dances light ?

ROBERT BRIDGES

469

A DREAM

ONCE a dream did weave a shade
O'er my Angel-guarded bed,
That an Emmet lost its way
Where on grass methought I lay.

Troubled, 'wildered, and forlorn,
Dark, benighted, travel-worn,
Over many a tangled spray,
All heart-broke I heard her say :

" O my children ! do they cry ?
Do they hear their father sigh ?
Now they look abroad to see :
Now return and weep for me."

Pitying, I dropped a tear ;
But I saw a glow-worm near,
Who replied : " What wailing wight
Calls the watchman of the night ?

A DREAM

" I am set to light the ground,
While the beetle goes his round :
Follow now the beetle's hum ;
Little wanderer, hie thee home."

WILLIAM BLAKE

THE LAND OF DREAMS

470

AWAKE, awake, my little Boy !
Thou wast thy Mother's only joy :
Why dost thou weep in thy gentle sleep ?
Awake ! thy Father does thee keep.

" O, what land is the Land of Dreams,
What are its mountains, and what are its streams ?
O Father ! I saw my Mother there,
Among the Lillies by waters fair.

" Among the lambs clothèd in white,
She walked with her Thomas in sweet delight.
I wept for joy, like a dove I mourn ;
O ! when shall I again return ?"

Dear Child, I also by pleasant streams
Have wandered all night in the Land of Dreams,
But tho' calm and warm the waters wide,
I could not get to the other side.

" Father, O Father ! what do we here,
In this Land of unbelief and fear ?
The Land of Dreams is better far
Above the light of the Morning Star."

WILLIAM BLAKE

THE GARDEN ✿ ✿ ✿

I KNOW a little garden-close
Set thick with lily and red rose,
Where I would wander if I might
From dewy dawn to dewy night,
And have one with me wandering.

And though within it no birds sing,
And though no pillared house is there,
And though the apple boughs are bare
Of fruit and blossom, would to God,
Her feet upon the green grass trod,
And I beheld them as before.

There comes a murmur from the shore,
And in the close two fair streams are,
Drawn from the purple hills afar,
Drawn down unto the restless sea ;
Dark hills whose heath-bloom feeds no bee,
Dark shores no ship has ever seen,
Tormented by the billows green
Whose murmur comes unceasingly
Unto the place for which I cry.

For which I cry both day and night,
For which I let slip all delight,
Whereby I grow both deaf and blind,
Careless to win, unskilled to find,
And quick to lose what all men seek.

481   2 H

THE GARDEN

Yet tottering as I am, and weak,
Still have I left a little breath
To seek within the jaws of death
An entrance to that happy place,
To seek the unforgotten face,
Once seen, once kissed, once reft from me
Anigh the murmuring of the sea.

WILLIAM MORRIS

FOLLOW

472

FOLLOW thy fair sun, unhappy shadow,
Though thou be black as night,
And she made all of light,
Yet follow thy fair sun, unhappy shadow.

Follow her whose light thy light depriveth,
Though here thou liv'st disgraced,
And she in heaven is placed,
Yet follow her whose light the world reviveth.

Follow those pure beams whose beauty burneth,
That so have scorchèd thee,
As thou still black must be,
Till her kind beams thy black to brightness turneth.

Follow her while yet her glory shineth :
There comes a luckless night,
That will dim all her light ;
And this the black unhappy shade divineth.

Follow still since so thy fates ordainèd ;
The Sun must have his shade,
Till both at once do fade—
The Sun still proud, the shadow still disdainèd.

THOMAS CAMPION

473 UP-HILL

Does the road wind up-hill all the way ?
  Yes, to the very end.
Will the day's journey take the whole long day ?
  From morn to night, my friend.

But is there for the night a resting-place ?
  A roof for when the slow dark hours begin.
May not the darkness hide it from my face ?
  You cannot miss that inn.

Shall I meet other wayfarers at night ?
  Those who have gone before.
Then must I knock or call when just in sight ?
  They will not keep you standing at the door.

Shall I find comfort, travel-sore and weak ?
  Of labour you shall find the sum.
Will there be beds for me and all who seek ?
  Yea, beds for all who come.

CHRISTINA ROSSETTI

474 LOVE

Love bade me welcome ; yet my soul drew back,
  Guilty of dust and sin.
But quick-eyed Love, observing me grow slack
  From my first entrance in,
Drew nearer to me, sweetly questioning
  If I lacked anything.

" A guest," I answered, " worthy to be here " :
  Love said, " You shall be he."
" I, the unkind, ungrateful ? Ah, my dear !
  I cannot look on Thee."
Love took my hand, and smiling did reply,
  " Who made the eyes but I ?"

THE GARDEN

" Truth, Lord ; but I have marred them ; let my shame
    Go where it doth deserve."
" And know you not," says Love, " who bore the blame ?"
    " My dear, then I will serve."
" You must sit down," says Love, " and taste my meat."
    So I did sit and eat.

GEORGE HERBERT

475   A ROYAL GUEST

    . . . YET if His Majesty our sovereign lord
        Should of his own accord
        Friendly himself invite,
And say, " I'll be your guest to-morrow night,"
How should we stir ourselves, call and command
All hands to work ! " Let no man idle stand !

    " Set me fine Spanish tables in the hall,
        See they be fitted all ;
        Let there be room to eat,
And order taken that there want no meat.
See every sconce and candlestick made bright,
That without tapers they may give a light.

    " Look to the presence : are the carpets spread,
        The dazie [1] o'er the head,
        The cushions in the chairs,
And all the candles lighted on the stairs ?
Perfume the chambers, and in any case
Let each man give attendance in his place !"

Thus, if the king were coming, would we do,
        And 't were good reason too ;
        For 'tis a duteous thing
To show all honour to an earthly king,
And after all our travail and our cost,
So he be pleased, to think no labour lost.

[1] Canopy over dais

A ROYAL GUEST

But at the coming of the King of Heaven
    All's set at six and seven :
    We wallow in our sin,
Christ cannot find a chamber in the inn.
We entertain Him always like a stranger,
And, as at first, still lodge Him in a manger.

EVE

            Eve, with her basket, was
            Deep in the bells and grass,
            Wading in bells and grass
            Up to her knees,
            Picking a dish of sweet
            Berries and plums to eat,
            Down in the bells and grass
            Under the trees.

            Mute as a mouse in a
            Corner the cobra lay,
            Curled round a bough of the
            Cinnamon tall. . . .
            Now to get even and
            Humble proud heaven and—
            Now was the moment or
            Never at all.

            " Eva !" Each syllable
            Light as a flower fell,
            " Eva !" he whispered the
            Wondering maid,
            Soft as a bubble sung
            Out of a linnet's lung,
            Soft and most silverly
            " Eva !" he said.

            Picture that orchard sprite,
            Eve, with her body white,
                        485

THE GARDEN

Supple and smooth to her
Slim finger tips,
Wondering, listening,
Listening, wondering,
Eve with a berry
Half-way to her lips.

Oh, had our simple Eve
Seen through the make-believe !
Had she but known the
Pretender he was !
Out of the boughs he came,
Whispering still her name,
Tumbling in twenty rings
Into the grass.

Here was the strangest pair
In the world anywhere,
Eve in the bells and grass
Kneeling, and he
Telling his story low. . . .
Singing birds saw them go
Down the dark path to
The Blasphemous Tree.

Oh, what a clatter when
Titmouse and Jenny Wren
Saw him successful and
Taking his leave !
How the birds rated him,
How they all hated him !
How they all pitied
Poor motherless Eve !

Picture her crying,
Outside in the lane,
Eve, with no dish of sweet
Berries and plums to eat,
Haunting the gate of the
Orchard in vain. . . .

Picture the lewd delight
Under the hill to-night—
" Eva !" the toast goes round,
" Eva! " again.   RALPH HODGSON

EVE

" WHILE I sit at the door,
Sick to gaze within,
Mine eye weepeth sore
For sorrow and sin :
As a tree my sin stands
To darken all lands ;
Death is the fruit it bore.

" How have Eden bowers grown
Without Adam to bend them !
How have Eden flowers blown,
Squandering their sweet breath,
Without me to tend them !
The Tree of Life was ours,
Tree twelvefold-fruited,
Most lofty tree that flowers,
Most deeply rooted :
I chose the Tree of Death.

" Hadst thou but said me nay,
Adam, my brother,
I might have pined away ;
I, but none other :
God might have let thee stay
Safe in our garden
By putting me away
Beyond all pardon.

" I, Eve, sad mother
Of all who must live,
I, not another,
Plucked bitterest fruit to give
My friend, husband, lover.

THE GARDEN

O wanton eyes run over ;
Who but I should grieve ?—
Cain hath slain his brother :
Of all who must die mother,
Miserable Eve !"

Thus she sat weeping,
Thus Eve our mother,
Where one lay sleeping
Slain by his brother.
Greatest and least
Each piteous beast
To hear her voice
Forgot his joys
And set aside his feast.

The mouse paused in his walk
And dropped his wheaten stalk ;
Grave cattle wagged their heads
In rumination ;
The eagle gave a cry
From his cloud station :
Larks on thyme beds
Forbore to mount or sing ;
Bees drooped upon the wing ;
The raven perched on high
Forgot his ration ;
The conies in their rock,
A feeble nation,
Quaked sympathetical ;
The mocking-bird left off to mock ;
Huge camels knelt as if
In deprecation ;
The kind hart's tears were falling ;
Chattered the wistful stork ;
Dove-voices with a dying fall
Cooed desolation
Answering grief by grief.

EVE

Only the serpent in the dust,
Wriggling and crawling,
Grinned an evil grin and thrust
His tongue out with its fork.

CHRISTINA ROSSETTI

478

ADAM

ADAM lay i-bowndyn,
    bowndyn in a bond,
Fowre thowsand wynter
    thowt he not to long ;

And al was for an appil,
    an appil that he tok,
As clerkes fyndyn wretyn
    in here Book.

Ne hadde the appil take ben,
    the appil taken ben,
Ne hadde never our lady
    a ben hevene qwen.

Blyssid be the tyme
    that appil take was !
Therefore we mown syngyn
    Deo gracias.

479

THE SEVEN VIRGINS

ALL under the leaves and the leaves of life
    I met with virgins seven,
And one of them was Mary mild,
    Our Lord's mother of Heaven.

" O what are you seeking, you seven fair maids
    All under the leaves of life ?
Come tell, come tell, what seek you
    All under the leaves of life ?"

THE GARDEN

" We're seeking for no leaves, Thomas,
    But for a friend of thine ;
We're seeking for sweet Jesus Christ,
    To be our guide and thine."

" Go down, go down, to yonder town,
    And sit in the gallery,
And there you'll see sweet Jesus Christ
    Nailed to a big yew-tree."

So down they went to yonder town
    As fast as foot could fall,
And many a grievous bitter tear
    From the virgins' eyes did fall.

" O peace, Mother, O peace, Mother,
    Your weeping doth me grieve :
I must suffer this," He said,
    " For Adam and for Eve.

" O Mother, take you John Evangelist
    All for to be your son,
And he will comfort you sometimes,
    Mother, as I have done."

" O come, thou John Evangelist,
    Thou'rt welcome unto me ;
But more welcome my own dear Son,
    Whom I nursèd on my knee."

Then he laid his head on His right shoulder,
    Seeing death it struck Him nigh—
" The Holy Ghost be with your soul,
    I die, Mother dear, I die.". . .

480 ## LULLY, LULLAY

Lully, lullay, lully, lullay ;
The fawcon hath born my make [1] away.

He bare hym up, he bare hym down,
He bare hym in to an orchard browne.

In that orchard there was an halle
That was hangid with purpill and pall.

And in that hall there was a bede,[2]
Hit was hangid with gold so rede.

And yn that bede there lythe a knyght,
His woundis bledying day and nyght.

By that bede side kneleth a may,
And she wepeth both nyght and day.

And by that bedde side there stondith a ston,
Corpus Christi wretyn ther'on.

481 ### BALME

. . . There grew a goodly tree him faire beside,
Loaden with fruit and apples rosie red,
As they in pure vermilion had beene dide,
Whereof great vertues over all were red : [3]
For happie life to all, which thereon fed,
And life eke everlasting did befall :
Great God it planted in that blessed sted
With his almightie hand, and did it call
The tree of life, the crime of our first father's fall.

In all the world like was not to be found,
Save in that soile, where all good things did grow,
And freely sprong out of the fruitfull ground,
As incorrupted Nature did them sow,
Till that dread Dragon all did overthrow.

[1] Mate   [2] Bed   [3] Told

THE GARDEN

Another like faire tree eke grew thereby,
Whereof who so did eat, eftsoones did know
Both good and ill : O mornefull memory :
That tree through one man's fault hath doen us all
    to dy.

From that first tree forth flowd, as from a well,
A trickling streame of Balme, most soveraine
And daintie deare, which on the ground still fell,
And overflowèd all the fertill plaine,
And it had deawèd bene with timely raine :
Life and long health that gratious ointment gave,
And deadly woundes could heale, and reare againe
The senselesse corse appointed for the grave.
Into that same he fell : which did from death him
    save. . . .

                              EDMUND SPENSER

482   MY MASTER HATH A GARDEN

My master hath a garden, full-filled with divers flowers,
Where thou may'st gather posies gay, all times and hours,
            Here nought is heard
            But paradise-bird,
            Harp, dulcimer, and lute,
                With cymbal,
                And timbrel,
            And the gentle sounding flute.

Oh ! Jesus, Lord, my heal and weal, my bliss complete,
Make thou my heart thy garden-plot, true, fair and neat
            That I may hear
            This music clear,
            Harp, dulcimer, and lute,
                With cymbal,
                And timbrel,
            And the gentle sounding flute.

THIS IS THE KEY

This is the Key of the Kingdom :
In that Kingdom is a city ;
In that city is a town ;
In that town there is a street ;
In that street there winds a lane ;
In that lane there is a yard ;
In that yard there is a house ;
In that house there waits a room ;
In that room an empty bed ;
And on that bed a basket—
A Basket of Sweet Flowers :
   Of Flowers, of Flowers ;
   A Basket of Sweet Flowers.

Flowers in a Basket ;
Basket on the bed ;
Bed in the chamber ;
Chamber in the house ;
House in the weedy yard ;
Yard in the winding lane ;
Lane in the broad street ;
Street in the high town ;
Town in the city ;
City in the Kingdom—
This is the Key of the Kingdom ;
   Of the Kingdom this is the Key.

ABOUT
AND
ROUND
ABOUT

ABOUT AND ROUNDABOUT

In Mr. Nahum's The Other Worlde, as I have said on page xxx, there were many passages written about and round-about the poems contained in it. Some of these I copied out. With others that I have added since, they appear in the following pages. If the reader prefer poems and poems only in such a collection as this, would he of his kindness and courtesy ignore everything else? Otherwise, will he please forgive any blunders he may discover?

1. "THIS IS THE KEY."

This jingle (like Nos. 15, 16 and others) is one of hundreds of nursery and dandling rhymes which I found in Mr. Nahum's book. Compared with more formal poems they are like wild flowers—pimpernel, eyebright, thyme, woodruff, and others even tinier, even quieter, but having their own private and complete little beauty if looked at closely. Who made them, how old they are ; nobody knows. But when Noah's Ark stranded on the slopes of Mount Ararat, maybe a blossoming weed or two was nodding at the open third-storey window out of which over the waters of the flood the dove had followed the raven, and there, rejoicing in the sunshine and the green, sat Japheth's wife dandling little Magog on her lap, and crooning him some such lullaby.

3.

On the one side is printed the old Scots, and on the other the best I can do to put it into the English of our own time. According to the dictionary the thistle-cock that cries shame on the sleepers still drowsing in their beds is the corn-bunting—

a cousin of the yellow-hammer. He has a small harsh mono-
tonous voice as if for the very purpose. Whereas the nightingale might seem to cry, " Nay, nay : it is in dreams you wander.
Happy ones ! Sleep on ; sleep on."

4. " I PASSED BY HIS GARDEN,"

Whatever fate befell the Sluggard, I should like to have
taken a walk in his garden, among those branching thistles,
green thorns and briers. Maybe he sailed off at last to the Isle
of Nightmare, or to the land where it is always afternoon, or
was wrecked in Yawning Gap. He must, at any rate, have
had an even heavier head than Dr. Watts supposed if he never
so much as lifted it from his pillow to brood awhile on that
still, verdurous scene. And the birds !

Indeed, to lie, between sleep and wake, when daybreak is
brightening of an April or a May morning, and so listen to the
far-away singing of a thrush or to the whistling of a robin
or a wren is to seem to be transported back into the garden of
Eden. Dreamers, too, may call themselves travellers.

Mr. Nahum's picture to this rhyme was of a man in rags
looking into a small round mirror or looking-glass, but at what
you couldn't see.

6. " THE MERCHANT BOWS " (line 7)

—(as do the happy to the New Moon, for luck), for his merchandise is being wafted over the sea under the guidance of
the Seaman's, or Ship, or Lode, or Pole Star. It shines in the
constellation of the Little Bear, and " is the cheefe marke
whereby mariners governe their course in saylings by nyghte."
To find the " marke," look towards the north some cloudless
night for the constellation of Seven Stars called the Plough or
the Dipper or Charles's Wain (or Waggon), which " enclyneth
his ravisshinge courses abouten the soverein heighte of the
worlde " day and night throughout the year. Its hinder stars
(Dubhe and Merak) are named " the pointers," because if you
follow the line of them with the eye into the empty skies, the
next brightish star it will alight on *is* the Seaman's Star. Close
beside the second of the seven is a mere speck of a star. And
that is called by country people Jack-by-the-middle-horse. On
this same star looked Shakespeare—as did the 1st Carrier in his
Henry IV. : " Heigh-ho, an't be not foure by the day, Ile be

hanged. Charles' waine is over the near Chimney, and yet our horse not packt "; and as did his 2nd Gentleman in *Othello* :

Montano.   What from the Cape can you discerne at Sea ?

1st Gentleman.   Nothing at all, it is a high-wrought Flood : I cannot 'twixt the Heaven, and the Maine Descry a Saile. . . .

2nd Gentleman. . . . Do but stand upon the Foaming Shore, The chidden Billow seemes to pelt the Clowds, The wind-shaked-Surge, with high and monstrous Maine, Seemes to cast water on the burning Beare, And quench the Guards of the ever-fixèd Pole. I never did like mollestation view On the enchafèd Flood. . . .

Faintly shimmering, too, in the northern heavens is that other numerous starry cluster, known the world over as *Seven* —to us as the Seven Sisters or the Pleiades. A strange seven ; for only six stars are now clearly visible to the naked eye, one having vanished, it would seem, within human memory. When ? where ?—none can tell. They play in light as close together as dewdrops in a cobweb hung from thorn to thorn. Nearby, on winter's cold breast burns the most marvellous of the constellations—the huntsman Orion, with his Rigel and Bellatrix and Betelgeuse ; his dog Sirius at his heels. " Seek him that maketh the Seven Stars and Orion, and turneth the shadow of death into the morning, and maketh the day dark with night . . . "

9. " LIKE A CHILD, HALF IN TENDERNESS AND MIRTH."

At a first reading, perhaps, this line will not appear to flow so smoothly as the rest. But linger an instant on the word *child*, and you will have revealed to yourself one of Shelley's, and indeed one of every poet's loveliest devices with words—to let the music of his verse accord with its meaning, and at the same time to please and charm the ear with a slight variation from the regular beat and accent of the metre. So, too, in the middle lines of the next stanza. This variation, which is called rhythm, is the very proof of its writer's sincerity. For if the sound of his verse (or of his voice) rings false, he cannot have completely realised what he was writing or saying. When a man says what he means, he says it *as if he meant it*. The *tune* of what he says sounds right. When a man does *not* mean what he says, he finds it all but impossible to say it as if he did. The *tune* goes wrong.

Just so with reading. So from a gay and tiny *Compendious English Grammar* of 1780 I have borrowed these four brief wholesome rules for reading :

(1) . . . Observe well the pauses, accents and emphases ; and never stop but where the sense will admit of it.

(2) Humour your voice a little, according to the subject. . . .

(3) Do not read too fast, lest [in lip or mind] you get a habit of stammering ; adding or omitting words ; and be sure that your understanding keep pace with your tongue.

(4) In reading Verse, pronounce every word just as if it were prose, observing the stops with great exactness, and giving each word its proper accent ; and if it be not harmonious, the Poet, and not the Reader, is to blame."

Better, perhaps, be sure of your ear before you blame the poet. But in general, if these rules are followed, there can be little danger of reading like a parrot, or like a small boy in his first breeches at a Dame's school. To *think* while one reads ; that is the main thing : so as not to be, as Sidney says,—just

    . . . like a child that some fair book doth find,
       With gilded leaves or coloured vellum plays,
       Or, at the most, on some fair pictures stays,
       But never heeds the fruit of writer's mind.

13. "Comes dancing from the East."

I found a story about this dancing in Mrs. Wright's *Rustic Speech and Folklore*. It is the story of a woman who lived in a district called Hockley, in the parish of Broseley. She said that she had heard of such " dancing " but did not believe it to be true, " till on Easter morning last, I got up early, and then I saw the sun dance, and dance, and dance, three times, and I called to my husband and said, ' *Rowland, Rowland, get up and see the sun dance !* ' I used," she said, " not to believe it, but now I can never doubt more." The neighbours agreed with her that the sun did dance on Easter morning, and that some of them had seen it. " Seeing," goes the old proverb, " is believing "—which is true no less of the " inward eye." I once tried to comfort a very little boy who was unhappy because there was a Bear under his bed. Candle in hand, I talked and talked, and proved that there wasn't a real bear for miles and miles around, not at any rate until we reached the Zoo, and there—black, brown, sloth, spectacled, grizzly and polar alike—all of them, poor creatures, were cabined, cribbed and shut up in barred cages. He listened, tears still shining in his eyes, his small face sharp and clear. " Why certainly, certainly *not*," I ended, " there can't be a real bear for miles around !" He smiled as if pitying me. " Ah yes, Daddie," he answered with a die-away sob, " but, you see, you's talking of *real* bears, and mine *wasn't* real."

14. " Us Idle Wenches."

It was a jolly bed in sooth,
  Of oak as strong as Babel.
And there slept Kit and Sall and Ruth
  As sound as maids are able.

Ay—three in one—and there they dreamed,
  Their bright young eyes hid under ;
Nor hearkened when the tempest streamed
  Nor recked the rumbling thunder.

For marvellous regions strayed they in,
  Each moon-far from the other—
Ruth in her childhood, Kit in heaven,
  And Sall with ghost for lover.

But soon as ever sun shone sweet,
  And birds sang, Praise for rain, O—
Leapt out of bed three pair of feet
  And danced on earth again, O !

17. Old May Song.

This, like No. 2, and the next song must be as old as the dew-ponds on the Downs. They were wont to be sung, I have read, by five or six men, with a fiddle, or flute, or clarionet accompaniment. When I was a boy I can remember one First of May seeing a Jack-in-the-Green in the street—a man in a kind of wicker cage hung about with flowers and leaves—with Maid Marian, Friar Tuck and the rest, dancing and singing beside him. A great friend of mine, when she was a little girl of eight, was so frightened at sight of this leafy prancing creature on her way to school that she turned about and ran for a mile without stopping.

10. THE DAISY.

There is far too little of Geoffrey Chaucer's—that most lovable, shrewd, compassionate, and natural of poets—in this book. There was much more of him, I noticed, in Mr. Nahum's Tome II. At first sight his words look a little strange ; but not for long ; and if every dotted letter is made a syllable of, his rhythm will flow like water over bright green waterweed.

It is a curious, though little thing, that while, among the one hundred and seventy varieties of flowers Shakespeare mentions, he has no less than fifty-seven several references to the rose, twenty-one to the green grass, eighteen to violets, and even to the serviceable but rank nettle a round dozen, he has but a scant five to Chaucer's beloved daisy. Flowers, it is true, as says Canon Ellacombe (who collected all such references into his delight-full book, *Plant-lore and Garden-craft of Shakespeare*), never sweeten the Plays for their own sake alone, and there are no foxgloves, snowdrops or forget-me-nots in them at all. Still, had he loved daisies as children do, he could hardly have resisted them even for " their own sake alone." Is not bairnwort another name for the daisy ?

" A yellow cup, it hath," says Pliny, " and the same is crowned, as it were with a garland, consisting of five and fifty little leaves, set round about it in manner of fine pales. These be flowers of the meadow, and most of such are of no use at all." No use at all, none—except only to make skylark of every heart whose owner has eyes in his head for a daisy's simple looks, its marvellous making, and the sheer happiness of their multitudes wide open in the sun or round-headed and adrowse in the evening twilight.

Chaucer's picture portrait is well known. So is that in his own words in the *Canterbury Tales*. But here is another, less familiar, by Robert Greene—of " Sir Jeffery Chaucer," as he calls him. Water chamlet is a rich coloured silken plush, and a whittell is a knife :

ABOUT AND ROUNDABOUT

His stature was not very tall,
Leane he was, his legs were small,
Hosed within a stock of red
A buttoned bonnet on his head,
From under which did hang, I weene,
Silver haires both bright and sheene,
His beard was white, trimmèd round,
His count'nance blithe and merry found,
A Sleevelesse Iacket large and wide,
With many pleights and skirts Side,
Of water Chamlet did he weare,
A whittell by his belt he beare,
His shooes were cornèd broad before,
His Inkhorne at his side he wore,
And in his hand he bore a booke,
Thus did this auntient Poet looke.

20. " BRAVE PRICK-SONG "

—which means, I gather, that while the nightingale was—even
into the dusk of dawn—yet singing her " *air* " or " *descant*,"
the lark joined in as if reading her notes from the daybreak
stars *pricking* the sky.

21. " CUCKOO, JUG, JUG, PU WE, TO WITTA WOO !"

Four birds, I suppose, have part in this : cuckoo, nightingale
(*yoog, yoog*), green-finch (?) and owl.

I rose anon, and thought I wouldè gone
Into the woods, to hear the birdis sing,
When that the misty vapour was agone,
And cleare and fairè was the morrowing ;
The dew, also, like silver in shining,
Upon the leaves, as any baumè sweet.

. . . . . .

And in I went to hear the birdis song,
Which on the branches, both in plain and vale,
So loudly y-sang, that all the wood y-rang,
Like as it should shiver in pieces smale ;
And as me thoughten that the nightingale
With so great might her voice began out-wrest,
Right as her heart for love would all to-brest.

JOHN LYDGATE

503

ABOUT AND ROUNDABOUT

22. "THE JEALOUS TROUT."

Thou that desir'st to fish with line and hook,
Be it in pool, in river, or in brook,
To bless thy bait and make the fish to bite,
Lo, here's a means ! if thou canst hit it right :
Take Gum of Life, fine beat, and laid in soak
In oil well drawn from that which kills the oak,
Fish where thou wilt, thou shalt have sport thy fill ;
When twenty fail, thou shalt be sure to kill.

> It's perfect and good,
> If well understood ;
> Else not to be told
> For silver or gold.

So advises Master Will. Lauson in the *Secrets of Angling*,
which was published in 1653 ; the ingredients (or *ingrediments*
as I used to say when I was a child) of his " gum of life " being
Cocculus Juliæ, Assafoetida, Honey, and Wheat-flour. The
" that which kills the oak," I suppose, is ivy. But it looks as
if there may have been a wink in his eye— to welcome the green
in his reader's.

Here, on the same theme, are a few lines from a poem by
Mr. Robert Bridges :

> . . . Sometimes an angler comes, and drops his hook
> Within its hidden depths, and 'gainst a tree
> Leaning his rod, reads in some pleasant book,
> Forgetting soon his pride of fishery,
> > And dreams, or falls asleep,
> > While curious fishes peep
> About his nibbled bait, or scornfully
> > Dart off and rise and leap. . . .

And these are by J. Wolcot :

> Why flyest thou away with fear ?
> Trust me there's naught of danger near,
> > I have no wicked hooke
> All covered with a snaring bait,
> Alas, to tempt thee to thy fate,
> > And dragge thee from the brooke. . . .

504

ABOUT AND ROUNDABOUT

> Enjoy thy stream, O harmless fish ;
> And when an angler for his dish,
> Through gluttony's vile sin,
> Attempts, a wretch, to pull thee out,
> God give thee strength, O gentle trout,
> To pull the raskall in !

A less common and more skilful sport than fly, hook and bait, or even " tickling " can afford is to share their watery chaos with the fish, and catch them with the hands. This needs rare skill and cunning and—a disguise! " For dyeing of your hairs," says Isaac Walton in *The Compleat Angler*, " do it thus : Take a pint of strong ale, half a pound of soot, and a little quantity of the juice of walnut-tree leaves, and an equal quantity of alum ; put these together, into a pot, pan, or pipkin, and boil them half an hour ; and having so done, let it cool ; and being cold, put your hair into it, and there let it lie ; it will turn your hair to be a kind of water or glass-colour or greenish ; and the longer you let it lie, the deeper coloured it will be. You might be taught to make many other colours, but it is to little purpose ; for doubtless the water-colour or glass-coloured hair is the most choice and the most useful for an angler, but let it not be too green."

" AND BIRDS HAD DRAWN THEIR VALENTINES." (line 4)

First thing in the early morning, if you go out on St. Valentine's Day, which is the 14th day of February, you will meet, if you meet anybody, your soon-to-be-loved one. So too the birds. In my young days, folks sent the daintiest pictures to their sweethearts on this day. Mr. Nahum had a drawer half full of them—with a few locks of hair and some withered flowers. And one or two of these Valentines were of beaten gold, with images of lovely things upon them, as if from another planet.

" This morning came up to my wife's bedside, I being up dressing myself, little Will Mercer to be her Valentine ; and brought her name writ upon blue paper in gold letters, done by himself, very pretty. . . ." Mr. Samuel Pepys's *Diary*.

> To-morrow is S. Valentine's day,
> All in the morning betime,
> And I a Maid at your Window
> To be your Valentine !
> *Ophelia's Song.*

545

ABOUT AND ROUNDABOUT

"JOAN STROKES A SILLABUB OR TWAIN."

If you would make a Lemon Sillabub (as advised by Mrs. Charlotte Mason, "a Professed Housekeeper, who from about 1740 had upwards of Thirty Years experience in Families of the First Fashion") take "a Pint of cream, a pint of white wine, the rind of two lemons grated, and the juice. Sugar to the taste. Let it stand some time; mill or whip it. Lay the froth on a sieve; put the remainder into glasses. Lay on the froth." Mr. Nahum must have had a fancy for Cookery Books; there were dozens of them in his tower room. Indeed, the next best thing to eating a good dish is to read how it is made; and somehow the old "cookbook" writers learned to write a most excellent and appetising English. Here is another recipe from *Delightes for Ladies*, of 1608—a dainty that would eat uncommonly well with a sillabub:— "*To make a marchpane.*—Take two poundes of almonds being blanched, and dryed in a sieve over the fire, beate them in a stone mortar, and when they bee small mixe them with two pounde of sugar beeing finely beaten, adding two or three spoonefuls of rose-water, and that will keep your almonds from oiling: when your paste is beaten fine, drive it thin with a rowling pin, and so lay it on a bottom of wafers, then raise up a little edge on the side, and so bake it, then yce it with rose-water and sugar, then put it in the oven again, and when you see your yce is risen up and drie, then take it out of the oven and garnish it with pretie conceipts, as birdes and beasts being cast out of standing moldes. Sticke long comfits upright in it, cast biskets and carrowaies in it, and so serve it; guild it before you serve it: you may also print of this *marchpane* paste in your molds for banqueting dishes. And of this paste our comfit makers at this day make their letters, knots, armes, escutcheons, beasts, birds, and other fancies." Also pygmy castles and suchlike, for dessert, which the guests would demolish with sugar-plums.

"Good thou, save mee a piece of Marchpane, and as thou lovest me, let the Porter let in Susan Grindstone and Nell. . . ."

Romeo and Juliet

23. "THE SUN ARISING."

"What other fire could be a better image of the fire which is there, than the fire which is here? Or what other earth than this, of the earth which is there ?" So said Plotinus, and " I know," said Blake, " that this world is a world of imagination and vision. I see everything I paint in this world, but everybody does not see alike. To the eye of a miser a guinea is far more beautiful than the sun, and a bag worn with the use of money has more beautiful proportions than a vine filled with grapes. The tree which moves some to tears of joy is in the eyes of others only a green thing which stands in the way. . . . Some scarce see Nature at all. But to the eyes of the man of imagination, Nature is Imagination itself. As a man is, so he sees. As the eye is formed, such are its powers. You certainly mistake, when you say that the visions of fancy are not to be found in this world. To me this world is all one continued vision.". . . Indeed, when Blake was a child, he saw on Peckham Rye a tree, full, not of birds, but of angels ; and his poems show how marvellously clear were the eyes with which he looked at the things of Nature.

In the year 1872, an old lady might have been seen driving across the Rye in her silvery carriage ; and she came to where, under a flowering tree, sat a small boy—the locks of hair upon his head like sheaves of cowslips, his eyes like speedwells, and he in very bright clothes. And he was a-laughing up into the tree. She stopped her carriage and said to him almost as if she were more angry than happy, " What are you laughing at, child ? " And he said, " At the sparrows, ma'am." " Mere sparrows ! " says she, " but why ? " " Because they were saying," says he, " here comes across the Rye a blind old horse, a blind old coachman, and a blind old woman." " But I am not blind," says she. " Nor are they not ' *mere* sparrows '," said the child. And at that the old lady was looking out of her carriage at no child, but at a small bush, in bud, of gorse.

24. " AND THANK HIM THEN "

—as does Robert Herrick's child, in his " Grace " :

> Here a little child I stand,
> Heaving up my either hand ;
> Cold as Paddocks though they be,
> Here I lift them up to Thee,
> For a Benizon to fall
> On our meat, and on us all. AMEN.

ABOUT AND ROUNDABOUT

A paddock is a frog or a toad, it seems. To either small cold hand there are four cold fingers and a thumb ; and in old times, says Halliwell, our ancestors had distinct names for each of the five toes and for each of the five fingers. The fingers were called thumb, toucher, longman, leche-man, little-man ; leche-man being the ring-finger, because in that " there is a sinew very tender and small that reaches to the heart." In Essex they used to call them (and still may)—Tom Thumbkin, Bess Bumpkin, Long Linkin, Bill Wilkin, and Little Dick. In Scotland : Thumbkin, Lickpot, Langman, Berrybarn and Pirlie Winkie.

And here are some more from Dr. Courtenay Dunn's *Natural History of the Child*—a book which is graced with as handsome a frontispiece as ever I've seen :

Thumb	- Tommy Tomkins or	Bill Milker.
Forefinger	- Billy Wilkins	,, Tom Thumper.
Third finger	- Long Larum	,, Long Lazy.
Fourth finger	Betsy Bedlam	,, Cherry Bumper.
Little finger	- Little Bob	,, Tippity, Tippity-Town-end.
Toes :		
Big toe	- Tom Barker	or Toe Tipe.
Toe 2 -	- Long Rachel	,, Penny Wipe.
Toe 3 -	- Minnie Wilkin	,, Tommy Tistle.
Toe 4 -	- Milly Larkin	,, Billy Whistle.
Little toe	- Little Dick	,, Tripping-go.

So (if you wish) you can secretly name not only your fingers, toes, rooms, chairs and tables, etc., but also the stars in their courses, the trees in your orchard, and have your own privy countersign for the flowers you like best. " Give a dog a bad name, and hang him," says the old proverb. Give anything a *good* name, and it is yours for ever. There is the tale of the unhappy gardener in the Isle of Rumm who without ill intention called a snapdragon an antirrhinum. And there arose out of the hillside a Monster named Zobj—but I haven't the space for the rest. The gardener of course meant well ; but when he heard the Voice counting his last moments, not in common English, but in what Wensleydale Knitters still remember of the Norse—Yahn, Jyahn, Tether, Mether, Mumph, Hither, Lither, Auver, Dauver, Dic—well, he died before he was due, so to speak.

ABOUT AND ROUNDABOUT

While we are on this subject, here is a Face Rhyme :

> Bo Peeper
> Nose Dreeper
> Chin Chopper
> White Lopper
> Red Rag
> And Little Gap.

This is another :

> Here sits the Lord Mayor :
> Here sit his men ;
> Here sits the cockadoodle ;
> Here sits the hen ;
> Here sits the little chickens ;
> Here they run in ;
> Chinchopper, chinchopper, chinchopper chin.

The next three are foot rhymes, very soothing at times to fractious babies. The first is common in London, etc. :

> This little pig went to market ;
> This little pig stayed at home ;
> This little pig had roast beef ;
> This little pig had the bone ;
> This little pig cried *Wee-wee-wee-wee-wee* !
> *All* the way home.

The second comes from the Isle of Wight :

> This gurt pig zays, I wants meat ;
> T'other one zays, Where'll ye hay et ?
> This one zays, In gramfer's barn ;
> T'other one zays, Week ! Week ! I can't get over the dreshel.

And this is from Scotland :

> This ain biggit the baurn,
> This ain stealt the corn,
> This ain stood and saw,
> This ain ran awa',
> An' wee Pirlie Winkie paid for a'.

And last ; here is a dance-babbie-on-knee (or This-is-the-way) rhyme ; also from Scotland :

> The doggies gaed to the mill,
> This way and that way ;

ABOUT AND ROUNDABOUT

They took a lick out o' *this* wife's poke
And they took a lick out o' *that* wife's poke,
And a loup in the lead, and a dip in the dam,
And gaed walloping, walloping, walloping, HAME.

And no doubt came to the conclusion expressed in the sixth
stanza of Robert Herrick's *Ternary of Littles, upon a Pipkin
of Jelly sent to a Lady*:

A little Saint best fits a little Shrine,
A little Prop best fits a little Vine,
As my small Cruse best fits my little Wine.

A little Seed best fits a little Soyle,
A little Trade best fits a little Toyle,
As my small Jarre best fits my little Oyle.

A little Bin best fits a little Bread,
A little Garland fits a little Head,
As my small stuffe best fits my little Shed.

A little Hearth best fits a little Fire,
A little Chappell fits a little Quire,
As my small Bell best fits my little Spire.

A little streame best fits a little Boat,
A little lead best fits a little Float,
As my small Pipe best fits my little note.

A little meat best fits a little bellie,
As sweetly, Lady, give me leave to tell ye,
This little Pipkin fits this little Jellie.

And the fact that this or any other poem is printed at this
end of the book instead of at the other does not mean that I am
any the less thankful to have it or that Mr. Nahum left it out
of his.

25. "I SING OF A MAIDEN."

Only the spelling of this lovely and ancient little carol has
been slightly changed.

29. "SLEEP STAYS NOT, THOUGH A MONARCH BIDS."
(line 11).

Why rather, sleep, liest thou in smoky cribs,
Upon uneasy pallets stretching thee,

ABOUT AND ROUNDABOUT

And hushed with buzzing night-flies to thy slumber,
Than in the perfumed chambers of the great,
Under the canopies of costly state,
And lulled with sound of sweetest melody ?
O thou dull god, why liest thou with the vile
In loathsome beds, and leavest the kingly couch
A watch-case or a common 'larum-bell ?
Wilt thou upon the high and giddy mast
Seal up the ship-boy's eyes, and rock his brains
In cradle of the rude imperious surge,
And in the visitation of the winds,
Who take the ruffian billows by the top,
Curling their monstrous heads, and hanging them
With deafening clamour in the slippery clouds,
That, with the hurly, death itself awakes ?
Canst thou, O partial sleep, give thy repose
To the wet sea-boy in an hour so rude ;
And in the calmest and most stillest night,
With all appliances and means to boot,
Deny it to a king ?   Then happy low, lie down !
Uneasy lies the head that wears a crown.
                                           Henry IV. Part ii.

30.

For many years I read this poem as if the accents in the
first line of each stanza fell on the first and third word—the
two " I's."   It was stupid of me, for clearly the accent should
fall (lightly) on the second syllable of the " remembers."
Apart from the accents or stresses in a line of verse, there is
the rise and fall of the voice, a kind of tune in the *saying* of it.
If the right tune is not caught, then the difference is as much
as if one sniffed a wallflower and it smelt like African mimosa.
And to me, as to hundreds of thousands of Englishmen, this
poem is as familiar, long-endeared and refreshing as wallflower,
Sweet William, or Old Man.   This is the second or third time
I have made remarks about the rhythm, lilt or tune of a poem ;
and it won't be the last.   May I be forgiven, for as Chaucer
wrote to his small son Louis when he was sharing with him his
love of astronomy : " Soothly me seemeth betre to writen unto
a child twice a good sentence, then he forget it ones."   As for
his elders, even thrice may be short commons.

ABOUT AND ROUNDABOUT

"THOSE FLOWERS MADE OF LIGHT." (line 12)

Hold up a flower between eye and sun, or even candle-flame, and it seems little but its own waxen hue and colour. Moonlight is too pale ; the petals remain opaque. In the moon's light, indeed, blueness is scarcely distinguishable from shadowiness ; red darkens but yellow pales, and the fairest flowers of all wake in her beams —jasmine, convolvulus, evening-primrose — as if they not only shared her radiance but returned a glowwormlike fumeness of their own.

Once, long before I came to Thrae, having plucked for my mother a few convolvulus flowers, I remember when I was just about to give them into her hand I discovered that the beautiful cups of delight had enwreathed themselves together, and had returned as it were to the bud, never to reopen. I was but a child, and this odd little disappointment was so extreme that I burst out crying.

32.

See just above, No. 30 : and for proof of the curious obedience of words to any bidden rhythm it is interesting to compare this poem with its next neighbours. Mr. Frost's colt is called " a little Morgan," because he was of a famous breed of horses of that name which are the pride of the State of Vermont.

35.

Only a single copy of the old play, *Mundus et Infans*, from which this fragment is taken, is known to be in existence. It was printed by Wynkyn de Worde in 1522 ; and was written roundabout 1500.

The lines need a slow reading to get the run and lilt of them : and even at that they jog and creak like an old farm-cart. But the boy, Dalyaunce, if one takes a little pains, will come gradually out of them as clear to the eye as if you had met him in the street to-day, on his way to " schole " for yet another " docking."

Clothes, houses, customs, food a little, thoughts a little, knowledge, too—all change as the years and centuries go by, but Dalyaunce under a thousand names lives on. It never occurred to me when I was young to think that the children in Rome talked Latin at their games, and that Solomon and Caesar, Prester John and the Grand Khan knew in their young days what it means to be homesick and none too easy to sit down. Yet there are knucklebones and dolls in London that the infant subjects of the Pharaohs played with, and at Stratford Grammar School, for all to see, is Shakespeare's school desk. As for Dalyaunce, " dockings " are not nowadays so harsh as once they were.

In proof of this, there is a passage from a book, telling of his own life as a small boy, written by Guibert de Nogent. He is speaking of his childhood, about the year when William the Conqueror landed at Hastings :

' So, after a few of the evening hours had been passed in that study, during which I had been beaten even beyond my deserts, I came and sat at my mother's knees. She, according to her wont, asked whether I had been beaten that day ; and I, unwilling to betray my master, denied it ; whereupon, whether I would or no, she threw back my inner garment (such as men call shirt), and found my little ribs black with the strokes of the osier, and rising everywhere into weals. Then, grieving in her inmost bowels at this punishment so excessive for my tender years, troubled and boiling with anger, and with brimming eyes, she cried, " Never now shalt thou become a clerk, nor shalt thou be thus tortured again to learn thy letters !" Whereupon, gazing upon her with all the seriousness that I could call to my face, I replied, " Nay, even though I should die under the rod, I will not desist from learning my letters and becoming a clerk !" '

Still, there were more merciful schoolmasters than Guibert de Nogent's, even in days harsh as his ; as this further extract from Mr. G. G. Coulton's enticing *Medieval Garner* shows :

' One day, when a certain Abbot, much reputed for his piety, spake with Anselm concerning divers points of Monastic Religion, and conversed among other things of the boys that were brought up in the cloister, he added : " What, pray, can we do with them ? They are perverse and incorrigible ; day and night we cease not to chastise them, yet they grow daily worse and worse."

Whereat Anselm marvelled, and said, " Ye cease not to beat them ? And when they are grown to manhood, of what sort are they then ?" " They are dull and brutish," said the other.

Then said Anselm, " With what good profit do ye expend your substance in nurturing human beings till they become

brute beasts ? . . . But I prithee tell me, for God's sake,
wherefore ye are so set against them ? Are they not human,
sharing in the same nature as yourselves ? Would ye wish
to be so handled as ye handle them ? Ye will say, ' Yes, if
we were as they are.' So be it, then ; yet is there no way but
that of stripes and scourges for shaping them to good ? Did
ye ever see a goldsmith shape his gold or silver plate into a
fair image by blows alone ? I trow not. What then ? That
he may give the plate its proper shape, he will first press it
gently and tap it with his tools ; then again he will more softly
raise it with discreet pressure from below, and caress it into
shape. So ye also, if ye would see your boys adorned with
fair manners, ye should not only beat them down with stripes,
but also raise their spirits and support them with fatherly
kindness and pity '. . .''

There was an old woodcut, hanging on Mr. Nahum's wall
in his tower room, showing a boy in the middle ages being
whipped in a kind of machine (something like a roasting-jack),
and a schoolmaster standing by, nicely smiling, in a gown.
When Coleridge was a bluecoat boy at Christ's Hospital with
Charles Lamb, he seems to have had a headmaster of this kind :
" ' Boy ! ' I remember Bowyer saying to me once when I was
crying the first day after my return after the holidays,—' Boy !
the school is your father ! Boy ! the school is your mother !
Boy ! the school is your brother ! the school is your sister !
the school is your first cousin, and your second cousin, and all
the rest of your relations ! Let's have no more crying.' . . .

" Mrs. Bowyer was no comforter, either. Val. Le Grice and
I were once going to be flogged for some domestic misdeed,
and Bowyer was thundering away at us, by way of prologue,
when Mrs. B. looked in and said, ' Flog them soundly, sir,
I beg !' This saved us. Bowyer was so nettled at the
interruption that he growled out, ' Away, woman, away !'
and we were let off."

Coleridge tells of yet another schoolmaster, whose name,
like Bowyer and birch, also began with a B. : " Busby was
the father of the English public school system. He was
headmaster of Westminster through the reign of Charles I.,
the Civil War, the Protectorate, the reign of Charles II., and
the Revolution of 1688. Under him Westminster became the
first school in the kingdom. When Charles II. visited the

school, Busby stalked before the King with his hat upon his head, whilst his most sacred majesty meekly followed him. In private Busby explained that his conduct was due to the fact that he could not allow, for discipline's sake, the boys to imagine there could be a greater man than himself alive." Quite rightly, of course.

There is, too, the story of the little Lion that went to school to the Bear. Being, though of royal blood, a good deal of a dunce, Master Lion bore many sound cuffings from Dr. Bruin on the road to learning, and found it hot and dusty. After such administrations, he would sometimes sit in the sun under a window, learning his task and brooding on a day when he would return to the school and revenge himself upon the Doctor for having treated him so sore. But Master Lion was all this time growing up, and so many were the cares of State when he had left his books and become a Prince and Heir Apparent, that for a time he had no thought for his old school. Being, however, in the Royal Gardens one sunny morning, and seeing bees busy about their hive, he remembered an old saying on the sweetness of knowledge and wisdom, and this once more reminded him of his old Master. Bidding his servants sling upon a rod half a dozen of the hives, he set out to visit Dr. Bruin. The hives were taken into his study, and the bees, being unused to flitting within walls out of the sunshine, angrily sang and droned about the head of the old schoolmaster as he sat at his desk. Their stings were of little account against his thick hide, but their molestation was a fret, and he presently cried aloud, " Would that the Prince had kept his gifts to himself ! " The Prince, who was standing outside the door, listening and smiling to himself, thereupon cried out : " Ah ! Dr. Bruin, when I was under your charge, you often heavily smit and cuffed me with those long-clawed paws of yours. Now I am older, and have learned how sweet and worthy is the knowledge they instilled. This too will be your experience. My bees may fret and buzz and sting a little now, but you will think of me more kindly when you shall be tasting their rich honey in the Winter that is soon upon us." And Dr. Bruin, peering out at the Prince from amid the cloud of the bees, when he heard him thus call Tit for Tat, he couldn't help but laugh.

And last—to return to Coleridge once more, who, in the bad

515

old days, so far as food goes, never "had a belly full" at Christ's Hospital, and whose appetite was only "damped, never satisfied,"—here is one of his earliest letters (to his elder brother George), which *may* have an (indirect) reference to Dr. Bowyer's birch :

Dear Brother,—You will excuse me for reminding you that, as our holidays commence next week, and I shall go out a good deal, a good pair of breeches will be no inconsiderable accession to my appearance. For though my present pair are excellent for the purpose of drawing mathematical figures on them, and though a walking thought, sonnet or epigram would appear in them in very *splendid* type, yet they are not altogether so well adapted for a female eye—not to mention that I should have the charge of vanity brought against me for wearing a looking-glass. I hope you have got rid of your cold—and I am

Your affectionate brother,

SAMUEL TAYLOR COLERIDGE

40.

This too should go to the lilt of its music, as then the accents would come clearly. I think, in the reading of it, there should be four stressed syllables to the first, second and fifth lines in each stanza : " Whâr hae ye been a' day, mŷ boy Tammy " ; and " The wee thing gie's her hând, and says, There, gâng and ask my Mâmmy." A line of verse like this resembles a piece of elastic ; if you leave it very slack you will get no music out of it at all ; stretch it a little too far, it snaps.

41. " ROSY APPLE, LEMON, OR PEAR."

This little jingle and Nos. 15, 16, 68, 75, etc., are Singing Game Rhymes, of which scores have been collected from the mouths of children near and far from all over the Kingdom, and are now to be found in print in Lady Gomme's two stout engrossing volumes entitled *Traditional Games.* In these more than seven hundred games are described, including Rakes and Roans, Rockety Row, Sally Go Round the Moon, Shuttle-feather, Spannims, Tods and Lambs, Whigmeleerie, Allicom-greenaie, Bob-Cherry, Oranges and Lemons, Cherry Pit, Thumble-bones, Lady on Yandor Hill, Hechefragy, and Snail Creep.

ABOUT AND ROUNDABOUT

A good many of these games have singing rhymes to them. And the words of them vary in different places. For the children in each of twenty or more villages and towns may have their own particular version of the same rhyme. As for the original from which all such versions must once have come— *that* may be centuries old. Like the Nursery Rhymes, they were most of them in the world ages before our great-great-great-grand-dams were babies in their cradles. The noble game of Hop Scotch, for instance, Lady Gomme tells us, was in favour before the year 1.

The most mysterious rhymes of all are said to refer to ancient tribal customs, rites and ceremonies—betrothals, harvest-homes, sowings, reapings, well-blessings, dirges, divinations, battles, hunting, and exorcisings—before even London was else than a few hovels by its river's side. Rhymes such as these having been passed on from age to age and from one piping throat to another, have grown worn and battered of course, and become queerly changed in their words.

These from Mr. Nahum's book have their own differences too. He seems to have liked best those that make a picture, or sound uncommonly sweet and so carry the fancy away. Any little fytte or jingle or jargon of words that manages *that* is like a charm or a talisman, and to make new ones is as hard as to spin silk out of straw, or to turn beech leaves into fairy money. When one thinks, too, of the myriad young voices that generation after generation have carolled these rhymes into the evening air, and now are still—well, it's a thought no less sorrowful for being strange, and no less strange for the fact that our own voices too will some day be as silent.

Summer's pleasures they are gone like to visions every one,
And the cloudy days of autumn and of winter cometh on.
I tried to call them back, but unbidden they are gone
Far away from heart and eye and for ever far away.
Dear heart, and can it be that such raptures meet decay ?
I thought them all eternal when by Langley Bush I lay,
I thought them joys eternal when I used to shout and play
On its bank at " clink and bandy," " chock " and " taw " and
    " ducking stone,"
Where silence sitteth now on the wild heath as her own
Like a ruin of the past all alone. . .

                         JOHN CLARE

ABOUT AND ROUNDABOUT

42. " IN PRAISE."

The loveliest and gayest song of praise and sweetness to a " young thing " I have ever seen.

" Ieloifer "—gelofer, gelofre, gillofre, gelevor, gillyvor, gillofer, jereiloure, gerrailour all these are ways of spelling Gillyflower, gelofre coming nearest to its original French : *giroflée*—meaning spiced like the clove. There were of old, I find, three kinds of gillyflowers : the clove, the stock and the wall. It was the first of these kinds that was meant in the earlier writers by the small clove carnation (or Coronation, because it was made into chaplets or garlands). Its Greek name was dianthus (the flower divine) ; and its twin-sister is the Pink, so called because its edges are, as it were, picked out, jagged, notched, scalloped. Country names for it are Sweet John, Pagiants, Blunket and Sops-in-Wine, for it spices what it floats in, and used to be candied for a sweetmeat. Blossoming in July, the Gillyflower suggests July-flower, and if Julia is one's sweetheart, it may also be a Julie-flower. So one name may carry many echoes. It has been truly described as a gimp and gallant flower, and, says Parkinson, who wrote *Paradisus Terrestris*, it was the chiefest of account in Tudor gardens. By 1700 indeed there were 360 kinds and four classes of clove gillyflower—the Flake, the Bizarre, the Piquette or picotee (*picotée* or pricketed), and the Painted Lady, the last now gone. Its ancestor, the dianthus, seems to have crossed the Channel with the Normans, for it flourishes on the battlements of Falaise, the Conqueror's birthplace, and crowns the walls of many a Norman Castle—Dover, Ludlow, Rochester, Deal—to this day.

43. " PYGSNYE "

must be Piggie's eye, or, from an old word, Twinkle-eye, just as we nowadays call a child or loved-one Goosikins or Pussikins, or Lambkin Pie, or Bunch-of-Roses, or Chickabiddy, or Come-kiss-me-quick. *Minion* means anything small, minikin, delicate, dainty, darling. Look close, for example, at the brown-green florets of a stalk of mignonette.

44. " A WORM'S LIGHT." (line 10)

Many years ago I had the curious pleasure of reading a little book—and one in small print too (Alice Meynell's lovely

ABOUT AND ROUNDABOUT

Flower of the Mind)—by *English* glowworm light. The worm was lifting its green beam in the grasses of a cliff by the sea, and shone the clearer the while because it was during an eclipse of the moon. But see No. 93.

50. "BUT NEVER CAM' HE."

. . . " O wha will shoe my bonny foot ?
  And wha will glove my hand ?
And wha will lace my middle jimp,
  Wi' a lang, lang linen band ?

" O who will kame my yellow hair,
  With a haw bayberry kame ?
And wha will be my babe's father,
  Till Gregory come hame ?"

" Thy father, he will shoe thy foot,
  Thy brother will glove thy hand,
Thy mother will bind thy middle jimp
  Wi' a lang, lang linen band !

" Thy sister will kame thy yellow hair,
  Wi' a haw bayberry kame ;
The Almighty will be thy babe's father,
  Till Gregory come hame." . . .

" Haw " is an old English word meaning (?) blue or braw, and bayberry is the all-spice tree ; so this sad one's yellow hair had for comb an uncommonly charming thing. In another version the comb is of " new silver," and in a third it is a red river kame, which, thinks Mr. Child, may be a corruption of red *ivory*. But give *me* (for such hair) the bayberry kind, and let it be haw.

51. "THE ORPHAN."

" The first sense of sorrow I ever knew," wrote Richard Steele, " was upon the death of my father, at which time I was not quite five years of age ; but was rather amazed at what all the house meant than possessed with a real understanding why nobody was willing to play with me. I remember I went into the room where his body lay, and my mother sat weeping alone by it. I had my battledore in my hand, and fell a-beating the coffin, and calling, papa ; for, I know not how, I had some slight idea that he was locked up there. My mother catched me in her arms, and transported beyond all patience of the silent grief she was before in, she almost smothered me in her embraces; and told me in a flood of tears, ' Papa could not hear me, and would play with me no more, for they were going to put him under ground, whence he could never come to us again.' "

53.

The first and third stanzas of this poem were (and are) my particular favourites, and especially the second line in each. Such poems are like wayside pools, or little well-springs of water. It does not matter how many wayfarers come thither to quench their thirst, there is abundance for all.

" THE PERISHING PLEASURES OF MAN." (line 18)

" But you mustn't imagine," said the old old Harper, " that I harp sad memories on my harp-strings because, being an ancient I am envious of my youth. Far from it. My only grief is that even if mine were the Harp that hung in Tara, I could not express the joy it is to be of years an hundred, and to remember that once I was nought—and all in the same bar."

And for yet another look behind, I cannot leave out this little rhyme from William Allingham, who made one of the happiest of all anthologies, " Nightingale Valley " :

> Four ducks on a pond,
> A grass-bank beyond,
> A blue sky of spring,
> White clouds on the wing ;
> What a little thing
> To remember for years—
> To remember with tears.

Or, last, this lovely scrap from the Scots—all distance and longing for home :

> O Alva hills is bonny,
> Dalycoutry hills is fair,
> But to think on the braes of Menstrie
> It maks my heart fu' sair.

ABOUT AND ROUNDABOUT

60.

Edward Thomas, who wrote this poem, knew by heart most of the villages, streams, high roads, by-roads, hills, forests, woods and dales of the southern counties of England, and came so to know them by the best of all methods. He walked through them on his feet ; and, when so inclined, sat down by the wayside or leaned over a farm or field gate and gazed and mused and day-dreamed. Here is another poem of his :

> If I should ever by chance grow rich
> I'll buy Codham, Cockridden, and Childerditch,
> Roses, Pyrgo, and Lapwater,
> And let them all to my elder daughter.
> The rent I shall ask of her will be only
> Each year's first violets, white and lonely,
> The first primroses and orchises—
> She must find them before I do, that is.
> But if she finds a blossom on furze—
> Without rent they shall all for ever be hers,
> Codham, Cockridden, and Childerditch,
> Roses, Pyrgo and Lapwater,—
> I shall give them all to my elder daughter.

Not, of course, to find a blossom on furze or gorse as soon as any sun is in the year's sky, is the rare feat ; and if in your wanderings over the hills and far away you should chance on secret hidden-away Pyrgo or Childerditch, sweet with its fragrance, then enquire for the beautiful, happy young Lady of the Manor. As a matter of fact, the scent of the furze-blossom is not exactly sweet, but nutlike and aromatic. This is what Edward Thomas's friend, W. H. Hudson, the great naturalist, wrote about it : " The gorse is most fragrant at noon, when the sun shines brightest and hottest. At such an hour when I approach a thicket of furze, the wind blowing from it, I am always tempted to cast myself down on the grass to lie for an hour drinking in the odour. The effect is to make me languid ; to wish to lie till I sleep and live again in dreams in another world, in a vast open-air cathedral where a great festival of ceremony is perpetually in progress, and acolytes, in scores and hundreds with beautiful bright faces, in flame yellow and orange surplices, are ever and ever coming toward me, swinging their censers until I am ready to swoon in that heavenly incense !". . .

" A Stoat." (stanza 5)

It is the gentle custom of gamekeepers to slaughter at sight (though not for food) the little preying beasts and birds of the woodlands—owls, hawks, crows, jays, stoats, weasels, and such like. They then nail up their carcases to a shed side, or to a barn door, or on a field-gate, leaving them to rot in the wind for a warning to their live mates—just as in the old days the precarious English kings spiked the heads of traitors on the turrets of the Tower. Foxes you " hunt " to death.

61. " The Howes of the Silent Vanished Races "
are, I suppose, the mounds, barrows, tumuli or Fairie Hills, some of them round, some of them long, some of them chambered, beneath which the ancient races of Britain, centuries before the coming of the Saxons and the Danes, buried their dead. So once slept the mummied Pharaohs beneath their enormous Pyramids. Age hangs densely over these solitary mounds, as over the Dolmens and Cromlechs—Stonehenge, the Whispering Knights—and the single gigantic Menhirs—the Tingle Stone, the Whittle Stone, the Bair-down-Man and the demoniac Hoar Stone.

These were utterly ancient and unintelligible marvels even when the monk Ranulph Higden wrote his *Polychronicon* in 1352 : The second wonder, he says, is at Stonehenge beside Salisbury. There great stones marvellously huge, be a-reared up on high, as it were gates, so that there seemeth gates to be set up upon other gates. Nevertheless it is not clearly known nor perceived how and to what end they be so a-reared up, and " so wonderlych yhonged." And yet, they are but as falling apple-blossom compared with the age of the world and the antiquity of the Universe :

1st *Gravedigger.*	Come my spade ; there is no ancient Gentlemen but Gardiners, Ditchers and Grave-makers ; they hold up *Adam's* profession.
2nd *Gravedigger.*	Was he a Gentleman ?
1st *Gravedigger.*	He was the first that ever bore Armes.

Hamlet.

ABOUT AND ROUNDABOUT

62. THE TWA BROTHERS

—and here is as romantic and tragic a tale of two friends :

> O Bessie Bell and Mary Gray,
> They war twa bonnie lasses ;
> They biggit a bower on yon Burn-brae,
> And theekit it o'er wi' rashes.

> They theekit it o'er wi' rashes green,
> They theekit it o'er wi' heather ;
> But the pest cam' frae the burrows-town,
> And slew them baith thegither.

> They thought to lye in Methven kirkyard,
> Amang their noble kin ;
> But they maun lye in Stronach haugh,
> To biek forenent the sin.

> O Bessie Bell and Mary Gray,
> They war twa bonnie lasses ;
> They biggit a bower on yon Burn-brae,
> And theekit it o'er wi' rashes.

Biggit and *theekit* means builded and thatched ; and the twelfth line is " to bask beneath the sun."

64.

A tragic tale is hidden, rather than told, in this old Scottish ballad. It resembles a half ruinous house in a desolate country, dense green with briar and bramble, echoing with wild voices— its memories gone. Mr. Nahum's picture for it was of a figure in a woman's bright clothes and scarlet hood, but with what looked to me like the head of his own skeleton deep within the hood. And on a stone nearby sat a little winged boy.

66. "HER HIGH-BORN KINSMAN."

. . . And there was a wind in the night as they fared onward, a wind in the mid-air, playing from out the clouds. And presently after, the twain descended into the valley, the one traveller's foot stumbling as he went, against the writhen roots that jutted from between the stones of the path they followed. And it seemed that the voice of one unseen cried, Lo ! And the traveller looked up from out of the valley of his

journey, and, behold, a wan moon gleamed between the
ravelled clouds ; and the face of his companion showed for
that instant clear against the sky in the shadow of its cloak.
And it was the face of a nobleman ; renowned for his patience ;
courteous and cold ; whose name is Death. . . .

68. "LONDON BRIDGE."

This is yet another singing-game rhyme. When London
was nothing but a cluster of beehive huts in the hill clearings
of the great Forest of Middlesex above the marshes and the
Thames, there can have been no bridge. There *may* have been
a bridge, it seems, in A.D. 44, eighty-seven years after the death
of Caesar ; and for centuries there was certainly a ferry,
Audery the Shipwight being one of its ferrymen, his oars the
shape of shovels, and his boat like a young moon on her back.

The rhyme appears to refer to the wooden bridge built in
994 at Southwark, which was destroyed in 1008 by King Olaf,
the Saint of Norway, to whose glory four London churches are
dedicated. Olaf had become the ally of Ethelred (the Unready),
and to defeat the Danes who had captured the city he first
screened his fighting ships with frameworks of osier for the
protection of his men, who then rowed them up to the Bridge
against the tide. They wapped and bound huge ropes or
hawsers round its timber piers, swept down with the slack
with the tide, and so brought the Bridge to ruin.

The first stone bridge, in building from 1196 to 1208, was
partially destroyed by fire four years afterwards. A picture
of the entrancing re-built Bridge of Elizabeth's time, with its
chapel, its many-storied gabled houses, its haberdashers',
goldsmiths' and booksellers' shops, its cut-waters or starlings
and many narrow arches, its gate-house with the spiked heads
atop, its drawbridge and pillory, and that strange timber
mansion, with not a nail in its wood, called Nonesuch, where
perhaps lived the Lord Mayor—all this may be gloated over
in any old seventeenth-century map of London. (John
Visscher's of 1616 shows a windmill in the Strand !) So narrow
were those high arches, and so vehemently flowed the tides
beneath them, that even at ebb it was dangerous for a novice
to shoot them in a boat. But between Windsor and Gravesend
it is said there were forty thousand watermen and wherrymen
in Shakespeare's day, yelling " Eastward Ho ! ", or " West-

ABOUT AND ROUNDABOUT

ward Ho!" for passengers. The Bridge was the glory of
London ; as the Thames it spanned was its main thoroughfare.
Fire was its chief enemy ; the Great Fire in 1616 and that in
1633, after which it long continued to be used though dark,
dismal and dangerous. The present monster of granite, over
which the people of London stream to and fro throughout the
day, like ants at the flighting, was built thirty yards west of
the old one and began to span the river in 1832.

70. " This City."

London, thou art of townès *A per se* [1]
Soveraign of cities, seemliest in sight,
Of high renoun, riches and royaltie ;
Of lordis, barons, and many a goodly knyght ;
Of most delectable lusty ladies bright ;
Of famous prelatis, in habitis clericall ;
Of merchauntis full of substaunce and of myght :
London, thou art the flow'r of Cities all.

Strong be thy wallis that about thee standis ;
Wise be the people that within thee dwellis ;
Fresh is thy ryver with his lusty strandis ;
Blith be thy chirches, wele sownyng be thy bellis ;
Rich be thy merchauntis in substaunce that excellis ;
Fair be their wives, right lovesom, white and small ;
Clere be thy virgyns, lusty under kellis [2] !
London, thou art the flow'r of Cities all. . . .

WILLIAM DUNBAR

71. " He opened House to All." (line 22)

The subject being good victuals, here is the " Bill of Fare
at the Christening of Mr. Constable's Child, Rector of Cockley
Cley, in Norfolk, January 2, 1682."

" A whole hog's head souc'd with carrots in the mouth, and
pendants in the ears, with guilded oranges thick sett.

2 Ox' cheekes stewed with 6 marrow bones.

A leg of Veal larded with 6 pullets.

A leg of Mutton with 6 rabbits.

A chine of bief, chine of venison, chine of mutton, chine of
veal, chine of pork, supported by 4 men.

[1] First and foremost   [2] Cap-nets of silk or of gold

525

ABOUT AND ROUNDABOUT

A Venison Pasty.
A great minced pye, with 12 small ones about it.
A gelt fat turkey with 6 capons.
A bustard with 6 pluver.
A pheasant with 6 woodcock.
A great dish of tarts made all of sweetmeats.
A Westphalia hamm with 6 tongues.
A Jowle of Sturgeon.
A great chargr of all sorts of sweetmeats with wine, and all sorts of liquors answerable."

And here is another from that inexhaustible Tom Tiddler's ground, *Rustic Speech and Folklore* for the " funeral meats " of a farmer who died near Whitby in 1760 : ' Besides what was distributed to 1,000 poor people who had 6d. each in money, there was consumed

> 110 dozen penny loaves,
> 6 large hams,
> 8 legs of veal,
> 20 stone of beef,
> 10 stone of mutton,
> 15 stone of Cheshire cheese, and
> 30 ankers of ale.'

For me the " great dish of tarts," the " guilded oranges " and " the great charger of sweetmeats "! But after all, fine fat feasts such as these are but a Town Mouse's crumb of Wedding Cake compared to Mac Conglinnes' Vision in No. 73, which is from the Gaelic of 1100/1200 A.D., as translated by Kuno Meyer. *Bragget*, line 33, appears to have been a concoction or decotion of ale, honey, sugar and spice, of which last ambrosial ingredients (according to the old rhyme) are made little girls.

72. " AND BRING US IN GOOD ALE "

really *good* ale, that is, before beer was made " so mortal small," 133 years before tea-leaves came from China (to be boiled and the decoction stored in a barrel) ; 140 before the first coffee-house in London ; and even, one might be tempted to add, before milk came from the cow, for as late as 1512 the two young sons of the fifth earl of Northumberland, Lord Percy aged eleven (who afterwards loved Anne Boleyn), and his younger brother, Maister Thomas Percy, were allowed for

ABOUT AND ROUNDABOUT

"braikfaste " even on " Fysch," or fast Days : " Half a Loif of houshold Brede, a Manchet, a Dysch of Butter, a Pece of Salt-fish, a Dysch of Sproits or iii White Herrynge," and a *Potell of Bere, i.e.* two quarts or Eight mugfuls.

" Hores," or heres, means *hairs*—cow's or dairymaid's. Butter is less hairy nowadays, though on the other hand *we* have margarine.

I thought perhaps " Godes good " referred to a " podinge " for Saturdays—a hodge-podge of the scraps and pieces left over through the week ; but I find it is really an old phrase for yeast.

73.

" I' sooth a Feast of Fats " (from the Irish of the twelfth century) like that dream of the rats in the " *Pied Piper of Hamelin* " as they scuttled to their doom in the cold Weser. For a feast of *sweets* there is Porphyrio's in the " Eve of St. Agnes " :

> " And still she slept an azure-lidded sleep,
> In blanchèd linen, smooth, and lavendered,
> While he from forth the closet brought a heap
> Of candied apple, quince, and plum, and gourd ;
> With jellies soother than the creamy curd,
> And lucent syrops, tinct with cinnamon ;
> Manna and dates, in argosy transferred
> From Fez ; and spicèd dainties, every one,
> From silken Samarcand to cedared Lebanon.

> These delicates he heaped with glowing hand
> On golden dishes and in baskets bright
> Of wreathèd silver : sumptuous they stand
> In the retirèd quiet of the night,
> Filling the chilly room with perfume light. . . ."

For a banquet of enchantment there is Lamia's, and of magical fruits, poor Laura's in " *Goblin Market* " ; Romeo too went feasting with the Capulets—but only his eyes ; so too Macbeth, but *his* eyes betrayed him. Bottom in his ass's ears asked only for a munch of your good dry oats, a handfull of pease, and a bottle of hay, then fell asleep before even Queen Titania could magick them up for him. As for the poor Babes, blackberries and dewberries were *their* last supper. These are but a few of scores of banqueting delights in poetry—but to include them all would need such a larder as Jack peeped into when he sat supping in the Giant's kitchen.

74. " PIGEON HOLES, STOOL-BALL, BARLEY-BREAK."

This fragment is a patchwork of the half-forgotten. " Pigeon holes " was a ball-game, played on the green, with wooden arches and little chambers as in a dovecot—a kind of open-air bagatelle. " Stool-ball " was popular with Nancies and Franceses on Shrove Tuesday. Barley-break was in Scotland a kind of " I spy," played in a stackyard, and in England a sort of " French and English," in three marked spaces or compartments, the middle one of which was called hell. And here—while we are on the subject of old and gallant pastimes— is a brief exposition of our noble and National Game of Cricket in its *early* days. It comes from a book with the queer title, " A Nosegay for the Trouble of Culling ; or, Sports of Childhood ":

" Cricket is a game universally played in England, not by boys only, for men of all ranks pique themselves on playing it with skill. In Mary-le-bone parish there is a celebrated cricket ground much frequented by noblemen and gentlemen.

The wicket consists of two pieces of wood fixed upright and kept together by another piece which is laid across the top and is called a bail ; if either of these pieces of wood be thrown down by the ball the person so hitting them becomes the winner.

The ball used in this game is stuffed exceedingly hard. Many windows and valuable looking-glasses have been broken by playing cricket in a room."

It was in a cricket match in the summer of 1775, when no less than three " balls " had rolled in between a Mr. Small's two stumps without stirring the bail, that it was decided to add stump iii.

As for " tansy " (line 5), here is a recipe for it (to go with the sillabub on p. 506) : " Take 15 eggs, and 6 of the whites ; beat them very well ; then put in some sugar, and a little sack ; beat them again, and put about a pint or a little more of cream ; then beat them again ; then put in the juice of spinage or of primrose leaves to make it green. Then put in some more sugar, if it be not sweet enough ; then beat it again a little, and so let it stand till you fry it, when the first course is in. Then fry it with a little sweet butter. It must be stirred and fryed very tender. When it is fryed enough, then put it in a dish, and strew some sugar upon it, and serve it in."

75. "MARY'S GONE A-MILKING."

And, according to Sir Thomas Overbury (who dipped his pen in nectar as well as ink), " *A Fair and Happy Milk-maid*," is " a country wench, that is so far from making herself beautiful by art, that one look of hers is able to put all face-physic out of countenance. . . .

" She doth not, with lying long abed, spoil both her complexion and conditions, . . . she rises, therefore, with chanticleer, her dame's cock, and at night makes the lamb her curfew. In milking a cow, and straining the teats through her fingers, it seems that so sweet a milk-press makes the milk the whiter or sweeter ; for never came almond glove or aromatic ointment on her palm to taint it. The golden ears of corn fall and kiss her feet when she reaps them, as if they wish to be bound and led prisoners by the same hand that felled them. Her breath is her own which scents all the year long of June, like a new made haycock. She makes her hand hard with labour, and her heart soft with pity : and when winter evenings fall early (sitting at her merry wheel), she sings a defiance to the giddy wheel of fortune. She doth all things with so sweet a grace, it seems ignorance will not suffer her to do ill, being her mind is to do well. . . . She dares go alone and unfold sheep in the night, and fears no manner of ill, because she means none : yet to say truth, she is never alone, for she is still accompanied with old songs, honest thoughts, and prayers, but short ones. . . .

" Thus lives she, and all her care is she may die in the spring-time, to have store of flowers stuck upon her winding-sheet."

76. "CYPRESSE BLACK AS ERE WAS CROW."

Cypresse (according to a memorandum from one of Mr. Nahum's books) is the fine cobweblike stuff we now call crape. Peaking-stickes, or poking-sticks, were gophering irons for frilling out linen, flounces, etc., etc., and not, as one might guess, curling tongs (since a pointed beard, and the V of hair on the forehead, used to be called peaks). A quoife or coif is a lady's head-dress, such as is still worn by nuns ; while as for " masks for faces," fine ladies in Shakespeare's day customarily wore

them (as old pictures show) when they went to see his plays.
Masks were useful too in disguising the faces of his players,
when as was the custom in the London theatres up to 1629—
boys took women's parts ; and in the streets eyes gleamed out
of the holes in them, worn *then* for keeping the skin fair,
untanned, and unfreckled, as Julia says of herself in Shakespeare's *Two Gentlemen of Verona* :

> But since she did neglect her looking-glasse,
> And threw her Sun-expelling masque away,
> The ayre hath starved the roses in her cheekes,
> And pinched the lily-tincture of her face. . . .

78. FAIRING. (line 5)

In this the earliest known letter of Shelley's—he too asks
for a fairing—the kickshaws and gewgaws sold in the booths
of a fair—and a toothsome one ; though I haven't yet been
able to discover what he meant by " hunting nuts " :

Monday, July 18, 1803.   (Horsham).

DEAR KATE,

We have proposed a day at the pond next Wednesday ;
and if you will come to-morrow morning I would be much
obliged to you ; and if you could any how bring Tom over to
stay all night, I would thank you. We are to have a cold
dinner over at the pond, and come home to eat a bit of roast
chicken and peas at about nine o'clock. Mama depends upon
your bringing Tom over to-morrow, and if you don't we shall
be very much disappointed.

Tell the bearer not to forget to bring me a fairing—which is
some ginger-bread, sweetmeat, hunting-nuts, and a pocket
book. Now I end.

> I am *not*,
>   Your obedient servant,
>   P. B. SHELLEY

Even before Mr. Nahum's tower-room, I loved the " bonny
brown hair " of this poem. Was it squirrel brown, or chestnut,
or hazelnut, or autumn-beech, or heather-brown, or walnut,
or old hay colour, or undappled-fawn, or dark lichen, or velvet
brown, or marigold or pansy or wallflower-brown—or yet
another ?—every one of which would look charming beneath
the rim of a round blue-ribanded " little straw hat."

ABOUT AND ROUNDABOUT

80. " WIDDECOMBE FAIR."

To an eye looking down, the steeple of Widdecombe Church
rises in the midst of Dartmoor like a lovely needle of ivory ;
and hidden beneath the turf around it lie, waiting, the bones of
Tom Pearse, Bill Brewer . . . Old Uncle Tom Cobley and all.

83. " THERE WERE THREE GIPSIES "

—and they were of England (Somerset), though to judge from
this old ballad they may have padded it down from the
Highlands :

> There cam' Seven Egyptians on a day,
> And wow, but they sang bonny !
> And they sang sae sweet, and sae very complete,
> Down cam' Earl Cassilis' lady.
>
> She cam' tripping adown the stair,
> And a' her maids before her ;
> As soon as they saw her weel-faur'd face
> They cast the glamourie owre her ;
>
> They gave to her the nutmeg,
> And they gave to her the ginger ;
> And she gave to them a far better thing,
> The seven gold rings off her finger.

There was a small black cobbled-up book entitled *Glamourie*
in a red leather case in Thrae, but, alas, it was in a writing I
could not easily decipher. On the fly-leaf was scrawled
" H.B.", and beneath it was the following :

> See, with eyes shut.
> Look seldom behind thee.
> In secret of selfship
> Free thee, not bind thee.
> Mark but a flower :
> 'Tis of Eden. A fly
> Shall sound thee a horn
> Wooing Paradise nigh.
> Think close. Unto love
> Give thy heart's steed the rein ;
> So—course the World over :
> Then homeward again.

ABOUT AND ROUNDABOUT

85. "WHATEVER THEY FIND THEY TAKE IT." (line 21)

There was a robber met a robber
On a rig of beans ;
Says a robber to a robber,
" Can a robber tell a robber
What a robber means ?"

And if not ; why not ? I had never seen this scrap of jingle until Mr. Ralph Hodgson gave it me. And the following version of an old game rhyme (with its rare " wood ") first met my eye by the kindness of another friend, Mrs. Lyon :

" My Mother said that I never should
Play with the gypsies in the wood,
The wood was dark ; the grass was green ;
In came Sally with a tambourine.

I went to the sea—no ship to get across ;
I paid ten shillings for a blind white horse ;
I up on his back and was off in a crack,
Sally, tell my Mother I shall never come back."

86.

This lament for matchless Robin Hood, who should shine in a far better place than between " Beggars " and " Gilderoy," is the only rhyme about him in this collection. The fact is, try as I might, I could not make up my mind which I liked best of his old greenwood ballads in Mr. Nahum's book. The oldest and best were all in formidable spelling, the most of them were long, and maybe I was at last a little lazy. They are all to be found in Professor Child. And if leaving out the merry outlaw will persuade anyone to get and read *English and Scottish Ballads*, I shall have omitted him to good purpose.

87. " GILDEROY."

A pretty song about a monstrously ugly scoundrel, though handsome of feature. Gilderoy was a highwayman, sparing for his prey neither man nor woman, and if there were " roses " on his shoes, they were blood-red. At last fifty armed avengers surrounded his house at night and set on. He killed eight of them before he was captured ; which, if true, was bonnie fighting. Nevertheless, such a villain he was that he was hanged, without trial, on a gibbet thirty feet high, and the bones of him (despite the last stanza of the ballad) dangled in chains forty feet above Leith Walk in Edinburgh for fifty years afterwards.

88. "AND HIS NAME WAS LITTLE BINGO."

In bounding health, it is said, a dog's nose and a woman's elbow are always cold. The reason for which is explained in a legend (referred to in Mrs. Wright's *Rustic Speech and Folk Lore*). It seems that in the midst of its forty days' riding on the Flood, the Ark one black night sprung a little leak. Father Noah having forgotten to bring his carpenter's bag on board, was at his wits' end to plug the hole in its timbers. In the beam of his rushlight he looked and he looked and he looked ; and still the water came rilling in and in. His dog, Shafet, was of course standing by, head on one side, carefully watching his master. And Noah, by good chance, at last casting his eye in his direction, seized the faithful creature and, thrusting his nose into the leak, for a while stopped the flow. But Noah, a merciful man, and partial to animals, quickly perceived that in a few minutes poor Shafet would perish of suffocation, and as, by this time, his wife had descended into the fo'c'sle to see what he was about, he released his dog's nose, and, instead of it, stuffed in her charming elbow. Q.E.D.

But not all dogs are as ready—as Launce in *The Two Gentlemen of Verona* knew :

" *Launce* : ' Nay, 'twill bee this howre ere I have done weeping. All the kinde of the *Launces*, have this very fault : I have received my proportion, like the prodigious Sonne, and am going with Sir *Protheus* to the Imperialls Court : I thinke *Crab* my dog, be the sowrest natured dogge that lives : My Mother weeping : my Father wayling : my Sister crying : our Maid howling : our Catte wringing her hands, and all our house in a great perplexitie, yet did not this cruell-hearted *Curre* shedde one teare : he is a stone, a very pibble stone, and has no more pitty in him then a dogge !"

90. "POOR OLD HORSE."

In the furrowed land
The toilsome and patient oxen stand.
Lifting the yoke-encumbered head,
With their dilated nostrils spread,

ABOUT AND ROUNDABOUT

They silently inhale
The clover-scented gale,
And the vapours that arise
From the well-watered and smoking soil.

For this rest in the furrow after toil
Their large and lustrous eyes
Seem to thank the Lord,
More than man's spoken word.

H. W. LONGFELLOW

91. "AY ME, ALAS."

Messalina's monkey was, I should fancy, of the kind called a marmoset, " blacke and greene." " Their agilitie and manner of doing is admirable, for that they seeme to have reason and discourse to go upon trees, wherein they seeme to imitate birds." There are so few of these far fair cousins of ours in poetry that I cannot forbear adding a note of Mr. Nahum's from Sir John Maundeville's *Travels*.

" . . . From that City, (that is to say Cassay—the City of Heaven), men go by Water, solacing and disporting themselves, till they come to an Abbey of Monks—that is fast by—that be good religious men after their Faith and Law. In that Abbey is a great Garden and a fair, where be many Trees of diverse manner of Fruits. And in this Garden, is a little Hill, full of delectable Trees. In that Hill and in that Garden be many divers Beasts, as of Apes, Marmosets, Baboons, and many other divers Beasts. And every day, when the Monks of this Abbey have eaten, the Almoner has the remnants carried forth into the Garden, and he smiteth on the Garden Gate with a Clicket of Silver that he holdeth in his hand, and anon all the Beasts of the Hill and of divers places of the Garden, come out, a 3000 or a 4000 of them ; they approach as if they were poor men come a-begging ; and the Almoner's servants give them the remnants, in fair Vessels of Silver, clean over gilt. And when they have eaten, the Monk smiteth eftsoons on the Garden Gate with the Clicket ; and then anon all the Beasts return again to their places that they came from. And they say that these Beasts be Souls of worthy men, that resemble in likeness the Beasts that be fair : and therefore they give them meat for the love of God."

ABOUT AND ROUNDABOUT

92. "O HAPPY FLY."

And here is another of these creatures—"a sleepy fly that
rubs its hands," in Mr. Hardy's words—William Blake's :

Little Fly,
Thy summer's play
My thoughtless hand
Has brushed away.

Am not I
A fly like thee ?
Or art not thou
A man like me ?

For I dance,
And drink, and sing,
Till some blind hand
Shall brush my wing.

If thought is life
And strength and breath,
And the want
Of thought is death ;

Then am I
A happy fly,
If I live
Or if I die.

But the Happy Fly is nowadays gone so dismally out of
favour that it would perhaps be prudent to draw attention
from him to Lovelace's " Grasshopper " :

O thou that swing'st upon the waving hair
Of some well-fillèd oaten beard,
Drunk every night with a delicious tear
Dropt thee from heaven, where thou wert reared !

The joys of earth and air are thine entire,
That with thy feet and wings dost hop and fly ;
And when thy poppy works, thou dost retire
To thy carved acorn-bed to lie.

Up with the day, the Sun thou welcom'st then,
Sport'st in the gilt plaits of his beams,
And all these merry days mak'st merry men,
Thyself, and melancholy streams.

ABOUT AND ROUNDABOUT

93. " LO, THE BRIGHT AIR ALIVE WITH DRAGONFLIES."

There is an old dialect children's rhyme about these lightlike shimmering *stingless* insects :

Snakestanger, snakestanger, vlee aal about the brooks ;
Sting aal the bad bwoys that vor the fish looks,
But let the góod bwoys ketch aal the vish they can,
And car'm away whooam to vry 'em in a pan ;
Bread and butter they shall yeat at zupper wi' their vish
While aal the littull bad bwoys shall only lick the dish.

And here is yet another rhyme on the *Firefly* (from Du Bartas), which I have borrowed (with other passages as curious) from a mine of such things, *Animal Lore of Shakespeare's Time*, by Miss Emma Phipson :

" New-Spain's *cucuio*, in his forehead brings
Two burning lamps, two underneath his wings :
Whose shining rayes serve oft, in darkest night,
Th' imbroderer's hand in royall works to light :
Th' ingenious turner, with a wakefull eye,
To polish fair his purest ivory :
The usurer to count his glistring treasures :
The learned scribe to limn his golden measures."

" There is a kind of little animal of the size of prawnes," says Champlain of these tiny winged things, " which fly by night, and make such light in the air that one would say that they were so many little candles. If a man had three or four of these little creatures, which are not larger than a filbert, he could read as well at night as with a wax light."

95. " THE SALE OF THE PET LAMB."

" The Pet Lamb " by William Wordsworth is certainly of a more delicate light and colour and music than this poem. But it is much better known. And there is a secret something in the words of Mary Howitt's that wins one at once to love the writer of it.

98.

This is another translation by Kuno Meyer from the ancient Irish—just the bare bones, that is, of a poem that in its original tongue must have been many times more musical with rhyme and gentle echo and cadence ; for the craft of Gaelic verse was an exceedingly delicate one.

I like it for the sake of its cat, its monk, and its age, but chiefly because it reminds me of my own faraway days at Thrae—brooding up there in solitude and silence over Mr. Nahum's books.

As for " white Pangur " and his kind, " it is needlesse," says Topsell, " to spend any time about [Puss's] loving nature to man, how she flattereth by rubbing her skinne against ones legges, how she whurleth with her voyce, having as many tunes as turnes ; for she hath one voice to beg and to complain, another to testifie her delight and pleasure, another among her own kind by flattring, by hissing, by spitting, insomuch as some have thought that they have a peculiar intelligible language among themselves." So also John de Trevisa, in 1387 : " The catte is a beaste of uncerten heare (hair) and colour ; for some catte is white, some rede, some blacke, some skewed (piebald) and speckled in the fete and in the face and in the eares. He is a beste in youth, swyfte, plyaunte, and mery, and lepeth and reseth (rusheth) on all thynge that is to- fore him ; and is led by a strawe and playeth therwith. He is a right hevy beast in aege, and ful slepy, and lyeth slily in wait for myce. And he maketh a ruthefull noyse and gastfull, whan one proffreth to fyghte with another, and he falleth on his owne fete whan he falleth out of hye places."

The writings of the ancient Egyptians show that, far from detesting to wet his paws, he would then *swim* in pursuit of fish. They painted a cat for the sound " miaou " in their hieroglyphics ; gazed into his changing moonlike eyes and revered him ; and embalmed him when dead.

Having borrowed him from Egypt, the Romans brought him to Britain (though we already had a wilding of our own, *Felis Catus*), with the ass, the goat, the rabbit, the peacock, not to speak of the cherry, the walnut, the crocus, the tulip, the leek, the cucumber, etc. The Monk's Pangur, then, came of a long lineage.

So valuable were cats in *Wales* in the eleventh century (two or three hundred years after Pangur), that their price was fixed by law : for a blind kitten a penny ; for a kitten with its eyes open, twopence ; for a cat of one mouse, fourpence, and so on. And to kill one of the Prince's granary cats meant payment of a tune of as much wheat as would cover up its body when suspended by its tail. In Scotland there has long been a complete Clan of Cats apart from the witches. As for the Cheshire Cat, he grins, I imagine, not because he has nine lives, is said to be melancholy, may look at a king, and has nothing to do with Catgut, Cat's cradle, and Cat-i'-the-pan, but because he has read in a dictionary that Dick Whittington sailed off to the Isle of Rats, not with a Cat, but with *acat* or *achat*, meaning goods for trading—Coals! Long may he grin! How but one country Gib or Tom may befriend the brightfaced Heartsease (so sturdy a little dear that it will bloom at burning noonday in a gravel path) Charles Darwin tells in his " *Origin of Species*," p. 57.

His " loving nature " to creatures *other* than man and the heartsease is referred to in the following old Scots nursery rhyme :

> There was a wee bit mousikie,
> That lived in Gilberaty, O,
> It couldna get a bite o' cheese,
> For cheetie-poussie-cattie, O.
>
> It said unto the cheesikie,
> " Oh fain wad I be at ye, O,
> If 't were na for the cruel paws
> O' cheetie-poussie-cattie, O."

99. " On what Wings dare He aspire."

The verb *dare* (I gather from Webster) was once used only in the past tense, the preterite ; for " dare he " therefore in this poem we should now write *dared he*.

100.

Andrew Marvell has three rare charms—his poetry is wholly his own ; it is as delightful as the sound of his name ; and the face in his portrait is as enchanting as either.

101-2.

The Phillip of these two poems is, I suppose, the hedge-sparrow or dunnock, that gentle and happy little cousin of the warblers—as light and lovely in voice as they are on the wing. As everyone knows, a bull-finch can be taught to whistle like a baker's boy, and will become so jealous of his mistress that he will hiss and ruff with rage at every stranger. Jackdaws and magpies, too, will become friends to a friend. But a lady whom I have the happiness to know has a nightingale that was hatched in captivity, and so has never shared either the delights or the dangers of the wild. So easy is he in her company that he will perch on her pen-tip as she sits at table, and sing as if out of a garden in Damascus.

102. "HE WOULD CHIRP."

" . . . As she (St. Douceline) sat at meat, if anyone brought her a flower, a bird, a fruit, or any other thing that gave her pleasure, then she fell straightway into an ecstasy, and was caught up to Him Who had made these fair creatures. . . . One day she heard a lonely sparrow sing, whereupon she said to her companions, ' How lonely is the song of that bird ! ' and in the twinkling of an eye she was in an ecstasy, drawn up to God by the bird's voice. . . ."

The above is from *A Medieval Garner*, and this, from a Note to " A Saint's Tragedy," by Margaret L. Woods : When the blessed Elizabeth " had been ill twelve days and more, one of her maids sitting by her bed heard in her throat a very sweet sound, . . . and saying, ' Oh, my mistress, how sweetly thou didst sing !' she answered, ' I tell thee, I heard a little bird between me and the wall sing merrily ; who with his sweet song so stirred me up that I could not but sing myself.' "

"LOVING REDBREASTS." (line 31)

My dear, do you know
How a long time ago,
  Two poor little children,
Whose names I don't know,
Were stolen away
On a fine summer's day,
  And left in a wood,
As I've heard people say.

And when it was night,
So sad was their plight,
  The sun it went down,
And the moon gave no light !

They sobbed and they sighed,
And they bitterly cried,
    And the poor little things,
They laid down and died.

· And when they were dead,
The robins so red
    Brought strawberry leaves,
And over them spread ;
And all the day long,
They sang them this song,—
Poor babes in the wood !
Poor babes in the wood !
    And don't you remember
The babes in the wood ?

105. " 'Tis a Note of Enchantment."

It was a note of enchantment such as this that haunted the memory of Edward Thomas when he was writing his poem called *The Unknown Bird*. I give only a few lines, but the rest of the beautiful thing may be found in his *Poems* :

Oftenest when I heard him I was alone,
Nor could I ever make another hear.
La-la-la ! he called seeming far-off—
As if a cock crowed past the edge of the world,
As if the bird or I were in a dream. . .

. . . O wild-raving winds ! if you ever do roar
By the house and the elms from where I've a-come,
Breathe up at the window, or call at the door,
And tell you've a found me a-thinking of home."

William Barnes

107. " Like a Lady Bright."

" They say," says Ophelia, " they say the owle was a Baker's daughter. Lord, we know what we are, but know not what we may be. God be at your Table." And thus runs the story :

Our Saviour being footsore, weary and hungry one darkening evening, went into a baker's shop and asked for bread. The oven being then hot and all prepared for the baking, the mistress of the shop cut off a good-sized piece of the risen dough to bake for him. At this her fair, greedy daughter, who sate watching what was forward from a little window, upraided her mother for this wasting of profit on such an outcast; and taking the platter out of her hands, she chopped the piece of dough into half, and half, and half again. Nevertheless when this mean small lump was put into the oven, it presently began miraculously to rise and swell until it exceeded a full quartern of wheaten bread. In alarm at this strange sight the daughter—her round blue eyes largely eyeing the stranger in the dim light—turned on her mother, and cried out: " O Mother, Mother, *Heugh, heugh, heugh.*" " As thou hast spoken," said our Saviour, " so be thou : child of the Night." Whereupon, the poor creature, feathered and in the likeness of an owl, fled forth into the dark towards the woodside.

109. " THE WHITE OWL."

When night is o'er the wood
　　And moon-scared watch-dogs howl,
Comes forth in search of food
　　The snowy mystic owl.
His soft, white, ghostly wings
　　Beat noiselessly the air
Like some lost soul that hopelessly
　　Is mute in its despair.

But now his hollow note
　　Rings cheerless through the glade
And o'er the silent moat
　　He flits from shade to shade.
He hovers, swoops and glides
　　O'er meadows, moors and streams ;
He seems to be some fantasy—
　　A ghostly bird of dreams.

Why dost thou haunt the night ?
　　Why dost thou love the moon
When other birds delight
　　To sing their joy at noon ?
Art thou then crazed with love,
　　Or is't for some fell crime
That thus thou flittest covertly
　　At this unhallowed time ?

F. J. PATMORE

541

ABOUT AND ROUNDABOUT

111. " HER SMALL SOUL." (line 23)

Smallest of all shrill souls among the English birds is the wren, but she has a remote relative that dwells in the dark and enormous forests of South America, the Humming Bird, and simply for their own sakes I cannot resist borrowing two more fragments from Miss Phipson's *Animal Lore*. The first comes out of Purchas's *Pilgrimes*, and was written by Antonia Galvano of New Spain :

" There be certaine small birds named *vicmalim*, their bil is small and long. They live of the dew, and the juyce of flowers and roses. Their feathers bee small and of divers colours. They be greatly esteemed to worke gold with. They die or sleepe every yeere in the moneth of October, sitting upon a little bough in a warme and close place : they revive or wake againe in the moneth of April after that the flowers be sprung, and therefore they call them the revived birds—*Vicmalim.*"

The second is Gonzalo Ferdinando de Oviedo's—his very name a string of gems :

" . . . I have seene that one of these birds with her nest put into a paire of gold weights [scales] altogether, hath waide no more then a *tomini*, which are in poise 24 graines, with the feathers, without the which she would have waied somewhat less. And doubtlesse, when I consider the finenesse of the clawes and feete of these birds, I know not whereunto I may better liken them then to the little birds which the lymners of bookes are accustomed to paint on the margent of church bookes, and other bookes of divine service. Their feathers are of manie faire colours, as golden, yellow, and greene, beside other variable colours. Their beake is verie long for the proportion of their bodies, and as fine and subtile as a sowing needle. They are verie hardy, so that when they see a man clime the tree where they have their nests, they fly at his face, and strike him in the eyes, comming, going, and returning with such swiftnesse, that no man should lightly beleeve it that had not seene it. . . ."

112. " IT CAUGHT HIS IMAGE "

And Shelley :

> . . . I cannot tell my joy, when o'er a lake
> Upon a drooping bough with nightshade twined,

ABOUT AND ROUNDABOUT

> I saw two azure halcyons clinging downward
> And thinning one bright bunch of amber berries,
> With quick long beaks, and in the deep there lay
> Those lovely forms imaged as in a sky. . . .

Anyone so happy as to be able to remember Mary Coleridge as a friend, will agree that to have seen her eyes is to have seen her own pool and Shelley's lake, imaging such lovely flitting halcyons.

114. " KING PANDION HE IS DEAD."

A wild and dreadful legend is hidden here—of a King who wronged his Queen and her sister, daughters of Pandion, and how they avenged themselves upon him, sacrificing his son to their hatred. That Queen, goes this old tale, became a nightingale, her sister a swallow (crimson still dying the feathers of her throat), the evil king a hoopoe, and the firstborn was raised to life again a pheasant.

115. " A SPARHAWK PROUD "

—a little bird but of a noble family. Listen, at least, to Auceps, the Faulkner or Falconer, in " *The Compleat Angler*." [I have inserted a few full stops in a sentence that has none] " . . . And first, for the Element that I use to trade in, which is the Air, an Element of more worth than weight, an Element that doubtless exceeds both the Earth and Water ; for though I sometimes deal in both ; yet the Air is most properly mine, I and my Hawks use that most, and it yields us most recreation. It stops not the high soaring of my noble generous *Falcon* ; in it she ascends to such an height, as the dull eyes of beasts and fish are not able to reach to ; their bodies are too gross for such high elevations. In the Air my troops of Hawks soar up on high, and when they are lost in the sight of men, then they attend upon and converse with the gods, therefore I think my *Eagle* is so justly styled, *Joves servant in Ordinary*. And that very *Falcon*, that I am now going to see, deserves no meaner a title, for she usually in her flight endangers her self, (like the son of *Daedalus*), to have her wings scorched by the Suns heat, she flyes so near it. But her mettle makes her careless of danger, for she then heeds nothing, but makes her

nimble Pinions cut the fluid air, and so makes her high way
over the steepest mountains and deepest rivers, and in her
glorious carere looks with contempt upon those high Steeples
and magnificent Palaces which we adore and wonder at ; from
which height I can make her to descend by a word from my
mouth (which she both knows and obeys), to accept of meat
from my hand, to own me for her Master, to go home with me,
and be willing the next day to afford me the like recreation. . . ."

120. "COME WARY ONE."

. . . Tak any brid,[1] and put it in a cage,
And do al thyn entente and thy corage
To fostre it tendrely with mete and drinke,
Of allé deyntees that thou canst bithinke,
And keep it al-so clenly as thou may ;
Al-though his cage of gold be never so gay,
Yet hath this brid, by twenty thousand fold,
Lever in a forest, that is rude and cold,
Gon eté wormes and seich wrecchednesse.
For ever this brid wol doon his bisinesse
To escape out of his cagé, if he may ;
His libertee this brid desireth ay. . . .
GEOFFREY CHAUCER

When I was a child of eight or nine I had a kind of passion
for sparrows, and used to set traps for them ; but even if I
succeeded in taking one alive, which was not always, I could
never persuade it to live in a cage above a day or two, however
much I pampered it. It drooped and died. Then, like a young
crocodile, I occasionally shed tears. One fine morning, I
remember, I visited a distant trap and, as usual, all but stopped
breathing at discovering that it was " down." Very cautiously
edging in my fingers towards the captive, I was startled out of
my wits by a sudden prodigious skirring of wings, and lo and
behold, I had caught—and lost—a starling. He fled away
twenty yards or so, and perched on a hillock. I see him now,
his feathers glistening in the sun, and his sharp head turned
towards me, his eyes looking back at me, as if foe at foe. And

[1] Bird

544

ABOUT AND ROUNDABOUT

that reminds me of the Griffons—the guardians of the mines
of the one-eyed Arimaspians.

"... From that land go men toward the land of Bacharie,
where be full evil folk and full cruel. . . . In that country be
many griffounes, more plentiful than in any other country.
Some men say that they have the body upward as an eagle, and
beneath as a lion ; and truly they say sooth that they be of
that shape. But a griffoun hath the body more great, and is
more strong, than eight lions, of such lions as be on this side
of the world ; and larger and stronger than an hundred eagles,
such as we have amongst us. For a griffoun there will bear
flying to his nest a great horse, if he may find him handy,
or two oxen yoked together, as they go at the plough. For he
hath his talons so long and so broad and great upon his feet, as
though they were hornes of great oxen, or of bugles (bullocks),
or of kine ; so that men make cups of them, to drink out of.
And of their ribs, and the quills of their wings, men make
bows full strong, to shoot with arrows and bow-bolts. . . ."

But a griffoun is only a gigantic starling, so to speak ; and
it's a pity mine and I were enemies. " If a sparrow come
before my window," wrote John Keats in one of his letters,
" I take part in its existence, and pick about the gravel."
Brick-traps are little help in this.

> A Robin Redbreast in a cage
> Puts all Heaven in a rage . . .
>
> A Skylark wounded in the wing,
> A Cherubim does cease to sing . . .
>
> The wild Deer wandering here and there
> Keeps the Human Soul from care . . .
>
> He who shall hurt the little Wren
> Shall never be beloved by Men . . .
>
> The wanton Boy that kills the Fly
> Shall feel the Spider's enmity . . .
>
> Kill not the Moth nor Butterfly,
> For the Last Judgment draweth nigh . . .
>
> The Beggar's Dog and Widow's Cat,
> Feed them, and thou wilt grow fat . . .

ABOUT AND ROUNDABOUT

To see a World in a Grain of Sand,
And a Heaven in a Wild Flower,
Hold Infinity in the palm of your hand,
And Eternity in an hour.

WILLIAM BLAKE

. . . What is heaven ? a globe of dew,
Filling in the morning new
  Some eyed flower whose young leaves waken
On an unimagined world :
Constellated suns unshaken,
Orbits measureless, are furled
  In that frail and fading sphere,
  With ten millions gathered there,
  To tremble, gleam, and disappear.

PERCY BYSSHE SHELLEY

The men who wrote these words, truly and solemnly
meant them. They are not mere pretty flowers of the fancy,
but the tough piercing roots of the tree of life that grew within
their minds.

126. "COME UNTO THESE YELLOW SANDS."

This poem and many others I copied out of Mr. Nahum's book
in their original spelling. At first I found the reading of
some of them very troublesome. It was like looking at a
dried-up flower or beetle. But there the things were ; and
after a good deal of trouble I not only began to read them more
easily, but grew to like them thus for their own sake. First,
because this was as they were actually written, before our
English printers agreed to spell alike ; and next, because the
old words with their look of age became a pleasure to me in
themselves. It was like watching the dried-up flower or beetle
actually and as if by a magic of the mind coming to life.
Besides, many of Shakespeare's small poems were already
known to me. It touched them with newness to see them
(though indeed *he* never so saw them), as they appeared (seven
years after his death), in the pages of the famous folio volume
of his *Plays* that was printed in 1623 by Isaac Jaggard and
Edward Blount.

Not only that ; for it is curious too to see how in the old days
English was constantly changing—its faded words falling like

dead leaves from a tree, and new ones appearing. In a book which William Caxton printed as far back even as 1490, he says : " And certainly our language now used varieth far from that which was used and spoken when I was born. For we Englishmen be born under the domination of the moon, which is never steadfast but ever wavering, waxing one season and waneth and decreaseth another season." So in our own day words, like human beings, come into the world and pass away : and many gradually change their meanings.

For if the spelling of a word alters its effect on the eye, it must also affect the *mind* of the reader ; and I must confess that " my lovynge deare," looks to me to tell of somebody more lovable even than " my loving dear." And what about shoogar-plummes, cleere greye eies, the murrkie fogghe, the moones enravysshynge ?

And what about—

> " Let's goe to Bedde," says Sleepihed ;
> " Tarrie a while," says Slowe ;
> " Putte on the Panne," says Greedie Nanne,
> " Wee'll suppe afore wee goe."

Not that I have *always* kept to the old spellings. I have followed my fancy ; and if anyone would like to see an old poem in its first looks that is here printed in our own way, all he need do is to go back to the book in which it first appeared.

128. "SHEE CARRIES ME ABOVE THE SKIE."

> . . . This palace standeth in the air,
> By necromancy placèd there,
> That it no tempest needs to fear,
>   Which way soe'er it blow it ;
> And somewhat southward toward the noon,
> Whence lies a way up to the moon,
> And thence the Fairy can as soon
>   Pass to the earth below it.
>
> The walls of spiders' legs are made
> Well mortisèd and finely laid ;
> He was the master of his trade
>   It curiously that builded :
> The windows of the eyes of cats,

ABOUT AND ROUNDABOUT

And for the roof, instead of slats,
Is covered with the skins of bats,
With moonshine that are gilded. . . .

MICHAEL DRAYTON

129. " WHO CALLS ? "

. . . Such a soft floating witchery of sound
As twilight Elfins make, when they at eve
Voyage on gentle gales from Fairy-Land,
Where Melodies round honey-dropping flowers,
Footless and wild, like birds of Paradise,
Nor pause, nor perch, hovering on untamed wing ! . . .

S. T. COLERIDGE

133. " FOR FEAR OF LITTLE MEN."

" Terrestrial devils," says Robert Burton, " are those Lares,
Genii, Fauns, Satyrs, Wood-nymphs, Foliots, Fairies, Robin
Goodfellows, Trulli, etc., which as they are most conversant
with men, so they do them most harm. . . . These are they
that dance on heaths and greens . . . and leave that green
circle, which we commonly find in plain fields, which others
hold to proceed from a meteor falling, or some accidental
rankness of the ground, so nature sports herself ; they are
sometimes seen by old women and children. . . . Paracelsus
reckons up many places in Germany, where they do usually
walk in little coats, some two feet long. A bigger kind there
is of them called with us hobgoblins, and Robin Goodfellows,
that would in those superstitious times grind corn for a mess
of milk, cut wood, or do any manner of drudgery work. They
would mend old irons in those Aeolian isles of Lipari, in former
ages, and have been often seen and heard. . . Dithmarus
Bleskenius, in his description of Iceland, reports for a certainty,
that almost in every family they have yet some such familiar
spirits. . . . Another sort of these there are, which frequent
forlorn houses. . . . They will make strange noises in the
night, howl sometimes pitifully, and then laugh again, cause
great flame and sudden lights, fling stones, rattle chains, shave
men, open doors and shut them, fling down platters, stools,
chests, sometimes appear in the likeness of hares, crows, black
dogs, etc.". . .

135.

So too with Hazel Dorn, in the following poem by Mr.
Bernard Sleigh, who has most kindly allowed me to print it
here for the first time.

> They stole her from the well beside the wood.
> Ten years ago as village gossips tell ;
> One Beltane-eve when trees were all a-bud
> In copse and fell.
>
> Ominous, vast, the moon rose full and red
> Behind dim hills ; no leaf stirred in the glen
> That breathless eve, when she was pixy-led
> Beyond our ken.
>
> For she had worn no rowan in her hair, —
> Nor set the cream-bowl by the kitchen door,—
> Nor whispered low the pagan faery prayer
> Of ancient lore ;
>
> But trod that daisied ring in hose and shoon,
> To hear entranced, their elf-bells round her ring ;
> The wizard spells about her wail and croon
> With gathering string.
>
> Swiftly her arms they bound in gossamer,
> With elvish lures they held her soul in thrall ;
> With wizard sorceries enveloped her
> Past cry or call.
>
> A passing shepherd caught his breath to see
> A golden mist of moving wings and lights
> Swirl upwards past the red moon eerily
> To starlit heights.
>
> While far off carollings half drowned a cry,
> Mournful, remote, of " Mother, Mother dear,"
> Floating across the drifting haze,—a sigh
> " Farewell, Farewell ! "

In the small hours of Beltane or May Day, vast fires have
been wont to be kindled on the hills of the Highlands—a
custom old as the Druids. Mr. Gilbert Sheldon tells me that
as lately as 1899 he saw the hills round Glengariff ablaze with

them. They must be set aflame with what is called need-fire. And need-fire is made by nine men twisting a wimble of wood in a balk of oak until the friction makes sparks fly. With these they ignite dry agaric, a fungus that grows on birch-trees, and soon the blaze is reddening the countryside under the night-sky. Need-fire in a window-nook or carried in a lantern is—like iron—an invincible defence against witches and witch-craft. Beltane cakes—to be eaten whilst squatting on the hills, or dancing and watching the fire—are made out of a caudle of eggs, butter, oatmeal and milk.

"No Rowan in her Hair."

So potent is the flower or berry or wood of the rowan or witchwood or quicken or whicken-tree or mountain ash against the wiles of the elf-folk, that dairymaids use it for cream-stirrers and cowherds for a switch.

> Rowan-tree and red thread
> Gar the Witches tyne their speed.

136. "True Thomas."

There are four copies in handwriting—two of them written about 1450—of a rhymed romance telling how Thomas in his youth, while dreaming daydreams under the Eildon Tree, was met and greeted by the Queen of fair Elfland. The ballad on p. 127 has been passed on from mouth to mouth.

Up to our own grandmothers' day, at least, this Thomas Rhymour of Ercildoune—a village nor far distant from where the Leader joins the Tweed—was famous as a Wise One and a Seer (a See-er—with the inward eye). He lived seven centuries ago, between 1210 and 1297. Years after he had returned from Elfland—as the ballad tells—while he sat feasting in his Castle, news was brought to him that a hart and a hind, having issued out of the forest, were to be seen stepping fair and softly down the stony street of the town, to the marvel of the people. At this, Thomas at once rose from among his guests; left the table; made down to the street; followed after these strange summoners: and was seen again no more.

"Ilka tett," line 7, means every twist or plait; a "fairlie," stanza 11, is a wonder, mystery, marvel; and the "coat" in the last stanza, being of " even cloth," was finer than the finest *napless* damask.

So, too, Young Tamlane, when a boy " just turned of nine," was carried off by the Elfin Queen :

> Ae fatal morning I went out
> Dreading nae injury,
> And thinking lang, fell soun asleep
> Beneath an apple tree.

> Then by it came the Elfin Queen
> And laid her hand on me ;
> And from that time since ever I mind
> I've been in her companie. . . .

He seems to have been an outlandish and unhuman creature —if this next rhyme tells of him truly (*gait*, meaning road ; *pin*, (?) knife ; *coft*, bought ; *moss*, peat-bog ; and *boonmost*— you can guess) :

> Tam o' the linn came up the gait,
> Wi' twenty puddings on a plate,
> And every pudding had a pin,
> " We'll eat them a'," quo' Tam o' the linn.

> Tam o' the linn had nae breeks to wear,
> He coft him a sheep's-skin to make him a pair,
> The fleshy side out, the woolly side in,
> " It's fine summer cleeding," quo' Tam o' the linn.

> Tam o' the linn he had three bairns,
> They fell in the fire, in each others' arms ;
> " Oh," quo' the boonmost, " I've got a het skin ; "
> " It's hetter below," quo' Tam o' the linn.

> Tam o' the linn gaed to the moss,
> To seek a stable to his horse ;
> The moss was open, and Tam fell in,
> " I've stabled mysel'," quo' Tam o' the linn.

138. " SABRINA."

This song is from " Comus," a masque written by Milton for the entertainment of the Earl of Bridgewater, lord lieutenant of Wales, at Ludlow Castle in 1634. That Castle's Hall is now open to the sky—" the lightning shines there ; snow

burdens the ivy." From a neighbouring room the two
princes, Edward V. and his brother, went to their dark death
in the Tower. Below the ruinous Castle flow together the
Teme and the Corve, on their way to the great Severn—of
which Sabrina, the daughter of Estrildis, is the Nymph, she
having been drowned in its waters by Guendolen, the jealous
queen of Locrine the son of Brut. Estrildis herself, the
daughter of King Humber, " so farre excelled in bewtie, that
none was then lightly found unto her comparable, for her
skin was so whyte that scarcely the fynest kind of Ivorie
that might be found, nor the snowe lately fallen downe from
the Elament, nor the Lylles did passe the same."

Milton's poems—*Lycidas*, for instance—frequently resemble
bunches of keys, each one of them fitting the lock of some
ancient myth or legend. In the lines I have omitted from No.
138 are many such locks awaiting the reader—a reference to
the following tale of Glaucus, for example :

There is a secret herb which, if nibbled by fish already
gasping to death in our air, gives them the power and cunning
to slip back through the grasses into their waters again. Of
this herb Glaucus tasted, and instantly his eyes dazzled in
desire to share their green transparent deeps. Whereupon
the laughing divinities of the rivers gave him sea-green hair,
sleeking the stream, fins and a fish's tail, and feasted him
merrily. His story is told by Keats in the third book of his
Endymion, while Leucothea's, another reference, is to be found
in the fifth of the *Odyssey*. As for the Sirens, here is the counsel
Circe gave Ulysses, the while his seamen lay asleep the night
after they had returned in safety from Pluto's dismal mansions :

> " . . . And then observe : They sit amidst a mead,
> And round about it runs a hedge or wall
> Of dead men's bones, their withered skins and all
> Hung all along upon it ; and these men
> Were such as they had fawned into their fen,
> And then their skins hung on their hedge of bones.
> Sail by them therefore, thy companions
> Beforehand causing to stop every ear
> With sweet soft wax, so close that none may hear
> A note of all their charmings. . . ."

ABOUT AND ROUNDABOUT

139.

These Songs are from the last act of " A Midsummer Night's Dream "—the Duke and his guests are retired, and now sleep far from Life's Play ; and Puck and the fairies are abroad in his palace.

" I am sent with Broome before."
>   When the cock begins to crow,
>   And the embers leave to glow,
>   And the owl cries, Tu-whit—Tu-whoo,
>   When crickets do sing
>   And mice roam about,
>   And midnight bells ring
>   To call the devout :
>   When the lazy lie sleeping
>   And think it no harm,
>   Their zeal is so cold
>   And their beds are so warm.
>   When the long—long lazy slut
>   Has not made the parlour clean,
>   No water on the hearth is put,
>   But all things in disorder seem ;
>   Then we trip it round the room
>   And make like bees a drowsy hum.
>   Be she Betty, Nan, or Sue,
>   We make her of another hue
>   And pinch her black and blue.

But when the Puritans came in, it seems, the fairies fled away. And Richard Corbet bewailed their exile :

> " Farewell, rewards and fairies ! "
>   Good housewives now may say,
> For now foul sluts in dairies
>   Do fare as well as they.
> And though they sweep their hearths no less
>   Than maids were wont to do,
> Yet who of late, for cleanliness,
>   Finds sixpence in her shoe ? . . .
>
> At morning and at evening both
>   You merry were and glad ;

ABOUT AND ROUNDABOUT

So little care of sleep or sloth
   These pretty ladies had ;
When Tom came home from labour,
   Or Ciss to milking rose,
Then merrily merrily went their tabour
   And nimbly went their toes.

Witness those rings and roundelays
   Of theirs, which yet remain,
Were footed in Queen Mary's days
   On many a grassy plain ;
But since of late, Elizabeth,
   And later, James came in,
They never danced on any heath
   As when the time hath been.

For times change, and with them changes the direction of
man's imagination. He turns his questing thoughts now this
way, now that ; and though our learned dictionaries may
maintain that fairy rings are but brighter circles in green grass
formed by " certain fungi, especially *marasmius oreades* "—
who knows ?—

He that sees blowing the wild wood tree,
And peewits circling their watery glass,
Dreams about Strangers that yet may be
   Dark to our eyes, Alas !

After all, Geoffrey Chaucer, even in *his* distant day, lamented
that England was bereft of the Silent Folk. Whisper, and they
will return—bringing with them Prince Oberon, who " is of
heyght but of III fote, and crokyd shulderyd. . . . And yf ye
speke to hym, ye are lost for ever."

140. " AWM. ' WHO FEASTS TONIGHT ? ' "

Another mere fragment—from p. 182 of Mr. C. M. Doughty's
Play, entitled *The Cliffs*. For the complete " feast " bestowed
on the world by this great traveller and poet, the reader must
seek out not only this volume, but his *Arabia Deserta*, and his
Dawn in Britain.

" ALL IN THEIR WATCHET CLOAKS." (line 15)

" Nan Page (my daughter) and my little sonne,
   And three or foure more of their growth, wee'l dress

ABOUT AND ROUNDABOUT

Like Urchins, Ouphes, and Fairies, greene and white,
With rounds of waxen Tapers on their heads,
And rattles in their hands . . . "
The Merry Wives of Windsor.

141. A HUNT'S-UP

was in old days the Tally-ho blared at daybreak to rouse the chase.

My houndes are bred of Southern kinde,
  So flewed, so sanded they ;
With crooked knees and dew-laps depe,
With eares the morning dew that sweepe
  Slowly they chase their praye ;
Their mouths, as tunable as belles
Each under each in concert swells.
The hunte is up, the morne is bright and gray,
Hunting us hence with hunte's up to the day. . . .

Beyond all beastys poor timorous Wat
  The hunter's skille doth trye,
See how the houndes, with many a doubte
The cold fault cleanly single out !
  Hark to their merrie crie !
They spende their mouthes, echoe replies,
Another chase is in the skies.
The hunte is up, the morne is bright and gray,
Hunting us hence with hunte's up to the day. . . .

These are two of the seven stanzas of a song richly larded with Shakesperean allusions, to be found in *The Diary of Master William Silence.*

In his book on English Poesy, Puttenham, who was born about 1520, says that a poet of the name of Gray won the esteem of Henry VIII. and the Duke of Somerset for " making certeine merry ballades, whereof one chiefly was, ' the hunte is up, the hunte is up." Henry VIII., moreover, was himself a versifier, and a musician, though, as I have read, a dull one. Here is the first stanza of one of his poems :

As the holly groweth green,
And never changeth hue,
So I am, ever hath been
Unto my lady true. . . .

which, with another equally surprising in sentiment, may be
found in full in that casket of antiquities, " Early English
Lyrics, chosen by E. K. Chambers and F. Sidgwick."

143. " WITH HIS COAT SO GRAY."

Though I be now a grey, grey friar,
Yet I was once a hale young knight,
The cry of my dogs was the only quoir
In which my spirit did take delight.

THOMAS LOVE PEACOCK

" D'YE KEN THAT A FOX WITH HIS LAST BREATH CURSED THEM ALL AS HE DIED IN THE MORNING."

" ' Hearken, Reynard, to my words,' (went on the King of
Beasts). ' To-day you shall answer with your life for these
sins you have committed.'. . . ' But nay, my lord,' (sighed the
fox), ' I am innocent of all these things. Your Majesty is great
and mighty ; I meagre and weak. If it is the King's pleasure
to kill me, I must die, for whether justly or unjustly, I am
your servant ; my only strength is in your justice and mercy.
To these I appeal, as none has yet appealed in vain. Yea, if
it be your Majesty's will that I shall die, then do I accept it
humbly. I say no more. But yet I cannot think it a worthy
thing for so great a King to wreak his vengeance upon a subject
so small.' "

148. " A FULLE FAYRE TYME."

What wonder May was welcome in medieval days –after the
long winters and the black cold nights when roads were all but
impassable, and men, " despisinge schetes " and nightgear,
went to their naked beds with nought but the stars or a
dip for candle and maybe their own bones and a scatter
of straw for warmth. Is not " Loud sing Cuckoo ! " our
oldest song ?

149. " LUBBER BREEZE"

I suppose, is the prevalent wind in Lubberland or Cocaigne,
where " the pigs run about ready roasted, and cry, Come eat
me ! "

And here is a picture of another kind of mill, that once long

ago sang to its waters, and dreamed above its image in the
weir :

> Only the sound remains
> Of the old mill ;
> Gone is the wheel ;
> On the prone roof and walls the nettle reigns.
>
> Water that toils no more
> Dangles white locks
> And, falling, mocks
> The music of the mill-wheel's busy roar. . . .
>
> Only the idle foam
> Of water falling
> Changelessly calling,
> Where once men had a work-place and a home.

EDWARD THOMAS

150. " THE AMPLE HEAVEN."

> The unthrifty sun shot vital gold,
>   A thousand pieces ;
> And heaven its azure did unfold
>   Chequered with snowy fleeces ;
>   The air was all in spice,
>   And every bush
> A garland wore ; thus fed my eyes,
>   But all the earth lay hush.
>
> Only a little fountain lent
>   Some use for ears,
> And on the dumb shades language spent—
>   The music of her tears.

HENRY VAUGHAN

" THE TIME SA TRANQUIL IS AND STILL." (line 13)

> Clear had the day been from the dawn,
>   All chequered was the sky,
> Thin clouds, like scarves of cobweb lawn,
>   Veiled heaven's most glorious eye.
>
> The wind had no more strength than this,
>   —That leisurely it blew—

ABOUT AND ROUNDABOUT

To make one leaf the next to kiss
That closely by it grew.

The rills, that on the pebbles played,
Might now be heard at will ;
This world the only music made,
Else everything was still. . . .

MICHAEL DRAYTON

153. "O FOR A BOOKE."

Nor—says John Bunyan :

Nor let them fall under Discouragement
Who at their Horn-book stick, and time hath spent
Upon (their) A, B, C while others do
Into their Primer, or their Psalter go.
Some boys with difficulty do begin
Who in the end, the Bays, and Lawrel win.

On the other hand ;

Some Boys have Wit enough to sport and play,
Who at their Books are Block-heads day by day.
Some men are arch enough at any Vice,
But Dunces in the way to Paradice.

So much for the reader, but the writer, too, may fall under discouragement. Listen to Cohim Cille, an Irish scribe of the eleventh century, in yet another translation from the Gaelic :

My hand is weary with writing,
My sharp quill is not steady,
My slender-beaked pen pours forth
A black draught of shining dark-blue ink.

A stream of the wisdom of blessed God
Springs from my fair-brown shapely hand ;
On the page it squirts its draught
Of ink of the green-skinned holly.

My little dripping pen travels
Across the plain of shining books,
Without ceasing for the wealth of the great—
Whence my hand is weary with writing.

ABOUT AND ROUNDABOUT

But to come back to the reader in his shadie nooke :

> Tales of my Nursery ! shall that still loved spot,
> That window corner, ever be forgot,
> Where through the woodbine—when with upward ray
> Gleamed the last shadow of departing day—
> Still did I sit, and with unwearied eye,
> Read while I wept, and scarcely paused to sigh !
> In that gay drawer, with fairy fictions stored,
> When some new tale was added to my hoard,
> While o'er each page my eager glance was flung,
> 'Twas but to learn what female fate was sung ;
> If no sad maid the castle shut from light,
> I heeded not the giant and the knight.
> Sweet Cinderella, even before the ball,
> How did I love thee—ashes, rags, and all !
> What bliss I deemed it to have stood beside,
> On every virgin when thy shoe was tried !
> How longed to see thy shape the slipper suit !
> But, dearer than the slipper, loved the foot.

As for "*the streete cryes all about*" : according to *London Lickpenny*, among the street-cries in the fifteenth century were : Hot Pease ! Hot Fine Oatcakes ! Whitings maids, Whitings ! Have you any old boots ? Buy a mat ! New Brooms, green brooms ! with a general hullabaloo of What d'ye lack ? and now and again a bawling of Clubs ! to summon the tag, rag, and bobtail to a row.

Of singing cries, we may still hear in the sunny summer London streets such sweet and doleful strains as Won't you buy my sweet blooming lavender : Sixteen branches a penny ! and in the dusks of November the muffin-man's bell. Besides these, we have Rag-a'-bone ! Milk-o ! Any scissors to grind ? Clo' props ! Water-creeses ! and, as I remember years ago,

> Young lambs to sell, white lambs to sell ;
> If I'd as much money as I could tell
> I wouldn't be crying, Young lambs to sell !

155. "WITH HEY ! WITH HOW ! WITH HOY."

In *Rustic Speech and Folk Lore* Mrs. Wright gives the decoys with which the country people all over England beguile their beasts and poultry into " shippon, sty, or pen " ; or holla them on their way, but much, I have found, depends on him who hollas !

For *Cows* : Coop ! Cush, cush !—while the milkmaid calls—Hoaf ! Hobe ! Mull ! Proo ! Proochy ! Prut !

For *Calves* : Moddie ! Mog, mog, mog ! Pui-ho ! Sook, sook !

For *Sheep* : Co-hobe ! Ovey !

For *Pigs* : Check-check ! Cheat ! Dack, dack ! Giss ! or Gissy ! Lix ! Ric-sic ! Shug, shug, shug ! Tantassa, tantassa pig, tow a row, a row ! Tig, tig, tig !

For *Turkeys* : Cobbler ! Peet, peet, peet ! Pen ! Pur, pur, pur !

For *Geese* : Fly-laig ! Gag, gag, gag ! Ob-ee ! White-hoddy !

For *Ducks* : Bid, bid, bid ! Diddle ! Dill, dill ! Wid ! Wheetie !

For *Pigeons* : Pees ! Pod !

And for *Rabbits* : Map !

" Yea, and I do vow unto thee," said the voice of the beautiful virgin speaking out of the rock ; " Call unto them but in their own names and language, and the strong and delicate creatures of the countries of the mind will flock into the living field of thy vision, and above the waters will befall the secret singing of birds, and thou shalt be a pilgrim. Mark how intense a shadow dwells upon this stone ! Therein too lurk marvels to be seen." The voice ceased, and I heard nothing but the tapping of a fragment of dry lichen which in the draught of the hot air caused by the burning sunlight stirred between rock and sand. And I cried, " O unfortunate one, I thirst ! "

156. " LAVENDER'S BLUE."

" A poor thing," as Audrey says, but homely and melodious and once *somebody's* own : such a somebody as inscribed on the walls of Burford Church :

> " . . . Love made me Poet
> And this I writt,
> My harte did do yt
> And not my witt."

ABOUT AND ROUNDABOUT

159. "There is a Garden in her Face."

Thomas Campion was "borne upon Ash Weddensday being the twelft day of February. An. Rg. Eliz. nono "—1567. He had one sister, Rose. He was educated at Peterhouse, Cambridge, and this was his yearly allowance of clothes : A gowne, a cap, a hat, ii dubletes, ii payres of hose, iiii payres of nether-stockes, vi payre of shoes, ii shirts, and two bandes. He was allowed also one quire of paper every quarter ; and half a pound of candles every fortnight from Michaelmas to Lady Day. He studied law, may for a time have fought as a soldier in France, and became a physician. He died on March 1, 1620, and was buried on the same day at St. Dunstan's in the West, Fleet Street, the entry in the register under that date being : "Thomas Campion, doctor of Phisicke, was buried."

I have taken these particulars from Mr. S. P. Vivian's edition of his poems, because it is pleasant to share even this little of what is known of a man who is not only a rare and true poet—though for two centuries a forgotten one—but also because he was one of the chief song-writers in the great age of English Music. Like all good craftsmen, he did his work "well, surely, cleanly, workmanly, substantially, curiously, and sufficiently," as did the glaziers of King's College Chapel, which is distant but a kingfisher's flight over a strip of lovely water from his own serene Peterhouse. It seems a little curious that being himself a lover of music he should have at first disliked rhymes in verse, though he lived to write such delicate rhymed poems as this.

In the preface to his *Book of Ayres*, he tells the secret of his craft : "In these English Ayres," he says, "I have chiefely aymed to couple my Words and Notes *lovingly* together, which will be much for him to doe that hath not power over both."

160. "What is there hid in the Heart of a Rose?"

There is a legend in *Sir John Mandeville's Travels*, which in our spelling runs thus : "Bethlehem is a little city, long and narrow and well walled, and on each side enclosed with good ditches. It was wont to be called Ephrata. . . . And toward the east end of the city is a full fair church and a gracious, and it hath many towers, pinnacles, and corners, full strong, and curiously made ; and within that church be forty-four pillars of marble, massive and fair.

"And between the city and the church is the field *Floridus*, that is to say, the ' Field of Flowers ' ; it being so named for this reason : A fair maiden was blamed with wrong and slandered. . . . for which cause she was demned to death and to be burnt in that place, to the which she was led. And, as the fire began to crackle about her, she made her prayers to our Lord,—that, as assuredly as she was not guilty of that sin, He would help her and make it to be known to all men, of His merciful grace. And when she had thus said, she entered into the fire, and anon was the fire quenched and out ; and the brands that were burning became red rose-trees, and the brands that were not kindled became white rose-trees, full of roses. And these were the first rose-trees and roses, both white and red, that ever any man saw ; and thus was this maiden saved by the grace of God. And therefore is that field clept the field of God, *Floridus*, for it is full of roses."

163. " THESE FLOWERS, AS IN THEIR CAUSES, SLEEP."
(line 4)

—while, also, flowers may themselves be the *causes* of poems, as, in a degree, a dewdrop in a buttercup is of the buttercup's causing. There the rhodora, or rhododendron :

In May, when sea-winds pierced our solitudes,
I found the fresh Rhodora in the woods,
Spreading its leafless blooms in a damp nook,
To please the desert and the sluggish brook.
The purple petals, fallen in the pool,
Made the black water with their beauty gay ;
Here might the red-bird come his plumes to cool,
And court the flower that cheapens his array.
Rhodora ! Let the sages ask thee why
This charm is wasted on the earth and sky . . .
Why thou wert there, O rival of the rose !
I never thought to ask, I never knew ;
But, in my simple ignorance, suppose
The self-same Power that brought me there brought you. . . .

R. W. EMERSON

ABOUT AND ROUNDABOUT

And here anemone and cyclamen—in an enchanting little poem of but the day before yesterday :

> Long ago I went to Rome
> As pilgrims go in Spring,
> Journeying through the happy hills
> Where nightingales sing,
> And where the blue anemones
> Drift among the pines
> Until the woods creep down into
> A wilderness of vines.
>
> Now every year I go to Rome
> As lovers go in dreams,
> To pick the fragrant cyclamen
> To bathe in Sabine streams,
> And come at nightfall to the city
> Across the shadowy plain,
> And hear through all the dusty streets
> The waterfalls again.
>
> MARGARET CECILIA FURSE

"THE PHOENIX BUILDS HER SPICY NEST." (line 18)

The Phoenix, in faith rather than by sight, is thus described by Pliny : "She is as big as an eagle, in colour yellow, and bright as gold, namely all about the neck, the rest of the bodie a deepe red purple ; the taile azure blue, intermingled with feathers among of rose carnation colour : and the head bravely adorned with a crest and pennache finely wrought, having a tuft and plume thereupon right faire and goodly to be seene."

Her life is but three hundred and nine years less in duration than that of the many-centuried patriarch Methuselah. When the lassitude of age begins to creep upon her, she wings across sea and land to the sole Arabian Tree. There she builds a nest of aromatic twigs, cassia and frankincense, and enkindling it with her own dying ardour she is consumed to ashes. And yet—while still they are of a heat beyond the tempering of the sun that shines down on them from the heavens, they magically stir, take body and awaken ; and she rearises to life renewed, in her gold, her rose carnation, her purple and azure blue.

ABOUT AND ROUNDABOUT

164. "The Bower of Bliss."

This and No. 348 are but the merest fragments of the *Faerie Queene* ; but they show of what an echoing mutable music are its words. And were ever light and colour so living, natural and crystal clear ? Reading this verse, hearing its sounds and seeing its sights in the imagination, you cannot think Thomas Nash was too fantastical when he wrote : " Poetry is the Honey of all Flowers, the Quintessence of all Sciences, the Marrow of Art and the very Phrase of Angels." Indeed, as Spenser's epitaph in Westminster Abbey says of him, he was the Prince of Poets of his time, whose divine spirit needs no other witness than the works which he left behind him. And poet of poets he has always remained. John Keats, when he was a boy, used to sit in a little summer-house at Enfield with his schoolfellow Cowden Clarke, simply drinking in this verse, and laying up store of purest English for his own brief life's matchless work. So, too, Abraham Cowley :

" How this love (for poetry) came to be produced in me so early is a hard question. I believe I can tell the particular little chance that filled my head first with such chimes of verse as have never since left ringing there. For I remember when I began to read, and to take some pleasure in it, there was wont to lie in my mother's parlour (I know not by what accident, for she herself never in her life read any book but of devotion), but there was wont to lie Spenser's works ; this I happened to fall upon, and was infinitely delighted with the stories of the knights and giants and monsters and brave houses which I found everywhere there (though my understanding had little to do with all this) ; and by degrees with the tinkling of the rhyme and dance of the numbers, so that I think I had read him all over before I was twelve years old. . . . "

170.

The poems of Robert Herrick and of Thomas Campion though known well in their own day remained for many years practically unread and forgotten. Thomas Traherne's (who died in 1674) had an even more curious fate, for they were discovered in manuscript and by chance on a bookstall so lately as 1896, and were first taken to be the work of Henry Vaughan. Here is a passage in prose from *Centuries of Meditation*, by the same writer, repeating this reverie of his childhood in other words : " The corn was orient and immortal wheat which never should be reaped nor was ever sown. I thought it had stood from everlasting to everlasting. The dust and stones of the street were as precious as gold ; the gates were at first the end of the world. The green trees when I saw them first through one of the gates transported and ravished me ; their sweetness and unusual beauty made my heart to leap, and almost mad with ecstasy, they were such strange and wonderful things. The men ! oh, what venerable and reverend creatures did the aged seem ! Immortal cherubims ! And young men glittering and sparkling angels ! and maids strange seraphic pieces of life and beauty ! Boys and girls tumbling in the street were moving jewels : I knew not that they were born or should die. But all things abided eternally as they were in their proper places. Eternity was manifest in the light of the day, and something infinite behind everything appeared, which talked with my expectation and moved my desire. . . ."

172. " BUT SILLY WE." (line 9)

This poem, I think carries with it the thought that in study of that great book, that fair volume, called the World, there is no full stop, no limit, pause, conclusion. Like bees, with their nectar and honeycomb, man stores up his knowledge and experience in books. These and his houses outlast him ; the things he makes ; and here and there a famous or happy or tragic name is for a while remembered. Else, we have our Spring and Summer—and dark cold skies enough, many of us —then vanish away, seeming but restless phantoms in Time's enormous dream. So far at least as this world is concerned. And generations of men—as of the grasses and flowers—follow one upon the other.

Oh, yes, my dear, you have a Mother,
And she, when young, was loved by another,
And in that mother's nursery
Played *her* mamma, like you and me.
When that mamma was tiny as you
She had a happy mother too :
On, on . . . Yes, presto ! Puff ! Pee-fee !—
And Grandam Eve and the apple-tree.

O, into distance, smalling, dimming,
Think of that endless row of women,
Like beads, like posts, like lamps, they seem—
Grey-green willows, and life a stream—
Laughing and sighing and lovely ; and, Oh,
You to be next in that long row !

And yet, " But silly we " is true of most of us and of most of
our time on earth. As Coventry Patmore says :

An idle Poet, here and there,
    Looks round him, but, for all the rest,
The world, unfathomably fair,
    Is duller than a witling's jest.
Love wakes men, once a life-time each ;
    They lift their heavy lids, and look ;
And, lo, what one sweet page can teach
    They read with joy, then shut the book :
And some give thanks, and some blaspheme,
    And most forget ; but, either way,
That and the Child's unheeded dream
    Is all the light of all their day.

Or again, in the words of Sir John Davies—long since dead :

. . . I know my Soul hath power to know all things,
Yet is she blind and ignorant in all :
I know I am one of Nature's little kings,
Yet to the least and vilest things am thrall.
I know my life's a pain and but a span,
I know my sense is mocked with everything ;
And, to conclude, I know myself a man
Which is a proud and yet a wretched thing.

175. " FOR SOLDIERS "

from an old book entitled, " A Posie of Gilloflowers, eche
differing from other in Colour and Odour, yet all sweete."
There were pretty and sonorous names for collections of poems
in the days of Humfrey Gifford (of whom nothing is known
but that he made this Posie)—such as *Wits Commonwealth ;
The Banket of Sapience ; The Paradise of Dainty Devices ;
A Gorgeous Gallery of Gallant Inventions ;* and *A Handfull of
Pleasant Delights.*

ABOUT AND ROUNDABOUT

" YE BUDS OF BRUTUS LAND "

sons of those, that is, who, according to the ancient myth
were descended from Brut or Brute, the Trojan, the conqueror
of Albion and its giants, the founder of London, after whom
the land is named Britain.

" SOLDIERS ARE PREST " (stanza 1)

that is, seized by the King's men, the press-gangs, and
carried away by force to fight in the wars.

" YOUR QUEEN."

" To the Most High, Mightie and Magnificent Empresse
Renowmed for Pietie, Vertue, and all Gratious Government
ELIZABETH by the Grace of God Queene of England Fraunce
and Ireland and of Virginia." So runs Spenser's dedication
of " The Faerie Queene," while in " The Shepheardes Calender "
for April, are the lines :

> See, where she sits upon the grassie greene,
> (O seemely sight)
> Yclad in Scarlot like a mayden Queene,
> And Ermines white.
> Upon her head a Cremosin coronet,
> With Damaske roses and Daffadillies set :
> Bayleaves betweene,
> And Primroses greene
> Embellish the sweete Violet.

In " A Midsummer Night's Dream," Oberon tells Puck how
he saw that " Faire Vestall " in danger of Love's sharp arrows—
and " The Imperiall Votresse passèd on In maiden meditation,
fancy free." But Shakespeare, if actually invited to Court,
it is said, " was in paine."

176. " THE BATTLE-HYMN."

The writer of this magnificent Battle-Hymn died in 1910,
at the age of ninety-one. If Henry Carey, who wrote our own
" National Anthem," had realised how much and how often
his fellow countrymen were to be fated to use his words, he
would perhaps have taken a little more trouble with them (as
much, at any rate, as Shelley and Flecker took in *their* versions

of it), and would have found a pleasanter rhyme than "over us" for "glorious," and than "voice" for "cause." If, on the other hand, he had read the following *Grace* which Ben Jonson made at the moment's call before King James, he might perhaps have refrained from rhyming altogether, and so, by sheer modesty, would have missed being immortalized :

> Our King and Queen the Lord God Blesse,
> The Paltzgrave, and the Lady Besse.
> And God blesse every living thing
> That lives, and breathes, and loves the King.
> God Bless the Counsell of Estate,
> And Buckingham the fortunate.
> God blesse them all, and keep them safe,
> And God blesse me, and God blesse Raph.

"The king," says John Aubrey, "was mighty enquisitive to know who this Raph was. Ben told him 'twas the drawer at the *Swanne* taverne, by Charing-crosse, who drew him good Canarie. For this drollery his majestie gave Ben an hundred poundes. . . ."

•

177.

"To those," is is said, "who have resided a long time by the falls of Niagara, the lowest whisper is distinctly audible." Their hearing accustoms itself to that unending and enormous roar, and becomes more exquisite. This is untrue of those whose finer sense is lulled by the roar of war : they become deafened, and cannot hear the voice of the one soldier—of which human "ones" every army is composed. And so war may poison even when its intention and its cause are honour and faith. In this particular poem (No. 177), the soldier is one of those who fought in the Transvaal in the years 1899-1901.

180.

Rupert Brooke, Wilfred Owen, Edward Thomas, Julian Grenfell, Charles Sorley, Francis Ledwidge, Alan Seeger, Joyce Kilmer—these are the names of but a few of the men, none of them old, many of them in the heyday of their gifts and genius, who besides proving themselves soldiers in the Great War had also proved themselves poets. Within his powers, every true poet lives in his country's service. These in that service died.

"... Old stairs wind upwards to a long corridor, the distant ends of which are unseen. A few candles gutter in the draughts. The shadows leap. The place is so still that I can hear the antique timbers talking. But something is without which is not the noise of the wind. I listen, and hear it again, the darkness throbbing ; the badly adjusted horizon of outer night thudding on the earth—the incessant guns of the great war.

And I come, for this night at least, to my room. On the wall is a tiny silver Christ on a crucifix ; and above that the portrait of a child, who fixes me in the surprise of innocence, questioning and loveable, the very look of warm April and timid but confiding light. I sleep with the knowledge of that over me, an assurance greater than that of all the guns of all the hosts. It is a promise. I may wake to the earth I used to know in the morning."   H. M. TOMLINSON

184.

The reader may speculate how it is that while room has been found here for this entrancing rhyme, none has been made for Macaulay's longer Lays, Browning's Cavalier Songs, and a host of poems equally gallant and spirited. Perhaps he will forgive their absence if he will consider what is said on page xxxiii, and if he will also remember that every chooser must make his choice.

There is, too, the story of the Woodcutter's son. This fuzz-headed boy, called Dick or Dickon, while playing on his elder pipe the tune of " Over the Hills " one dappled sunshine morning in the woods, fortuning to squinny his eye sidelong over his pipe, perceived a crooked and dwarf old man to be standing beside him where before was only a solitary bearded thistle. This old man, the twist of whose countenance showed him to be one with an ear for woodland music, invited the Woodcutter's son to descend with him into the orchards of the Gnomes—and to help himself. This he did, and marvellously he fared. On turning out his pockets that night—the next day being a Sunday—his Mother found (apart from the wondrous smouldering heap of fruits, amethyst, emerald, rubies and the topaz, which he had given her) two or three strange unpolished stones, and these also from the Old Man's orchards.

And she climbed up with her candle, he being abed, and asked him why he had burdened himself with such things of little seeming value, when he might have carried off their weight in diamonds big as dumplings. "Well, you see, mother dear," he drowsily replied, "I chose of the best and brightest till my eyes dazzled ; and then there was a bird that called, Dick ! Dick ! Dick ! Dick ! and those magic pebbles were among her eggs."

185. "WE BE THE KING'S MEN."

The Song of Soldiers from Act I., Scene 1., Part i. of that mighty play, *The Dynasts.* "The time is a fine day in March, 1805. A highway crosses the ridge, which is near the sea, and the south coast is seen bounding the landscape below, the open Channel extending beyond."

186. BUDMOUTH DEARS

—from *The Dynasts*, Act II., Scene I., Part iii.—the song sung in Camp on the Plain of Vittoria by Sergeant Young (of Sturminster Newton) of the Fifteenth (King's) Hussars on the eve of the longest day in the year 1813 and of Wellington's victory.

187. "TRAFALGAR"

—from *The Dynasts*, Act V., Scene VII., Part i. Boatmen and burghers with their pipes and mugs are sitting on settles round the fire in the taproom of the *Old Rooms* Inn at Weymouth. The body of Nelson on board his battered *Victory* has lately been brought to England to be sepulchred in St. Paul's. And this is the Song the Second Boatman sings.

The "Nothe," line 8, is the promontory that divides for Weymouth, where lived Nelson's Captain Hardy, its harbour or back-sea on the north, and the Portland Roads, its front-sea on the south "Roads," meaning protected seas where ships may *ride* at anchor. On this tempestuous and fateful night, October 21, 1805, the breakers were sweeping clean across the spit of land called the Narrows. On the further side runs for a round ten miles that enormous wall of pebbles—Chesil Beach, whose stones the tides sort out so precisely—the least in size towards Lyme Regis—that a coast-man can tell even in a thick mist where he has landed on the beach, merely by measuring them

ABOUT AND ROUNDABOUT

with his eye. About ten miles up this water swim in Spring the swans of the Swannery of Abbotsbury with their cygnets, each mother-bird striving to decoy as many strange young ones into her train as she can. So deals a proud and powerful nation with the lesser kingdoms of the earth.

About four years and a half before Trafalgar, on April 2nd, 1801, Nelson and Parker had won the Battle of the Baltic—as Thomas Campbell (who was then twenty-four), in his well-known poem tells :

> . . . Like leviathans afloat
> Lay their bulwarks on the brine ;
> While the sign of battle flew
> On the lofty British line :
> It was ten of April morn by the chime :
> As they drifted on their path,
> There was silence deep as death ;
> And the boldest held his breath,
> For a time. . . .

So accustomed, indeed, are we mere landsmen to the exploits of the Navy on the High Seas that we easily forget it was once to our forefathers a novelty and a wonder—such a wonder as might be compared with the fabulous Castles in Spain or the Gardens of Babylon, as the old nameless poet of the following lines recounts :

> Cease now the talke of wonders ! nothing rare
> Of floateing ilandes, castles in the aire !
> Of wooden walls, graves walkeing, flieing steedes,
> Or Trojan horse ! The present truth exceeds
> Those ancient fables ; floating iles great store,
> Sent from the British Ile, now guard her shore,
> And castles strong without foundation stande
> More safe on waters pavement then on lande. . . .

189. " BRAVE SAILORS."

And here is one of them—come home to his sweetheart, and she (until stanza 6) not recognizing him :

> As I walked out one night, it being dark all over,
> The moon did show no light I could discover,
> Down by a river side where ships were sailing,
> A lonely maid I spied, weeping and bewailing.

ABOUT AND ROUNDABOUT

I boldly stept up to her, and asked her what grieved her,
She made me this reply, " None could relieve her,
For my love is pressed, she cried, to cross the ocean,
My mind is like the Sea, always in motion."

He said, " My pretty fair maid, mark well my story,
For your true love and I fought for England's glory,
By one unlucky shot we both got parted,
And by the wounds he got, I'm broken hearted.

" He told me before he died his heart was broken,
He gave me this gold ring, take it for a token,—
' Take this unto my dear, there is no one fairer,
Tell her to be kind and love the bearer.' "

Soon as these words he spoke she ran distracted,
Not knowing what she did, nor how she acted,
She run ashore, her hair showing her anger,
" Young man, you've come too late, for I'll wed no stranger."

Soon as these words she spoke, her love grew stronger,
He flew into her arms, he could wait no longer,
They both sat down and sung, but she sung clearest,
Like a Nightingale in spring, " Welcome home, my dearest."

He sang, " God bless the wind that blew him over."
She sang, " God bless the ship that brought him over,"
They both sat down and sung, but she sung clearest,
Like a Nightingale in spring, Welcome home, my dearest.

To get any rhythm into this doggerel is like persuading a
donkey to gallop. And yet how clearly one sees the dark
night, the disguised sailor and his sweetheart talking together
on the river strand, and the ships on its bosom in the gloom ;
while the wistful, deceitful tale he tells her is as old as
Romance. Once get cantering, too; how pleasing is the motion !

192. " Dark Rosaleen."

From his childhood, which was spent in a little shop in
Dublin, Mangan had a dark and troubled life. But always a
passionate love for his country, Ireland—his Dark Rosaleen—
burned on in his imagination as it is revealed in the wild and
haunting music of this poem.

ABOUT AND ROUNDABOUT

197.

There are so many words in this poem strange to an English ear that it seems better to explain them here so as not to interrupt the actual reading of it too much. After all, the little that is not plain speaks in its music, and that is a very large part of what we call its " meaning." For the meaning of a poem is *all* the interest, thought, pictures, music, and happiness that we can get out of it—it is all that it *does* to us.

Stanza (1) " loaning " is a green path in the fields, and " ilka " means every ; " wede " means faded or vanished. (2) " bught " is a sheep-fold ; " scorning " I suppose means cracking jokes at one another ; " dowie " means sad and drooping ; " daffing " and " gabbing " is larking and gossiping ; a " leglin " is a milkpail. (3) " hairst " means harvest ; " bandsters ," sheaf-binders ; " lyart " is faded with age ; " runkled " wrinkled ; " fleeching " is wheedling or coaxing or flirting. (4) " swankies " means the blithe lads of stanza 2 ; " bogle " means goblin or bogey—an evening game like " I spy," I should think. (5) " Dool and wae " means sorrow or grief and woe.

199.

Robert Hayman, a Merchant of Bristol at the age of twenty-five, was a nephew of Sir Walter Raleigh's. He became Governor of a Plantation called *The British Hope* in Newfoundland. In 1628 he settled in Guiana (of whose gilded and barbaric Amazonian princesses his uncle tells in Hakluyt's *Voyages*). He made his will in 1633, and nothing more was afterwards heard of him—at least by the people of Bristol.

Poetry shines out of his stumbling verses like the setting sun through a thicket of thorns. Their " Totnes " is an uncommonly old town, mainly consisting of that " long street " where, when a boy, he met " godly Drake." At its East-Gate is the Brutus-stone—for here Brut of Troy is said first to have trodden English soil, having landed from the Dart. Twenty miles distant to westward of the town lies on its rivers Plymouth—the Spaniards' wasps' nest—its Drake in stone now gazing out to sea from its Hoe. Twenty miles to the east on the coast is Hayes Barton, where Raleigh was born about 1552. And seven miles down the Dart is the village of Green-way, the home of his half-brother Sir Humphrey Gilbert, the discoverer of Newfoundland, who was in that year a boy of about sixteen. Here amid-stream juts up the Anchor Rock upon which, runs the story, the discoverer of tobacco and of the potato used to sit and smoke his pipe. In 1587 Gilbert and Raleigh sailed together in search of the as yet Unfoundland, but on that voyage in vain.

200. "FOR HALLY NOW IS DEAD."

Hally was Henry, Prince of Wales, the eldest son of James I., Queen Elizabeth's godson, and a beloved patron of the arts and poetry to whom Sir Walter Raleigh looked for happy favours. He was little of body and quick of spirit, and, like Alexander, delighted " to witch the World with noble horsemanship." He died when he was nineteen. In Windsor Castle may be seen a suit of armour made for this young prince when he was a boy—a suit which for grace and craftsmanship is said to be one of the most beautiful things of its kind in the world.

202. "HENRY BEFORE AGINCOURT."

Here, again, the verse of this ancient fragment jolts, jars, and moves cumbrously as a cannon over rocky ground. But how wide and moving a picture it presents, and how noble is its utterance.

203. "ALEXANDER THE GREAT."

This is the translaton of another ancient Irish poem made by Kuno Meyer. Plutarch wrote Alexander's Life (comparing him with Julius Caesar), in which the young prince is pictured as if by Velasquez. Here are a few words from the translation of this life which Sir Thomas North made from the French of Amiot :

" The ambition and desire he (Alexander) had of honour showed a certain greatness of mind and noble courage, passing his years. . . . For when he was asked one day (because he was swift of foot) whether he would assay to run for victory at the Olympian Games, ' I could be content ' (said he), ' so I might run with Kings '." When, too, " they brought him news that his Father had taken some famous city, or had won some great battle, he was nothing glad to hear it, but would say to his playfellows : ' Sirs, my Father will have all : I shall have nothing left me to conquer with you that shall be ought worth ' . . ."

" Is it even so ? " said my lady.
" Even so !" said my lord.

205. "AND THE KINGS ASLEEP."

. . . Not a stone-cast from the summit of the hill where all snow was now parched and evaporated away, stood a cairn of boulders and thereon sate three Eagles whose eyes surveyed the kingdoms of the world, its seas and Man's lost possessions. And the Eagle that was eastwards of the three, a little rimpled her wings and cried : " Where now ? where now ? " And the Eagle that shook upon her plumes the dazzle of the dying sun stretched out her corded neck and yelped : " Man ! Man ! " And the midmost Eagle stooped low its golden head and champed between its talons with its beak upon the boulder : " The Earth founders," she mewed. And a stillness was upon the hill as though of a myriad watching eyes.

207. "DANCE SEDATELY"

—and here are two old rhymes for the dancing to. One for a Morris Dance :

Skip it and trip it nimbly, nimbly,
  Tickle it, tickle it lustily ;
Strike up the tabour for the wenches' favour,
  Tickle it, tickle it lustily.

Let us be seene in Hygate Freene,
  To dance for the honour of Holloway.
Since we are come hither, let us spare for no leather
  To dance for the honour of Holloway.

And this for a Flower Dance :

Where's my lovely parsley, say ?
My violets, roses, where are they ?
My parsley, roses, violets fair,
Where are my flowers ? Tell me where ?

ABOUT AND ROUNDABOUT

And yet another for one's Lonesome Low :

> The king's young dochter was sitting in her window,
> Sewing at her silken seam ;
> She lookt out o' the bow-window,
> And she saw the leaves growing green,
> My luve ;
> And she saw the leaves growing green.

> She stuck her needle into her sleeve,
> Her seam down by her tae,
> And she is awa' to the merrie greenwood,
> To pu' the nit and the slae,
> My luve ;
> To pu' the nit and the slae.

The " dochter " is of course daughter, " nit " is nut, and " slae " sloe.

209.

Pause an instant on the fifth word in the third stanza and you can actually *hear* the birds laughing—yaffle, blackcap, bullfinch and jay, and the droning and the whistling and the whir-r-r.

210. FA LA LA.

Scattered through this volume are many songs, a few of them—both words and music—exceedingly ancient. Mr. Nahum had a cofferful of old hand-written music (square crotchets and quavers and handsome clefs) ; and many outlandish instruments were hung up in the dust and silence in one of his cupboards. I remember some small living thing set a string jangling when for the first time the door admitted me to a sight of their queer shapes and appearances. In an old book of 1548, *The Complaynt of Scotland*, there is a list of names, not only of old folk-tales such as " The tayl of the wolfe of the varldes end " ; and " The tayl of the giantes that eit quyk men," but of songs and dances for long in common love and knowledge even in those old times. Here are a few of the songs :

> God You, Good Day, Wild Boy.
> Broom, Broom on Hill.

ABOUT AND ROUNDABOUT

Trolly lolly leman, dow.
All musing of Marvels, amiss have I gone.
O Mine Heart, hey, this is my Song.
Shall I go with You to Rumbelow Fair ?
That Day, that Day, that Gentle Day.
Alas, that Samyn Sweet Face !
In ane Mirthful Morrow.

And here some Dances :

> All Christian Men's Dance.
> Long Flat Foot of Garioch.
> The Lamb's Wind.
> Leaves Green.
> The Bace of Voragon.
> The Loch of Slene.
> The Bee.
> Shake a Trot, and
> The Vod and the Val.

The tunes to these were played at that day on four kinds
of bagpipe (including a drone bagpipe), a trump, a recorder,
a " fiddell," and a " quhissil "—which is the pleasantest way
of spelling *whistle* I have yet seen. The melodies and words
of most of them are, apparently, all now clean forgotten.

" Fa la la " (No. 210) is of a different kind, being one of
hundreds of madrigals, " ayres " and ballets of which both the
words and the music were written in England in the first twenty
years or so of the seventeenth century. There is, of course, a
hoard of learning that one may study on this English music—
William Byrd's, John Dowland's, Thomas Ford's, Thomas
Campion's, John Bartlet's, Philip Rosseter's, Robert Ayres'
and others—which in its own day was as famous in the countries
of Europe as English poetry is now. It was the coming of
foreign music and musicians to England—the Italians and
Handel and Mendelssohn—that put it ungratefully out of mind.
To-day its dust has at last been brushed away. The Madrigals
are being printed and sung again, and Dr. Fellowes has lately
published a volume containing the words of hundreds of such
lively, nimble and heart-entrancing rhymes—intended by their
writers to carry with them a double charm—not only their own
verbal melody, grace and beauty, but also their music's.

My own knowledge is scanty indeed, but I gather that a

madrigal is intended to be sung, unaccompanied with instruments, by voices only—three to five, six, or seven, it may be, and men's and women's or boys', coursing, echoing, interweaving, responding and rilling together like the countless runnels and wavelets of a brook over its stones, or a wood full of singing birds at evening. An Ayre is different. It is for the voice—singing its melody to the accompaniment of lute, viol or virginal, as a nightingale may sing at dusk above the murmur of a softly-brawling brook. A Ballet, the most ancient of all three, went hand in hand and foot to foot with a dance.

All I wish to make clear is that the printed words of Nos. 210 and 212, for instance, can give only a fraction of the pleasure their poets intended, who in writing had always the singing voice and often the twangling string in mind. Their very age to my fancy gives them an enticing strangeness, grace, and freshness. For in their company the imagination returns to the days when first they rang out in the taverns and parlours and palaces and streets of a London that from every steeple and tower was within sight of green fields ; a noble city of but about three hundred thousand people (including children) wherein you might any day find William Shakespeare, Ben Johnson, Chapman and the rest talking together in its taverns, the *Mermaid* or the *Triple Tun*, while that ill-fortuned traveller and statesman, Sir Walter Raleigh, fallen upon evil days, sat mewed up in the Tower of London, engrossed in his *History of the World*.

None the less there are human beings who remain deaf to the magic both of words and music—that, like the deaf adder, *stop* their ears : " I know very well," wrote Sir William Temple, " that many who pretend to be wise by the forms of being grave, are apt to despise both poetry and music as toys and trifles too light for the use or entertainment of serious men. But whoever find themselves wholly insensible to these charms, would I think do well to keep their own counsel, for . . . while this world lasts, I doubt most but the pleasure and requests of these two entertainments will do so too ; and happy those that content themselves with these, or any other so easy and so innocent ; and do not trouble the world or other men, because they cannot be quiet themselves, though nobody hurts them !

ABOUT AND ROUNDABOUT

" When all is done, human life is at the greatest and the best but like a froward child, that must be played with and humoured a little to keep it quiet till it falls asleep, and then the care is over."

211. " THE ONELY PRETTY RING TIME."

" Amo, amas,
I love a lass,
As cedar tall and slender ;
Sweet cowslip's face
Is her nominative case,
And she's of the feminine gender.
Horum quorum,
Sunt divorum,
Harum, scarum, Divo ;
Tag rag, merry derry, periwig and hatband,
Hic—hoc—hârum, genitivo."

JOHN O'KEEFE

There was a mayde come out of Kent,
Deintie love, deintie love ;
There was a mayde cam out of Kent,
Daungerous be :
There was a mayde cam out of Kent,
Fáyre, propre, small and gent,
As ever upon the grounde went,
For so should it be.

" When you speake (Sweet)
I'ld have you do it ever. When you sing,
I'ld have you buy and sell so : so give Almes,
Pray so : and for the ord'ring your Affayres,
To sing them too. When you do dance, I wish you
Nothing but that : move still, still so :
And owne no other function. . . .
My prettiest Perdita."

The Winter's Tale.

" Such pretie things would soon be gon
If we should not so them remembre."

212.

There *might* be an instant's check or faltering at the eighth
line, but make it " when the WINDS BLOW and the SEAS FLOW "
— the great flood of air and water banking up as it were into
the words as does the Atlantic in a gale at the Spring Equinox —
and all's well.

213. " AND THE FLEAS THAT TEASE IN THE HIGH PYRENEES."

" The flee is a lyttell worme, and greveth men mooste ; and
scapeth and voideth peril with lepynge and not with runnynge,
and wexeth slowe and fayleth in colde tyme, and in somer tyme
it wexeth quiver and swyft ; and spareth not kynges."

214. " I LOVED A LASS."

George Wither, says Aubrey, could make verses as fast as
he could write them. So, too, could Shakespeare. " What
he thought," said his editors, " he uttered with that easinesse
that we have scarse received from him a blot in his papers."

Still :—" So, So-a ! fair and softly ! " said the old Shropshire
farmer to Job his plough-horse when he kicked up his heels as
if to break into a gallop ; " So, So-a ! When thou'rt a racer,
my dear, or born a high-blood Arab, there'll be time enough for
that. *Some goes their best slow.*"

If the lass's " fives " in the fourth stanza (of 214) were the
fives of to-day she must have had a quite comfortable foot, a
size or two larger, at any rate, than the bride's in Sir John
Suckling's *Ballad upon a Wedding* :

> . . . Her feet beneath her petticoat
> Like little mice stole in and out,
>   As if they feared the light ;
> But oh, she dances such a way !
> No sun upon an Easter-day
>   Is half so fine a sight.
>
> Her cheeks so rare a white was on,
> No daisy makes comparison ;
>   Who sees them is undone :
> For streaks of red were mingled there,
> Such as are on a Catharine pear,
>   The side that's next the sun.

ABOUT AND ROUNDABOUT

Her lips were red ; and one was thin
Compared to that was next her chin
(Some bee had stung it newly) ;
But, Dick, her eyes so guard her face,
I durst no more upon them gaze,
Than on the sun in Júly. . . .

218. " AND ST. JOHN'S BELL RINGS FOR MATINS.''

June 24 is not only the birthday of St. John the Baptist, but
also the year's Sun Day, for about this day, following through
the night but a little way beneath the horizon, he rises at dawn
furthest North of East in his annual journey (see p. xiv). As
once on May-day so it was then formerly the custom, all
England over, to set bonfires blazing on the hilltops, around
which the country people danced and sang. The dairy-maid
who had the breath, and was fleet enough of foot to ring
around, between dusk and daybreak, nine such merry bonfires
before they were burnt out, assured her heart of a happy
marriage within the year.

219. " O IT'S DABBLING IN THE DEW MAKES THE MILKMAIDS
FAIR !"

The aïr to gi'e your cheäks a hue
O' rwosy red, so feaïr to view,
Is what do sheäke the grass-bleädes grae
At breäk o' dae, in mornén dew ;
Vor vo'k that will be rathe abrode,
Will meet wi' health upon their road.

But biden up till dead o' night,
When han's o' clocks do stan' upright,
By candlelight, do soon consume
The feäce's bloom, an' turn it white.
An' moon-beäms cast vrom midnight skies
Do blunt the sparklen ov the eyes.

Vor health do weäke vrom nightly dreams
Below the mornen's eärly beams,
An' leäve the dead-aïr'd houses' eaves,
Vor quiv'ren leaves, an' bubblen streams,
A-glitt'ren brightly to the view,
Below a sky o' cloudless blue.

WILLIAM BARNES

581

ABOUT AND ROUNDABOUT

The words in this poem are spelt as they are spoken in the County of Dorset. "Rathe" means early; and "below" beneath. There is a half-secret rhyme in each fourth line.

223. "MUSIC, WHEN SOFT VOICES DIE, VIBRATES IN THE MEMORY."

There is sweet music here that softer falls
Than petals from blown roses on the grass,
Or night-dews on still waters between walls
Of shadowy granite, in a gleaming pass;
Music that gentlier on the spirit lies,
Than tir'd eyelids upon tir'd eyes;
Music that brings sweet sleep down from the blissful skies.

TENNYSON

224. "A BELL IN MOSCOW." (stanza 4)

Of this I saw the picture in Thrae. It was named Czar Kolokol, and, when cast, was of the weight of about twenty-six hundred heavy men. It now stands clapperless on the ground with a breach in its metal side. Through this breach the people go into its silence to pray.

225.

This " Country Rhime," with Nos. 121 and 434, is taken from *A Book for Boys and Girls*, written by John Bunyan. It came out into the world on May 12th, 1686, two years before Bunyan died on Snow Hill in London; and two years after the publication of the Second Part of *The Pilgrim's Progress*, " wherein is set forth the manner of the setting out of Christian's Wife and Children, their dangerous journey, and safe arrival at the Desired Country."

When Bunyan was young he loved ringing the bells with the ringers in the steeple of the village church of Elstow, where he was born, and where his grandfather, Thomas Bonyon, was " a common baker of human bread."

All these " Homely rhimes " are followed in this particular *Book for Boys and Girls* by comparisons " ; as here : first the bells ; then a lesson about them. They are parables. But in Mr. Nahum's copying, many of the lessons were omitted ;

perhaps because he preferred to think out his own. Not that the poetry that is intended to teach, to praise virtue, and to instil wisdom in the heart and mind of its readers is any the less poetry for this reason. Nevertheless, *every* beautiful thing in this world—the hyssop in the wall and the cedar of Lebanon, Solomon in all his glory and the ring on his finger, carries with it joy and wonder of the life that is ours, and gratitude to the Maker of all. And poets who, when writing, are too intent upon teaching, are apt to forfeit their rarest poetry.

232.

Dorothy was William Wordsworth's only sister and his friend Coleridge's close friend. What she squandered on these two poets—her self, her talk, her imagination, her love—only they could tell. " She gave me eyes, she gave me ears," once wrote her brother ; she shared his visionary happiness. With Coleridge she used to walk and talk so nearly and dearly that again and again in her *Journal* she uses all but the very words— that " thin gray cloud," the line on Spring, or on the one red leaf, for instance—which are so magically his own in *Christabel* (No. 345).

233. " To Autumn."

I read this—perhaps the loveliest of John Keats's odes, many times before I realised that the whole of it is addressed to the musing apparition or phantasm of Autumn whom in its second stanza he describes as if she were in image there before him. This, perhaps, was partly because the poem is usually printed with a full stop after " clammy cells," and partly because of my own stupidity.

Thomas Hood, in his scarcely less beautiful Ode, sees Autumn first as an old man :

> I saw old Autumn in the misty morn
> Stand shadowless like Silence, listening
> To silence, for no lonely bird would sing
> Into his hollow ear from woods forlorn,
> Nor lowly hedge nor solitary thorn ;
> Shaking his languid locks all dewy bright
> With tangled gossamer that fell by night,
>   Pearling his coronet of golden corn.

ABOUT AND ROUNDABOUT

And later, in his fourth stanza :

> The squirrel gloats on his accomplished hoard,
> The ants have brimmed their garners with ripe grain,
>   And honey bees have stored
> The sweets of Summer in their luscious cells ;
> The swallows all have winged across the main ;
> But here the Autumn melancholy dwells,
>   And sighs her tearful spells
> Amongst the sunless shadows of the plain.
>   Alone, alone,
>   Upon a mossy stone,
> She sits and reckons up the dead and gone,
> With the last leaves for a love-rosary,
> Whilst all the withered world looks drearily,
> Like a dim picture of the drownèd past
> In the hushed mind's mysterious far away,
> Doubtful what ghostly thing will steal the last
> Into that distance, gray upon the gray. . . .

237. "A Foolish Thing."

> I thee advise
> If thou be wise
> To keep thy wit
> Though it be small :
> 'Tis rare to get,
> And far to fet,
> 'Twas ever yet
> Dear'st ware of all.

GEORGE TURBERVILLE

" Far to fetch " it certainly is ; but here is a little counsel to this end from the old Irish *Instructions of King Cormac* (of the ninth century). Of Carbery I know no more, but doubtless there is much to hear :

" O Cormac, grandson of Conn," said Carbery, " what is the worst for the body of man ?"

" Not hard to tell," said Cormac. " Sitting too long, lying too long, long standing, lifting heavy things, exerting oneself beyond one's strength, running too much, leaping too much, frequent falls, sleeping with one's leg over the bed-rail, gazing at glowing embers, wax, biestings [very new milk], new ale, bull-flesh, curdles, dry food, bog-water, rising too early, cold, sun, hunger, drinking too much, eating too much, sleeping too much, sinning too much, grief, running up a height, shouting against the wind, drying oneself by a fire, summer-dew, winter-dew, beating ashes, swimming on a full stomach, sleeping on one's back, foolish romping.". . .

" O Cormac, grandson of Conn," said Carbery, " I desire to know how I shall behave among the wise and the foolish, among friends and strangers, among the old and the young, among the innocent and the wicked."

" Not hard to tell," said Cormac.

> " Be not too wise, nor too foolish,
> Be not too conceited, nor too diffident,
> Be not too haughty, nor too humble,
> Be not too talkative, nor too silent,
> Be not too hard, nor too feeble.

If you be too wise, men will expect too much of you ;
If you be too foolish, you will be deceived ;
If you be too conceited, you will be thought vexatious ;
If you be too humble, you will be without honour ;
If you be too talkative, you will not be heeded ;
If you be too silent, you will not be regarded ;
If you be too hard, you will be broken ;
If you be too feeble, you will be crushed."

But what the exact total of all these " too's " may be is a riddle only the Higher Mathematics can solve.

" OUR PLAY IS DONE "

—after which, in Elizabeth's day, " the characters (one or more) were wont to kneel down upon the stage and to offer a solemn prayer for the sovereign, or other patron " :

" My tongue is wearie ; when my Legs are too, I will bid you good night ; and so kneele down before you : But (indeed) to pray for the Queene."   *Henry IV.*

245. " AH ! WOULD 'TWERE SO."

I know that all beneath the moon decays,
And what by mortals in this world is brought
In Time's great periods shall return to nought ;
That fairest states have fatal nights and days ;

ABOUT AND ROUNDABOUT

I know how all the Muse's heavenly lays,
With toil of spright which is so dearly bought,
As idle sounds, of few or none are sought ;
And that nought lighter is than airy praise.

I know frail beauty's like the purple flower,
To which one morn oft birth and death affords ;
That love a jarring is of minds' accords,
Where sense and will invassall reason's power.

Know what I list, this all can not me move,
But that— O me ! I both must write and love !

WILLIAM DRUMMOND

246.   " NO CRANE TALKS." (line 16)

" I hear the crane, if I mistake not, cry
Who in the clouds forming the forked Y,
By the brave orders practized under her,
Instructeth souldiers in the art of war.
For when her troops of wandring cranes forsake
Frost-firmèd Strymon, and (in autumn) take
Truce with the northern dwarfs, to seek adventure
In southern climates for a milder winter ;
A-front each band a forward captain flies,
Whose pointed bill cuts passage through the skies,
Two skilful sergeants keep the ranks aright,
And with their voyce hasten their tardy flight ;
And when the honey of care-charming sleep
Sweetly begins through all their veines to creep
One keeps the watch, and ever carefull-most,
Walks many a round about the sleeping hoast,
Still holding in his claw a stony clod,
Whose fall may wake him if he hap to nod.
Another doth as much, a third, a fourth,
Untill, by turns the night be turnèd forth."

So also, according to travellers, talk, argue in parliament,
camp, and keep watch the wandering tribes of the gaudy-dyed
Baboons.

249.

If this poem is read softly, pausingly, without haste, the very
words will seem like snowflakes themselves, floating into the
mind ; and then, the beauty and the wonder.

ABOUT AND ROUNDABOUT

251.

Here again, as in music, there are rests in the second, fourth and fifth lines of each stanza. Is there any magic to compare with that still solemn unearthly radiance when the world is masked with snow ; and the very sparkling of the mind is like hoar-frost on the bark of a tree.

253. " THE WILD WOODS."

Allan Cunningham's in Scotland, and these—Mr. Robert Frost's—in Vermont U.S.A. :

> Whose Woods these are I think I know,
> His house is in the village though
> He will not see my stopping here
> To watch his woods fill up with snow.
>
> My little horse must think it queer,
> To stop without a farmhouse near
> Between the woods and frozen lake
> The darkest evening of the year.
>
> He gives his harness bells a shake
> To ask if there is some mistake,
> The only other sounds the sweep
> Of easy wind and downy flake.
>
> The woods are lovely dark and deep ;
> But I have promises to keep
> And miles to go before I sleep :
> And miles to go before I sleep.

255.

There may be a few small verbal puzzles in this fifteenth-century carol—otherwise as clear, sharp and shining as a winter moon.

Kechoun is kitchen, and Stephen (who waited on the King at bed and board) stepped out of it into the hall, " boar's head on hand." *Kyst*, means cast ; *eylet*, aileth ; *wod* is mad. So too *brede*, I fancy. When the roasted capon or cock crowed in its dish, Herod, in wrath and fear cried on his torturers, " by two and all by one " to rise up and kill.

In later times a clay or earthenware box made all of a piece, with a slit in it, was carried by apprentices through the streets on St. Stephen's day, for money. And never a Catholic missionary once sailed for the Indies, Barbary, or the Islands of the Anthropophagites, but a box was hung by the priests in the church for alms against his return. From the former old custom comes our " Boxing Day."

In the Isle of Man, however, the Christmas Box was called the Wren Box, and for this reason : There dwelt of old a Lorelei, siren or sea-elf, in the emerald green creeks and caves of a solitary precipitous island. She was as lovely as she was cruel, and her shrill sweet voice rose amid the roaring and soughing of the waves in her steep rocky habitation as shines a poisonous flower in the dark of a forest. Thus she would at daybreak enchant to their doom sailors following their craft on the sea. Leaning to listen to this music creeping by them on the waters, they drew in to her haunts. Of their bones were coral made ; while she lived on ; sang on. She was hunted down at last in her sea-grottoes by those who, like Ulysses, had stopped their ears against her incantations. Brought finally to bay, her beauty and bright hair suddenly dwindled and dimmed, and she escaped in the shape of—Jenny Wren. Alas, for Jenny Wren ! condemned ever after for the woes of this siren to be pursued with sticks and stones by young loons, cullions and Jerry Sneaks, on every St. Stephen's Day. As goes the rhyme :

" Oh, where are you going ? " says milder to melder ;
" Oh, where are you going ? " says the younger to the elder.
" Oh, I cannot tell," says Festel to Fose ;
" We're going to the woods," says John the Red Nose.
    " We're going to the woods," says John the Red Nose.

" Oh, what will you do there ? " says milder to melder ;
" Oh, what will you do there ? " says the younger to the elder.
" Oh, I do not know," says Festel to Fose ;
" To shoot the cutty wren," says John the Red Nose.
    " To shoot the cutty wren," says John the Red Nose.

" Oh, fwhat of her corpsums ? " etc. etc.,

and a sinister company they look, especially " milder " !

ABOUT AND ROUNDABOUT

257.

Lullay, lullay, thou lytill child,
Sleep and be well still ;
The King of bliss thy father is,
As it was his will.

The other night I saw a sight,
  A mayd a cradle keep :
" Lullay," she sung, and said among,
  " Lie still, my child, and sleep."

" How should I sleep ? I may not for weep,
  So sore am I begone :
Sleep I would ; I may not for cold,
  And clothes have I none.

" For Adam's guilt mankind is spilt
  And that me rueth sore ;
For Adam and Eve here shall I live
  Thirty winter and more."

258. "WELCOME TWELFTH DAY"

and here is a rhyme (entitled Jolagiafir) for a memory-game
they used to play in old times on Twelfth Night after the bean
or silver-penny had been discovered in the Twelfth Cake, and
the Wassail Bowl has gone round with the Mince Pies.

On the first day of Christmas, my true love sent to me
A partridge in a pear-tree.

On the second day of Christmas, my true love sent to me
Two turtle doves and a partridge in a pear-tree.

On the third day of Christmas, my true love sent to me
Three French hens, two turtle doves and
A partridge in a pear-tree.

And so on to—

On the twelfth day of Christmas, my true love sent to me
Twelve lords a-leaping, eleven ladies dancing,
Ten pipers piping, nine drummers drumming,
Eight maids a-milking, seven swans a-swimming,
Six geese a-laying, five gold rings,

ABOUT AND ROUNDABOUT

Four colly birds, three French hens,
Two turtle doves, and
A partridge in a pear-tree.

And here is a recipe for Lamb's Wool, with which to fill
" the Bowl " : Take " the pulpe of rosted apples, in number
four or five according to the greatnesse of the apples (especially
the pome water), and mix it heartily in a wine quart of faire
water "— or old ale—" with a due and fair lacing of nutmegs,
sugar and ginger "—until the company can wait no longer.
And here's another " Twelve "; from Scotland :

What will be our twelve, boys ?
What will be our twelve, boys ?
Twelve's the Twelve Apostles ;
Eleven's maidens in a dance ;
Ten's the Ten Commandments ;
Nine's the Muses o' Parnassus ;
Eight's the table rangers ;
Seven's the stars of heaven ;
Six the echoing waters ;
Five's the hymnlers o' my bower ;
Four's the gospel-makers ;
Three, three thrivers ;
Twa's the lily and the rose,
That shine baith red and green, boys :
My only ane, she walks alane,
And evermair has dune, boys.

259.

It looks as if this carol—of Henry VI.'s reign—was once a
singing game : On the one side in the blaze of the Yule Log
the Holly men with gilded and garlanded pole ; and on the
other Ivy with her maidens ; each side taunting the other, and
maybe tugging for prisoners. " Ivy-girls," too, used to be
burned by companies of boys, and Holly-boys by girls—all
yawping and jodelling at the sport.
" Poppynguy " may perhaps be the jay, but it would be
pleasanter company for the lark, if here it means the green
woodpecker. His other names are rain-bird, hew-hole, wood-
sprite, woodweele, woodspeek and yaffle, the very sound of

which is like the echo of his own laughter in the sunny green tops of the wood.

260. "WHEN ISICLES HANG BY THE WALL."

There is a peculiar magic (which may perhaps be less apparent to the Greenlanders) in icicles. Nor are its effects unknown to the four-footed. In certain remote regions of Siberia there is said to be a little animal called the Iccè-vulff (or Ice-wolf). He has prick-ears, is a fierce feeder, and wears a coat so wondrous close and dense that three or four of our English moles' skins laid one atop the other would yet fall short of its match. But he seldom attains to a ripe age, and for this reason. As soon as he is freed from his dam's snow-burrow, he hastes off to the dwellings of the men of those parts, snuffing their dried seal-steaks and blubber, being a most incorrigible thief and a very wary. And such is his craft that he mocks at gins, traps and pitfalls. But he has a habit which is often to his undoing. It is in this wise : The heat of these hovels is apt to melt a little the snow upon them, its water trickling and coursing softly down till long, keen icicles are formed, upon which, whether hungry or fed, taking up his station in a plumb line beneath them, he will squat and gloat for an hour together, having a marvellous greedy pleasure in clear glasslike colours. Hearing his breathing or faint snuffing, any human who wakes within will of a sudden violently shake the wall between. This dislodges the pendent icicles, and the squatting Iccè-vulff is pierced to his death as with a sword.

Winter indeed makes crystal even of ink. It has the power of enchanting every imagination ; and particularly Coleridge's :

> Therefore all seasons shall be sweet to thee,
> Whether the summer clothe the general earth
> With greenness, or the redbreast sit and sing
> Betwixt the tufts of snow on the bare branch
> Of mossy apple-tree, while the nigh thatch
> Smokes in the sun-thaw ; whether the eave-drops fall
> Heard only in the trances of the blast,
> Or if the secret ministry of frost
> Shall hang them up in silent icicles,
> Quietly shining to the quiet Moon. . . .

ABOUT AND ROUNDABOUT

264. " Woe weeps out Her Division when She sings."

This means, I think, that she adds her own grieved cadences
to the melody, as may one, among many voices, singing in
harmony.

265. " Is like a Bubble."

This rainbow "bubble"—like Shelley's "many-coloured
dome of glass" in his *Adonais*—seems, before our very eyes, to
be floating up into the empty blue heavens, until it smalls into
a bead of gold, and vanishes. It brings to memory—though
I am uncertain of the first line—an epitaph in the church at
Zennor, a village clustered above the Atlantic on the dreamlike
coast of Cornwall—an epitaph cut in fine lettering into its slate
slab, while at each corner of the slab Cherubs' heads puff out
their round cheeks, representing the winds of the world :

> Sorrow, and sin, false hope, and trouble —
> These the Four Winds that daily vex this Bubble :
> His breath a Vapour, and his life a Span ;
> 'Tis Glorious Misery to be born a Man.

266. " O, Sweet Content."

> There is a jewel which no Indian mines
> Can buy, no chymic art can counterfeit ;
> It makes men rich in greatest poverty ;
> Makes water wine, turns wooden cups to gold,
> The homely whistle to sweet music's strain :
> Seldom it comes, to few from heaven sent,
> That much in little, all in naught—Content.

" Art Thou poor . . . Art Thou rich."

The subject being riches, here from Hugh Rhodes, is a
nourishing crumb or two of advice. *Cautions* the poem is
called, and it may be found in the *Book of Nurture* :

> He that spendeth much ,
> And getteth nought ;
> He that oweth much,
> And hath nought ;
> He that looketh in his purse
> And findeth nought,—
> He may be sorry,
> And say nought.

He that may and will not,
He then that would shall not.
He that would and cannot
May repent and sigh not.

He that sweareth
    Till no man trust him ;
He that lieth
    Till no man believe him ;
He that borroweth
    Till no man will lend him ;
Let him go where
    No man knoweth him.

He that hath a good master,
    And cannot keep him ;
He that hath a good servant,
    And is not content with him ;
He that hath such conditions,
    That no man loveth him ;
May well know other,
    But few men will know him.

And, to make trebly sure :

Three false sisters : " Perhaps," " May be," " I dare say."
Three timid brothers : " Hush !" " Stop !" " Listen !"

269. " LORD RAMESES OF EGYPT SIGHED."

The most ancient poem I know of consists of such a sigh.
It comes from an Egyptian tomb, was composed about 5000
years ago, and might have been written by some melancholy
soul at his sick-room window yesterday afternoon. For, after
all, these ancients whose mummies are now a mere wonder
for the curious, all lived, as Raleigh says, " in the same newness
of time which we call ' old time.' "

" Death is before me to-day
Like the recovery of a sick man,
Like going forth into a garden after sickness.

" Death is before me to-day
Like the odour of myrrh,
Like sitting under the sail on a windy day. . . .

ABOUT AND ROUNDABOUT

" Death is before me to-day
Like the course of the freshet,
Like the return of a man from the war-galley to his house. . . .

" Death is before me to-day
As a man longs to see his house
When he has spent years in captivity."

272. " These Strong and Fair. . . ."

And here is another poem by William Barnes which I have
ventured to spell not as it appears in its original dialect, but
in the usual way :

If souls should only shine as bright
In heaven as in earthly light,
And nothing better were the case,
How comely still, in shape and face,
Would many reach that happy place,—
The hopeful souls that in their prime,
Have seemed a-taken before their time—
      The young that died in beauty.

But when one's limbs have lost their strength
A-toiling through a lifetime's length,
And over cheeks a-growing old
The slowly-wasting years have rolled
The deepening wrinkles' hollow fold ;
When life is ripe, then death do call
For less of thought, than when it fall
      On young folks in their beauty. . . .

But still the dead shall more than keep
The beauty of their early sleep ;
Where comely looks shall never wear
Uncomely, under toil and care,
The fair, at death be always fair,
Still fair to living, thought and love,
And fairer still to God above,
      Than when they died in beauty.

273.

I remember actually coming upon this poem (in Mr. Nahum's
second book), and how I twisted my head and looked up at

the quiet dark-socketed skull in its alcove in the turret room.
It had no alarm for me then, though I can recall cold moments
of dread or confusion, when I was a boy, at the thought of
death. Then—or was it some time after ?—I turned the page
and found the following poem by Thomas Campion, and, in
Mr. Nahum's writing, this scrawl at the foot of it : " Yes,
but the vision first."

> The man of life upright,
>   Whose guiltless heart is free
> From all dishonest deeds,
>   Or thought of vanity ;
>
> The man whose silent days
>   In harmless joys are spent,
> Whom hopes cannot delude
>   Nor sorrow discontent :
>
> That man needs neither towers
>   Nor armour for defence,
> Nor secret vaults to fly
>   From thunder's violence :
>
> He only can behold
>   With unaffrighted eyes
> The horrors of the deep
>   And terrors of the skies.
>
> Thus scorning all the cares
>   That fate or fortune brings,
> He makes the heaven his book,
>   His wisdom heavenly things ;
>
> Good thoughts his only friends,
>   His wealth a well-spent age,
> The earth his sober inn
>   And quiet pilgrimage.

" . . . Yet suffer us, O Lord, not to repine, whether in the
morning, at noon, or at midnight, that is to say, in our cradle,
in our youth, or old age, we go to take our long sleep ; but
let us make this reckoning of our years, that if we can live no
longer, *that* is unto us our old age ; for he that liveth so long
as thou appointest him (though he die in the pride of his
beauty) dieth an old man. . . ."

ABOUT AND ROUNDABOUT

274. " ADIEU ! FAREWELL EARTH'S BLISS."

This solemn dirge was written in " time of pestilence,"—such
a time as Daniel Defoe tells of in his " Journal of the Plague
Year." The Elizabethan poets brooded endlessly on the
mystery of death. A music haunts their words like that of
muffled bells, as in John Fletcher's poem :

> . . . Come hither, you that hope, and you that cry,
>   Leave off complaining !
> Youth, strength, and beauty, that shall never die,
>   Are here remaining.
> Come hither, fools, and blush you stay so long
>   From being blessed,
> And mad men, worse than you, that suffer wrong,
>   Yet seek no rest ! . . .

And in William Davenant's :

> Wake, all the dead ! What ho ! what ho !
> How soundly they sleep whose pillows lie low !
> They mind not poor lovers, who walk above
> On the decks of the world in storms of love.
> No whisper now nor glance shall pass
> Through wickets or through panes of glass,
> For our windows and doors are shut and barred.
> Lie close in the church, and in the churchyard !
> In every grave make room, make room !
> The world's at an end, and we come, we come ! . . .

275. " I WHO LOVED WITH ALL MY LIFE LOVE WITH ALL
MY DEATH."

> Not full twelve years twice-told, a weary breath
> I have exchanged for a wishèd death.
> My course was short, the longer is my rest,
> God takes them soonest whom he loveth best ;
> For he that's born to-day and dies to-morrow,
> Loseth some days of mirth, but months of sorrow.

And this reminds me of an epitaph I chanced on in the
graveyard at Manorbier whose ruinous castle towers above the

green turf of its narrow ocean inlet, as if it were keeping a
long tryst with the clocked church tower on the height :

> Weep not for her ye friends that's dear,
> Weep for your sins, for death is near—
> You see by her, she [was] cut down soon.
> Her morning Sun went down at noon.

And then there are these two unforgettable fragments, the
one from the Scots of John Wedderburn (1542), and the other
of a century before, its authorship unknown :

WHO'S AT MY WINDOW ?

> Who's at my window, who, who ?
> Go from my window, go, go !
> Who calleth there so like a stranger ?
> Go from my window—go !

> Lord, I am here, a wretched mortal
> That for Thy mercy does cry and call—
> Unto Thee, my Lord Celestial,
> See who is at my window, who.

THE CALL.

> . . . Come home again, come home again ;
> Mine own sweet heart, come home again !
> You are gone astray
> Out of your way,
> Therefore, sweet heart, come home again !

277. "HARK ! NOW EVERYTHING IS STILL."

> Death stands above me, whispering low
> I know not what into my ear ;
> Of his strange language all I know
> Is, there is not a word of fear.
>   WALTER SAVAGE LANDOR

" 'TIS NOW FULL TIDE 'TWEEN NIGHT AND DAY."
(line 17)

Leave me, O Love, which reachest but to dust ;
And thou, my mind, aspire to higher things ;
Grow rich in that which never taketh rust ;
Whatever fades, but fading pleasure brings.

ABOUT AND ROUNDABOUT

Draw in thy beams, and humble all thy might
To that sweet yoke where lasting freedoms be ;
Which breaks the clouds, and opens forth the light,
That doth both shine and give us sight to see.

O, take fast hold ! let that light be thy guide
In this small course which birth draws out to death—
And think how evil becometh him to slide,
Who seeketh heaven, and comes of heavenly breath.

Then farewell, world ; thy uttermost I see :
Eternal Love, maintain thy life in me.

SIR PHILIP SIDNEY

278.

Of the *Lyke-wake Dirge* is known neither the age nor the author. The body from which the " saule " or spirit within is fled away lies in its shroud, and the dirge tells of that spirit's journey. Its word " sleet," says Mr. Sidgwick, means either salt, for it was the custom to place in a wooden platter beside the dead, earth and salt for emblems, the one of corruption, the other of the immortal ; or, as some suppose, " sleet " should be *fleet*, meaning embers or water or house-room. " Whinnies " means gorse. To explain the full meaning of Bridge of Dread would need many pages—but does not much of that meaning haunt in the very music and solemnity of the words ?

279.

Next this poem in Mr. Nahum's book was " Lead, Kindly Light," and there was a strange picture for it hanging in the round tower—the picture of a small becalmed ship, clumsy of rig and low in the water which was smooth and green as glass. In the midst of the ship there was piled high what might be taken for a vast heap of oranges, their fair reddish colour blazing in the rays of the sun that was about to plunge out of the greenish sky below the line of the west. But what even more particularly attracted my eye at the time was that ship's figurehead—a curious head and shoulders as if with wings, and of a kind of far beauty or wonder entirely past me to describe. Many years afterwards I read that this poem was written by John Henry Newman (one who even in his young days at Oxford was " never less alone than when alone "), when his

mind was perplexed and unhappy, and he himself had time
to ponder awhile, because the boat in which he was sailing to
England had been for some days becalmed off the coast of Spain.

281. "FEAR NO MORE."

Philaster.   Fie, fie,
        So young and so dissembling ! fear'st thou not
          death ?
        Can boys contemn that ?

Bellario.   O, what boy is he
        Can be content to live to be a man,
        That sees the best of men thus passionate,
        Thus without reason ?

Philaster.   O, but thou dost not know what 'tis to die.

Bellario.   Yes, I do know, my Lord !
        'Tis less than to be born ; a lasting sleep,
        A quiet resting from all jealousy ;
        A thing we all pursue ; I know besides
        It is but giving over of a game
        That must be lost.

From *Philaster :* FRANCIS BEAUMONT and JOHN FLETCHER

284. "ALL THE FLOWERS."

" . . . But those which perfume the air most delightfully,
not passed by as the rest, but being trodden upon and crushed,
are three—that is, burnet, wild thyme, and watermints.
Therefore you are to set whole alleys of them, to have the
pleasure when you walk or tread."

An Essay on Gardens, FRANCIS BACON

    Bring, too, some branches forth of Daphne's hair,
    And gladdest myrtle for the posts to wear,
    With spikenard weaved and marjorams between
    And starred with yellow-golds and meadows-queen.

The very names indeed of the aromatic herbs seem to " perfume the air "—bergamot, lavender, meadowsweet, costmary,
southernwood, woodruff, balm, germander. And flowers even
though dead remain sweet in their dust, as every bowl of pot-
pourri proclaims. To have " a repository of odours " always

with them, when streets were foul and pestilence was a peril, gentle-people would in old times carry fresh nosegays or pomanders. The pomanders were of many kinds; an orange stuffed with cloves, etc., for the hand; or—for pocket or chatelaine—some little curiously-devised receptacle of silver containing tiny phials of precious essences—possibly no bigger than a plum. Or they might be compounded of rare ingredients: "Your only way to make a good pomander is this. Take an ounce of the purest garden mould, cleansed and steeped seven days in change of motherless rose water. Then take the best labdanum, benjoin, both storaxes, ambergris, civet, and musk. Incorporate them together, and work them into what form you please. This, if your breath be not too valiant, will make you smell as sweet as any lady's dog."

285.

I have pondered over the thirteenth and eighteenth lines of this poem, but am not yet certain of all that they were intended to convey. But what scope for the imagination is in it! The next epitaph is by Stephen Hawes, whose *Passetyme of Pleasure or History of Graunde Amoure, and La Bel Pucel,* was printed by Wynkyn de Worde in 1509:

> O mortal folk, you may behold and see
> How I lie here, sometime a mighty knight.
> The end of joy and all prosperity
> Is death at last, thorough his course and might:
> For though the day be never so long,
> At last the bells ringeth to evensong.

And the lines following are said to have been found between the pages of Sir Walter Raleigh's Bible in the Gate House at Westminster, having been written by him, it is surmised, during the night before he—an ageing man of sixty-six—was beheaded:

> Even such is Time, that takes in trust
> Our youth, our joys, our all we have,
> And pays us but with earth and dust;
> Who, in the dark and silent grave,
> When we have wandered all our ways,
> Shuts up the story of our days.
>
> But from this earth, this grave, this dust,
> My God shall raise me up, I trust.

ABOUT AND ROUNDABOUT

286. "SIDNEY, O SIDNEY IS DEAD."

" Sir Philip Sydney, Knight," says John Aubrey, " was the most accomplished courtier of his time. He was not only of an excellent witt, but extremely beautiful ; he much resembled his sister. He was a person of great courage. Among others Mr. Edmund Spenser made his addresse to him, and brought his *Faery Queen.* Sir Philip was busy at his study, and his servant delivered Mr. Spenser's booke to his master, who layd it by, thinking it might be such kind of stuffe as he was frequently troubled with. When Sir Philip perused it, he was so exceedingly delighted with it, that he was extremely sorry he was gonne, and where to send for him he knew not. After much enquiry he learned his lodgeing, and sent for him, and mightily caressed him. . . . From this time there was a great friendship between them, to his dying day. . . . His body was putt in a leaden coffin (which after the firing of Paule's, I myself sawe), and with wonderfull greate state was carried to St. Paule's church, when he was buried in our Ladie's Chapell. There solempnized this funerall all the nobility and great officers of Court."

Here is part of a letter written to him, by his father, Sir Henry Sidney, in 1566, when Philip was a boy at Shrewsbury School :

SON PHILIP. . . . Above all things, tell no untruth. No, not in trifles. The custom of it is nought : and let it not satisfy you that, for a time, the hearers take it for a truth ; yet after it will be known as it is, to your shame. For there cannot be a greater reproach to a gentleman, than to be accounted a liar. . . . Remember, my son ! the noble blood you are descended of by your mother's side : and think that only by virtuous life and good action you may be an ornament to that illustrious family ; otherwise, through vice and sloth, you may be counted *labes generis*, " a spot of your kin," one of the greatest curses that can happen to man.

This next fragment is from a letter written on October 18, 1580, by Sir Philip Sidney himself to his younger brother Robert (then seventeen). This Robert six years afterwards fought with him at Zutphen. He grew up a gallant gentleman, was created Earl of Leicester, and in his leisure wrote words to fit the music of John Dowland—afterwards lutenist to Charles I.

MY DEAR BROTHER,

For the money you have received, assure yourself (for it is true), there is nothing I spend so pleaseth me ; as that which is for you. If ever I have ability, you shall find it so : if not, yet shall not any brother living be better beloved than you, of me. . . . Look to your diet, sweet Robin ! and hold your heart in courage and virtue. Truly, great part of my comfort is in you ! . . . . Be careful of yourself, and I shall never have cares. . . . I write this to you as one, that for myself have given over the delight in the world ; but wish to you as much, if not more, than to myself. . . . God bless you, sweet Boy ! and accomplish the joyful hope I conceive of you. . . . Lord how I have babbled ! Once again, farewell, dearest Brother !

Your most loving and careful brother,

PHILIP SIDNEY

And here in a few words is a fleeting glimpse of this renowned man as he appeared amidst the splendour and magnificence of the Tournament, during the Anjou Fetes in London, in 1581, five years before his death :

" Then proceeded Master Philip Sidney, in very sumptuous manner with armour part blue and the rest gilt and engraven. . . . He had four pages that rode on his four spare horses " (richly caparisoned in gold and pearls and feathers of silver) " who had cassock hats and Venetian hose all of cloth of silver laid with gold lace and hats of the same with gold bands and white feathers : and each one a pair of white buskins.". . . . There followed him in as rich and splendid array his gentlemen, yeomen, and trumpeters.

287. " HIS PICTURE IN A SHEET."

Of John Donne's Book of Poems there was nothing in Mr. Nahum's first volume, much in the others. But what I then read of them I little understood. It is a poetry that awaits the mind as the body grows older, and when we have ourselves learned the experience of life with which it is concerned. Not that the simplest poetry will then lose anything of its grace and truth and beauty—far rather it shines the more clearly, since age needs it the more.

"*His Picture in a sheet*" refers to a drawing (prefixed to Donne's *Poems*) of his stone effigy. This shows him draped with a shroud, and may now be seen in St. Paul's Cathedral, of which he was the dean, and in whose pulpit a few days before his death he preached his last valedictory or farewell sermon.

"LIVING TO ETERNITY."

How happy is he born and taught
That serveth not another's will ;
Whose armour is his honest thought,
And simple truth his utmost skill ! . . .

Who God doth late and early pray
More of his grace than gifts to lend ;
And entertains the harmless day
With a well chosen book or friend ;

This man is freed from servile bands
Of hope to rise or fear to fall :
Lord of himself, though not of lands,
And having nothing, yet hath all.

Sir Thomas More was such a man. On Monday, July 5th, 1535, the night before he was beheaded, he wrote (" with a cole ") this letter of farewell to his daughter Margaret Roper. He had seen her for the last time when she openly met and kissed him in the midst of his enemies and of the throngs on Tower Wharf, as he came from Judgment :

" Oure Lorde Blesse you good daughter, & youre good husbande, & youre lyttle boye, & all yours, & all my children, & all my Godde chyldren and all oure frendes. . . . I cumber you good *Margaret* much, but I would be sory, if it should be any longer than to morow. For it is saint *Thomas* even, & the utas of saint *Peter* : & therfore to morow long I to go to God : it were a day verye mete & convenient for me. I never liked your maner toward me better, than whan you kissed me laste : for I love when doughterly love, and deere charitye, hath no leysure to loke to worldlye curtesy. Farewell my dere chylde, & pray for me & I shall for you & all youre frendes, that we maye merilye mete in heaven. . . . ."

ABOUT AND ROUNDABOUT

288. "Do Thou the same."

So too Walter Savage Landor :

... Quieter is his breath, his breast more cold
　　Than daisies in the mould,
Where children spell, athwart the churchyard gate,
　　His name, and life's brief date.
Pray for him, gentle souls, whoe'er you be,
　　And, O, pray too for me !

290. "A pretty Bud."

" To die young," in William Drummond's words, " is to do
that soon, and in some fewer days, which once thou must do ;
it is but the giving over of a game, that after never so many
hazards must be lost."

291. "A-left asleep."

May ! Be thou never graced with birds that sing,
　　Nor Flora's pride !
In thee all flowers and roses spring—
　　Mine, only died.
　　In obitum MS. X° Maij. 1614, WILLIAM BROWNE

293. "Sunk Lyonesse."

There is a legend—recorded in an ancient monastic chronicle
—that in the days of Arthur there stretched between Land's
End and the Scillies a country of castles, of fair towns, and
landscapes, named Lyonesse. When the tumult of the last
great Arthurian battle was over, there befell a cataclysm of
nature, and in a night of tempest this whole region was engulfed
beneath the seas.

What truth is in this legend no certain history relates.
But when the vast Atlantic breakers begin to lull after storm,
to lie listening in the watches of the night is to hear, it would
seem, deep-sunken belfries of bells sounding in the waters,
and siren-like lamentations. I have myself heard this, and
fantasy though it may be, if the ear is once beguiled into its
deceit, the bells clash and chime on and on in the imagination,
mingled with the enormous lully of the surges, until at last,
one falls asleep.

ABOUT AND ROUNDABOUT

299. "SING NO SAD SONGS FOR ME"

—and here is another such happy and tender word of farewell—
but from one unknown :

> When from the world I should be ta'en,
> And from earth's necessary pain,
> Then let no blacks be worn for me,
> Not in a ring, my dear, by thee.
> But this bright diamond, let it be
> Worn in rememberance of me.
> And when it sparkles in your eye,
> Think 'tis my shadow passeth by.

302. "READEN OV A HEAD-STWONE."

This poem, again, is spelt as the words would be pronounced
by the country people of Dorset, the country in which William
Barnes was born and lived nearly all his long life. Their way
of speech is slower than in common English, and the words,
especially those with the two dots, or diaeresis, over them,
should be lingered over a little in pronouncing them.

Londoners have a way of being scornfully amused at country
speech—in their ignorance that it is older and far more beautiful
than their own clipped and nasal manner of talking. But
half an hour with the great *Dialect Dictionary* will prove how
inexhaustibly rich the English language once was and still is
in words made, used, and loved by folk unlearned in books, but
with keen and lively eyes in their heads, quick to see the
delight and livingness of a thing, and with the wits to give it
a name fitting it as close as a skin.

303. "CARE IS HEAVY."

> Dear God, though Thy all-powerful hand
> Should so direct my earthly fate
> That I may seem unfortunate
> To them who do not understand
> That all things follow Thy decree,
> Staunchly I'll bear what e'er's Thy will—
> Praying Thee but to grant me still
> That none shall come to harm through me ;
> For, God, although Thou knowest all,

ABOUT AND ROUNDABOUT

I am too young to comprehend
The windings to my journey's end ;
I fear upon the road to fall
In the worst sin of all that be
And thrust my brother in the sea.

CONAL O'RIORDAN

304. " MOTHER, NEVER MOURN."

" It was my own mother (wrote Thomas Cantimpratanus about 1260) who told me the story which I am about to relate. My grandmother had a firstborn son of most excellent promise, comely beyond the wont of children, at whose death she mourned . . . with a grief that could not be consoled, until one day, as she went by the way, she saw in her vision a band of youths moving onwards, as it seemed to her, with exceeding great joy ; and she, remembering her son and weeping that she saw him not in this joyful band, suddenly beheld him trailing weary footsteps after the rest. Then with a grievous cry the mother asked : ' How comes it, my son, that thou goest alone, lagging thus behind the rest ? ' Then he opened the side of his cloak and showed her a heavy water-pot, saying : ' Behold, dear mother, the tears which thou hast vainly shed for me, through the weight whereof I must needs linger behind the rest ! Thou therefore shalt turn thy tears to God : then only shall I be freed from the burden wherewith I am now grieved.' "

But not all dreamers are so rebuked or so comforted. St. Augustine, a loving son, pined in vain :

" If the dead could come in dreams," he wrote, " my pious mother would no night fail to visit me. Far be the thought that she should, by a happier life, have been made so cruel that, when aught vexes my heart, she should not even console in a dream the son whom she loved with an only love."

310. TOM O' BEDLAM.

This poem has been at hide-and-seek with the world for many years past. Mr. Frank Sidgwick has now played Seek, however, and has tracked it down in the British Museum in a manuscript, No. 24665, inscribed " Giles Earle—his book, 1615." In this manuscript the poem consists of eight stanzas

ABOUT AND ROUNDABOUT

of ten lines each, with a chorus of five lines. The version in this book is only of twenty-five lines, as they were arranged by Mrs. Meynell in her beautiful Anthology, *The Flower of the Mind*. Here are the chief differences which Mr. Sidgwick has very kindly allowed me to collect from his account of his search :

Line 1, " moon " is *morn*. Line 2, "lovely" is *lonely*, " marrow " is *morrow*. Line 10, " rounded " is *wounded*. Line 16, " a heart " is *a host*. And line 21, " with " is *by*. It is a happy exercise of the wits to choose between them and to find reasons for one's choice. When and by whom the poem was written is not yet known. It remains a shining jewel in the crown of the most modest of all men of genius, Mr. Anon.

314. " What's in there."

This far-carrying rhyme belongs to the ancient and famous game of Dump. " He who speaks first in it, " says Dr. Gregor, " or laughs first, or lets his teeth be seen, gets nine nips, nine nobs, nine double douncornes, an' a gueed blow on the back o' the head."

The *faht* and *fahr*, I suppose, are the pleasant Scots way of saying *what* and *where*.

316.

So may the omission of a few commas effect a wonder in the imagination. To the imagination indeed there is nothing absurd in, " I saw the sun at twelve o'clock at night "—for one can actually *see* in the " little nowhere of the mind " both burning sun and black night *together* : as once in a dream I myself was enchanted by three moons in the sky, shining in their silver above waters as wide as those of Milton's curfew. So, too, even mere day-by-day objects will take on themselves a strangeness and beauty never seen or " marked " before, if (like Marcus Aurelius and his loaf of bread) we will only " glut " the eye on them. " I see a rose," said an old woman on her deathbed, " but if, in childhood and youth, I had seen it closer, what a rose on the threshold it had been ! "

Here is another old nursery " nonsense " rhyme that makes almost as lively pictures in the mind :

> There was a man of double deed
> Who sowed his garden full of seed ;

And when the seed began to grow,
'Twas like a garden full of snow ;
And when the snow began to fall,
Like birds it was upon the wall ;
And when the birds began to fly ,
'Twas like a shipwreck in the sky ;
And when the sky began to crack,
'Twas like a stick upon my back ;
And when my back began to smart,
'Twas like a pen-knife in my heart ;
And when my heart began to bleed,
Then I was dead —and dead indeed.

319. " It had become a glimmering Girl."

" The Tuatha De Danaan—the divine Children of Danu which forgotten centuries ago invaded Ireland —can take all shapes, and those that are in the waters take often the shape of fish. A woman of Burren, in Galway, says, ' There are more of them in the sea than on the land . . .,' and another Galway woman says, ' Surely those things are in the sea as well as on land. My father was out fishing one night off Tyrone. And something came beside the boat that had eyes shining like candles. And then a wave came in, and a storm rose all in a minute, and whatever was in the wave, the weight of it had like to sink the boat. And then they saw that it was a woman in the sea that had the shining eyes. So my father went to the priest, and he bid him always to take a drop of holy water and a pinch of salt out in the boat with him, and nothing could harm him.' "

W. B. YEATS

321. " One without."

Was it the sound of a footfall I heard
On the cold flag stone ?
Or the cry of a wandering far night bird,
On the sea-winds blown ?
Was that a human shape that stood ?
In the shadow below,
Or but the mist of the moonlit wood
As it hovered low ?

ABOUT AND ROUNDABOUT

Was it the voice of a child that called
From the hill side steep ?
Or, O, but the wind as it softly lulled
The world to sleep ?

ELIZABETH RAMAL

325. " BROOME, BROOME ON HILL."

The story is of how a bright lady comes to keep her tryst
with a knight-at-arms in the golden broom of Hive Hill. She
finds him under a charm, an enchantment, asleep ; and having
left her ring on his finger for proof of her coming, she steals
away. Presently after he awakes—her presence gone. To
leave a quiet and happy room vacant at night is sometimes to
have this experience, as it were, *reversed*. There comes a
feeling that you being gone, gentler visitants may enter and
share its solitude—while its earthly occupant sleeps overhead,
and one by one the stars sink to their setting.

326. " THE CHANGELING."

When larks gin sing
Away we fling,
And babes new-born steal as we go ;
An elf instead
We leave in bed,
And wind out, laughing, Ho, ho, ho !

329. " MARIANA."

It is difficult to read this poem slowly and intently enough
if one is to experience to the *full* the living things and sights
and sounds that by its words are charmed into the mind—the
hushed solitude, the desolation. Take even, of all there is,
but the " peering mouse " in the sixth stanza—his sharp nose
sniffing the air beneath the small wooden arch of his dark-
glimmering mousery, where miche and shriek and gambol his
fellows behind the mouldering wainscot. Or stay for a moment
looking down on the " marsh mosses " in the third stanza—
of a green as lively as a fairy's mantle in the sunlight, gilding
the waters of the blackened sluice. So piece by piece the
words of the poem build up in the imagination this solitary
house with its forsaken Mariana, whom Tennyson himself had

ABOUT AND ROUNDABOUT

seen in the dream conferred on him by another poet, Shakespeare, in *Measure for Measure* :

Isabella.   Can this be so ? did *Angelo* so leave her ?

Duke.   Left her in her teares, and dried not one of them
            with his comfort : swallowed his vowes whole,
            pretending in her discoveries of dishonour : in
            few, bestowed on her her owne lamentation,
            which she yet weares for his sake : and he, a
            marble to her teares, is washed with them, but
            relents not.

Isabella. What a merit were it in death to take this poore
           maid from the world. . . .

332. " YES TOR."

Turn your back on Okehampton and break out due South
into the wilds of Dartmoor, and there, " summering " together
" beneath the empty skies," lie titanic Yes Tor and High
Willes, rearing their bare vast shapes 700 yards into the air.

333. " TO HEARE THE MANDRAKE GRONE." (stanza 2)

Of the dangerous plant Mandrake (" its root in something
the shape and appearance of a man ") is concocted Mandra-
gora, one of the " drowsy syrups." " The leaves and fruit
be also dangerous, for they cause deadly sleep, and peevish
drowsiness." The fruit is " of the bigness of a reasonable pippin,
and as yellow as gold when it is thoroughly ripe " : fair without,
ashes within. It is said that the mandrake's screams, when it
is dragged out of the ground, will send the hearer mad. So the
gatherer should first seal his ears, then tie the plant to a dog's
tail and hike him on to haul it out of its haunt! " Avicenna
the Arabian physician asserts that a Jew at Metz had a man-
dragore with a human head, and the legs and body of a cock,
which lived five weeks, and was fed on lavender and earth-
worms, and, when dead, was preserved in spirits." Even up to
the nineteenth century dreaders or wishers of witchcraft were
wont to carry these monstrous little Erdmannikens in bosom
or pocket for an amulet or charm.

The " Basilisk," old books maintain, is a fabulous beast
whose icy glare freezes the gazer, and is mortal. Approach
her then with a mirror ; and courage be your guide !

610

ABOUT AND ROUNDABOUT

" HEMLOCK, HENBANE, ADDERS-TONGUE." (line 10)

Hemlock is that tall, dim-spotted plant of a sad green colour, and of a scent " strong, heady and bad," which is " very cold and dangerous," especially when " digged in the dark."

Clammy henbane is woolly-leafed, with hollow dark-eyed flowers of a purple-veined dingy yellow. " It lusts to grow in rancid soil, To 'stil its deadly oil."

Moonwort is the meek-looking little flowering fern that has the power to break locks, and to make any horse that chances to tread upon it cast his shoes.

The livid-flowered, cherrylike-fruited dwale, enoron, or night-shade is the most " daungerous " plant in England. While leopard's bane—though it bears a bright-yellow daisy-like flower, and witches are said to fear sun-colour—is venomous to animals.

I am uncertain of adder's tongue, for the fern of this name cures sore eyes ; and cuckoo-pint which is also so called, is " a remedy for poison and the plague " !

Of these six insidious plants only one is openly mentioned by Shakespeare, and they appear to have few country names, unlike, for example, the purple orchis, " which has so many," says Nicholas Culpeper, " that they would fill a sheet of paper " : long-purples, dead-men's fingers, crake-feet, giddy-gandy, neat-legs, geese and goslings, and gander-gooses, being a few choice specimens.

334. " THE RAVEN."

Underneath an old oak tree
There was of swine a huge company,
That grunted as they crunched the mast :
For that was ripe, and fell full fast.
Then they trotted away, for the wind grew high :
One acorn they left, and no more might you spy.
Next came a Raven, that liked not such folly :
He belonged, they did say, to the witch Melancholy !
Blacker was he than blackest jet,
Flew low in the rain, and his feathers not wet.

He picked up the acorn and buried it straight
By the side of a river both deep and great.
　　Where then did the Raven go ?
　　He went high and low,
Over hill, over dale, did the black Raven go.

ABOUT AND ROUNDABOUT

Many Autumns, many Springs
Travelled he with wandering wings :
Many Summers, many Winters —
I can't tell half his adventures.

At length he came back, and with him a She,
And the acorn was grown to a tall oak tree,
They built them a nest in the topmost bough,
And young ones they had, and were happy enow.
But soon came a Woodman in leathern guise,
His brow, like a pent-house, hung over his eyes.
He'd an axe in his hand, not a word he spoke,
But with many a hem ! and a sturdy stroke,
At length he brought down the poor Raven's own oak.
His young ones were killed ; for they could not depart,
And their mother did die of a broken heart.

The boughs from the trunk the Woodman did sever ;
And they floated it down on the course of the river.
They sawed it in planks, and its bark they did strip,
And with this tree and others they made a good ship.
The ship, it was launched ; but in sight of the land
Such a storm there did rise as no ship could withstand.
It bulged on a rock, and the waves rush'd in fast :
Round and round flew the raven, and cawed to the blast.
He heard the last shriek of the perishing souls—
See ! see ! o'er the topmast the mad water rolls !
  Right glad was the Raven, and off he went fleet,
And Death riding home on a cloud he did meet,
And he thanked him again and again for this treat :
  They had taken his all, and REVENGE IT WAS SWEET !

S. T. COLERIDGE

" Seventeen or eighteen years ago," wrote Coleridge in 1817,
" an artist of some celebrity was so pleased with this doggerel
that he amused himself with the thought of making a Child's
Picture Book of it ; but he could not hit on a picture for the
four lines beginning, ' Many Autumns, many Springs.' I
suggested a *Round-about* with four seats, and the four seasons,
as children, with Time for the shew-man."

ABOUT AND ROUNDABOUT

335. " A THOUSAND DARLING IMPS." (stanza 19)

" Aeriel spirits," says Robert Burton, " are such as keep quarter most part in the air, cause many tempests, thunder, and lightnings, tear oaks, fire steeples, houses, strike men and beasts, make it rain stones, . . . wool, frogs, etc., counterfeit armies in the air, strange noises, swords, etc."

Nothing vexed Linnet Sara more than to be asked if there were any such darling imps or spectres or ghosts or blackamoors in Thrae. All such to her were nothing but idle fiddle-faddle. But Reginald Scot, who wrote *The Discoverie of Witchcraft* (1584), had another kind of kitchen company when he was young.

" . . . Our mothers maide," he says, of his childhood, " so terrified us with . . . bull beggers, spirits, witches, urchens, elves, hags, fairies, satyrs, pans, faunes, sylens, kit with the cansticke, tritons, centaurs, dwarfes, giants, imps, calcars, conjurors, nymphes, changlings, Incubus, Robin goodfellowe, the spoorne, the mare, the man in the oke, the hellwaine, the fierdrake, the puckle, Tom thombe, hob gobblin, Tom tumbler, boneles, and such other bugs, that we were afraid of our own shadowes : in so much as some never feare the divill, but in a dark night ; . . ."

There seems to be no mention here of the salamander—a creature at least as rarely seen by mortal eyes as the puckle or firedrake.

" When I was about five years old," says Benvenuto Cellini, " my father happened to be in a basement-chamber of our house, where they had been washing, and where a good fire of oak logs was still burning ; he had a viol in his hand and was playing and singing alone beside the fire. The weather was very cold. Happening to look into the fire, he espied in the middle of the most burning flames a little creature like a lizard, which was sporting in the core of the intensest coals. Becoming aware of what the thing was, he had my sister and me called, and pointing it out to us children, gave me a great box on the ears, which caused me to cry with all my might. Then he pacified me by saying, ' My dear little boy, I am not striking you for anything that you have done, but only to make you remember that the lizard you see in the fire is a salamander, a creature which has never been seen before by any of whom we have credible information.' So saying he gave me some pieces of money, and kissed me."

" BELL AND WHIP AND HORSE'S TAIL " (stanza 22)

— such in old days was the Witch's vile punishment if she escaped drowning : to be whipped, tied to a horse's tail, and rung through the crowded streets.

" Agramie," I suppose, is agrimony, which, if worn by the wary, will enable the wearer to detect witches. Their eyes too will betray them, for *there* you will find no tiny image of yourself reflected as in the eyes of the honest. And if you would be rid of their company, pluck a sprig of scarlet pimpernel, and repeat this charm :

> Herbe pimpernell, I have thee found
> Growing upon Christ Jesus' ground :
> The same guift the Lord Jesus gave unto thee,
> When he shed his blood on the tree,
> Arise up, pimpernell, and goe with me.
> And God blesse me,
> And all that shall wear *thee*. AMEN.

" Say this fifteen dayes together, twice a day, morning earlye fasting, and in the evening full."

Indeed, at last, whatever the peril, a quiet heart and heaven's courage, are charm enough :

> I say that we are wound
> With mercy round and round
> As if with air : . . .
>   GERALD MANLEY HOPKINS

336. " THE WATER KELPY " (stanza 8)

is a fiend that haunts in rivers and desolate waters. It is of horse-shape, and the sound of its neighings is a boding of death to the traveller.

" Thus did the evil creatures often press me hard, but, as was meet, I served them well with my war-sword ; they had no joyous fill by eating me, wicked destroyers, sitting round their feast nigh the bottom of the sea ; but in the morning, wounded by the sword, slain by the dagger, they lay up along the sea-strand, so that they could never more hinder seafarers on their course in the deep channel.

ABOUT AND ROUNDABOUT

Light came from the east, the bright beacon of the Lord ;
the waves were stilled, and I could descry the sea-headlands,
those wind-swept walls."

Beowulf, translated by C. B. TINKER

" ' And what is the sea ?' asked Will.
' The sea !' cried the miller. ' Lord help us all, it is the
greatest thing God made ! That is where all the water in the
world runs down into a great salt lake. There it lies, as flat
as my hand and as innocent-like as a child ; but they do say
when the wind blows it gets up into water-mountains bigger
than any of ours, and swallows down great ships bigger than
our mill, and makes such a roaring that you can hear it miles
away upon the land. There are great fish in it five times bigger
than a bull, and one old serpent as long as our river and as old
as all the world, with whiskers like a man, and a crown of
silver on her head.' "

ROBERT LOUIS STEVENSON

341. " THE WANDERING SPECTRE."

" . . . The usewall Method for a curious Person to get a
transient Sight of this otherwise invisible Crew of Subter-
raneans, . . . is to put his left Foot under the Wizard's right
Foot, and the Seer's Hand is put on the Inquirer's Head, who
is to look over the Wizard's right Shoulder . . . then will he
see a Multitude of Wights, like furious hardie Men, flocking to
him haistily from all Quarters, as thick as Atoms in the Air. . . .
Thes thorow Fear strick him breathless and speechless."

So says " Mr. Robert Kirk, Minister at Aberfoill," in his
Secret Commonwealth of 1691.

Of these invisible wights the womenkind " are said to Spin
very fine, to Dy, to Tossue, and Embroyder, but whether only
curious Cob-webs, impalpable Rainbows . . . I leave to con-
jecture."

343. " AND CLOOTIE'S WAUR NOR A WOMAN WAS."
(stanza 19)

A strip or patch of wild weedy uncropped ground (like the
Sluggard's garden) that in England is called *No Man's Land*,
the Scots country folk call *Clootie's Croft* (or Clootie's little
field). They hand it over by name, as it were, to the Fiend,

hoping that he may rest content with its harvest of nettle and bramble and burr, and not range elsewhere. It is an old belief that if, like Christian, the wayfarer meets Apollyon straddling across his path, he may have to withstand him not only with sword and staff, but with his wits. Just so, too, in old times, sovereign princes would test strangers with dark questions and riddles. In this ballad the Fiend disguised as a knight comes wooing at a Widow's door, in the next he is abroad on the high road. Jennifer and the wee boy kept up their hearts, their wits about them, their eyes open, and " had the last word " ; which, says Mr. Sidgwick, is a mighty powerful charm against evil spirits—as against Witches are the herbs vervain, dill, basil, hyssop, periwinkle and rue. Iron, too ; the cross, and running water.

Here is another such encounter from *The White Wallet*—packed with poems new and old. You can almost hear the voices of the two speakers standing together in the quiet and dust of the morning road :

MEET-ON-THE-ROAD.

" Now, pray, where are you going, child ?" said Meet-on-the-Road.

" To school, sir, to school, sir," said Child-as-It-Stood.

" What have you in your basket, child ?" said Meet-on-the-Road.

" My dinner, sir, my dinner, sir," said Child-as-It-Stood.

" What have you for your dinner, child ?" said Meet-on-the-Road.

" Some pudding, sir, some pudding, sir," said Child-as-It-Stood.

" Oh, then I pray, give me a share," said Meet-on-the-Road.

" I've little enough for myself, sir," said Child-as-It-Stood.

" What have you got that cloak on for ?" said Meet-on-the Road.

" To keep the wind and cold from me," said Child-as-It-Stood.

" I wish the wind would blow through you," said Meet-on-the-Road.

" Oh, what a wish ! Oh, what a wish !" said Child-as-It Stood.

ABOUT AND ROUNDABOUT

" Pray what are those bells ringing for ?" said Meet-on-the-Road.

" To ring bad spirits home again," said Child-as-It-Stood.

" Oh, then, I must be going, child !" said Meet-on-the-Road.
" So fare you well, so fare you well," said Child-as-It-Stood.

And here, for titbits and *bonnes bouches*, are Seven Ancient Riddles from *Popular Rhymes*—in case :

i.
The fiddler and his wife,
  The piper and his mother,
Ate three half-cakes, three whole cakes,
  And three quarters of another.

ii.
A house full, a yard full,
And ye can't catch a bowl full.

iii.
As I was going o'er London Bridge,
  I heard something crack ;
Not a man in all England
  Can mend that !

iv.
I had a little sister,
  They called her Pretty Peep ;
She wades in the waters,
  Deep, deep, deep !
She climbs up the mountains,
  High, high, high ;
My poor little sister,
  She has but one eye.

v.
As I was going o'er yon moor of moss,
I met a man on a gray horse ;
He whipp'd and he wail'd,
I ask'd him what he ail'd ;
He said he was going to his father's funeral,
Who died seven years before he was born !

617

vi.

As I looked out o' my chamber window,
I heard something fall ;
I sent my maid to pick it up,
But she couldn't pick it all.

vii.

Black within, and red without,
Four corners round about.

ANSWERS.

i. 1¾ cakes each ; since, if Mr. Piper marries, his wife will
be Mr. and Mrs. Fiddler's dear daughter-in-law. ii. Smoke ;
iii. Ice ; iv. A Star ; v. The poor soul in the coffin was by
trade a dyer ; vi. Snuff (!) ; vii. A Chimney (in Days of Yore).

344. " THE FAUSE KNICHT."

Such visitants, it would appear, have marvellous power even
over faces or shapes in stone :

He's tied his steed to the kirk-stile,
    Syne wrang-gaites round the kirk gaed he ;
When the Mer-Man entered the kirk-door,
    Away the sma' images turned their e'e. . . .

Wrang-gaites must mean widdershins, left to right, West
to East, the opposite to *deiseal* (deshal)—to the right, Sunwards.

Here is another such visitor—one who considerately intrudes
not all at once but little by little, bone by bone :

THE STRANGE VISITOR.

A wife was sitting at her reel ae night ;
    And aye she sat, and aye she reeled, and aye she wished for
        company.

In came a pair o' braid braid soles, and sat down at the fire-
        side ;
    And aye she sat, and aye she reeled, and aye she wished for
        company.

In came a pair o' sma' legs, and sat down on the braid braid
        soles ;
    And aye she sat, and aye she reeled, and aye she wished for
        company.

ABOUT AND ROUNDABOUT

In came a pair o' muckle muckle knees, and sat down on the
    sma' sma' legs ;
  And aye she sat, and aye she reeled, and aye she wished for
    company.
In came a pair o' sma' sma' thees, and sat down on the muckle
    muckle knees ;
  And aye she sat, and aye she reeled, and aye she wished for
    company.
In came a pair o' muckle muckle hips, and sat down on the
    sma' sma' thees ;
  And aye she sat, and aye she reeled, and aye she wished for
    company.
In came a sma' sma' waist, and sat down on the muckle
    muckle hips ;
  And aye she sat, and aye she reeled, and aye she wished for
    company.
In came a pair o' braid braid shouthers, and sat down on the
    sma' sma' waist ;
  And aye she sat, and aye she reeled, and aye she wished for
    company.
In came a pair o' sma' sma' arms, and sat down on the braid
    braid shouthers ;
  And aye she sat, and aye she reeled, and aye she wished for
    company.
In came a pair o' muckle muckle hands, and sat down on the
    sma' sma' arms ;
  And aye she sat, and aye she reeled, and aye she wished for
    company.
In came a sma' sma' neck, and sat down on the braid braid
    shouthers ;
  And aye she sat, and aye she reeled, and aye she wished for
    company.
In came a great big head, and sat down on the sma' sma' neck ;
  And aye she sat, and aye she reeled, and aye she wished for
    company.

" What way hae ye sic braid braid feet ?" quo' the wife.
" Muckle ganging, muckle ganging."
" What way hae ye sic sma' sma' legs ?"
" *Aih-h-h* !—late—and *wee-e-e* moul."

" What way hae ye sic muckle muckle knees ?"
" Muckle praying, muckle praying."
" What way hae ye sic sma' sma' thees ?"
" *Aih-h-h* ! late and *wee-e-e* moul."
" What way hae ye sic big big hips ? "
" Muckle sitting, muckle sitting."
" What way hae ye sic a sma' sma' waist ?"
" *Aih-h-h* ! late—and *wee-e-e* moul."
" What way hae ye sic braid braid shouthers ?"
" Wi' carrying broom, wi' carrying broom."
" What way hae ye sic sma' sma' arms ?"
" *Aih-h-h* ! late—and *wee-e-e* moul."
" What way hae ye sic muckle muckle hands ?"
" Threshing wi' an iron flail, threshing wi' an iron flail."
" What way hae ye sic a sma' sma' neck ?"
" *Aih-h-h* ! late—and *wee-e-e* moul."
" What way hae ye sic a muckle muckle head ?"
" Muckle wit, muckle wit."
" What do you come for ?"
" For YOU !"

345. " CHRISTABEL."

I have included only these few stanzas of this familiar
magical poem because a book is but one book, and to print
everything as lovely or almost as lovely would need many.

In reading it, as Coleridge explained, all that is necessary to ensure its lilt and cadence is to remember that
every line, however few or many its words or syllables, has
four accents, and that these fall in accord with the meaning
of the lines as one reads them with clear eyes, attentive ear,
and understanding. In his tale of Genevieve there is yet
another false and lovely Fiend :

> . . . But when I told the cruel scorn
> That crazed that bold and lovely Knight,
> And that he crossed the mountain-woods,
> Nor rested day nor night ;
>
> That sometimes from the savage den,
> And sometimes from the darksome shade,
> And sometimes starting up at once
> In green and sunny glade,—

ABOUT AND ROUNDABOUT

There came and looked him in the face
An angel beautiful and bright ;
And that he knew it was a Fiend,
This miserable Knight——

" A TOOTHLESS MASTIFF BITCH."

Here is a description of one *with* teeth—a dog seldom seen
now. It is taken from a German book on husbandry, translated by Barnaby Goodge, and is quoted in *Animal Lore :*
" First the mastie that keepeth the house : for this purpose
you must provide you such a one, as hath a large and a mightie
body, a great and a shrill voyce, that both with his barking
he may discover, and with his sight dismay the theefe, yea,
being not seene, with the horror of his voice put him to flight ;
his stature must neither be long nor short, but well set, his
head great, his eyes sharpe, and fiery, . . . his countenance like
a lion, his brest great and shaghayrd, his shoulders broad, his
legges bigge, his tayle short, his feet very great ; his disposition
must neither be too gentle, nor too curst, that he neither fawne
upon a theefe, nor flee (fly) upon his friends ; very waking,
no gadder abroad, not lavish of his mouth, barking without
cause. Neither maketh it any matter though he be not swift :
for he is but to fight at home, and to give warning of the
enemie." And his name is little Bingo !

347. "ONCE A FAIR AND STATELY PALACE."

The radiant palace of this poem is indeed far away—the
other side of dream and night. Its monstrous word, *Porphyro-
gene,* means a prince, a child-Royal, one born in the chamber
of some Eastern palace walled with rare porphyry.

350. "SWEET WHISPERS ARE HEARD BY THE TRAVELLER."
(stanza 6)

On a poet's lips I slept
Dreaming like a love-adept
In the sound his breathing kept ;
Nor seeks nor finds he mortal blisses,
But feeds on the aërial kisses
Of shapes that haunt thought's wildernesses.

ABOUT AND ROUNDABOUT

He will watch from dawn to gloom
The lake-reflected sun illume
The yellow bees in the ivy-bloom,
Nor heed nor see, what things they be ;
But from these create he can
Forms more real than living man,
Nurslings of immortality ! . . .

PERCY BYSSHE SHELLEY

352. " MY A DILDIN."

This, 353, 355 and 356 are four more Singing-Game Rhymes,
worn down into almost nonsensical jingle by multitudinous
tongues in long long usage. (See No. 41, page 36).

And—since in my humble opinion it is not easy to get too
much of this kind of good thing—here is another :

Bobby Shaft is gone to sea,
With silver buckles at his knee ;
When he'll come home he'll marry me,
Pretty Bobby Shaft !

Bobby Shaft is fat and fair,
Combing down his yellow hair ;
He's my love for evermair,
Pretty Bobby Shaft !

352. " WE ARE COME TO COURT."

King Edelbrode cam owre the sea,
Fa la lilly.
All for to marry a gay ladye,
Fa la lilly.

Her lilly hands, sae white and sma',
Fa la lilly.
Wi' gouden rings were buskit braw,
Fa la lilly. . . . .

And here is a Bride of Elizabeth's day whom I chanced on
in that packed and inexhaustible book, *Shakespeare's England.*
When " buskit braw," she must have been as lovely to see as a
hawthorn in May or a wax candle in a silver shrine :

" The bride being attired in a gown of sheeps russet, and a
kirtle of fine worsted, her head attired with a billiment of gold,
and her hair as yellow as gold hanging down behind her, which

622

was curiously combed and pleated, according to the manner in those days : she was led to church between two sweet boys, with bride-laces and rosemary tied about their silken sleeves. . . . Then was there a fair bride-cup of silver and gilt carried before her wherein was a goodly branch of rosemary, gilded very fair, hung about with silken ribands of all colours : next was there a noise of musicians, that played all the way before her : after her came all the chiefest maidens of the country, some bearing great bride-cakes, and some garlands of wheat, finely gilded, and so she passed to the Church."

As for the silken ribands they may have been of Drakes colour or Ladies blush or Gozelinge colour or Marigold or Isabel or Peas porridge tawny or Popingay blew or Lusty gallant, but they were certainly not Judas colour, Devil in the hedge, or Dead Spaniard.

355. "AND FEED HER WI' NEW MILK AND BREAD."

The Yellow-haired Laddie sat down on yon brae,
Cries—Milk the ewes, Lassie ! let nane o' them gae !
And ay she milked, and ay she sang—
The Yellow-haired Laddie shall be my gudeman !
And ay she milked, and ay she sang—
The Yellow-haired Laddie shall be my gudeman ! . . .

ALLAN RAMSAY

357. QUOTH JOHN TO JOAN.

This old song, which was set to music in the reign of Henry VIII., comes (like Dallyaunce of No. 35), out of a Morality Play, *Lusty Juventus*, the author of which is said to be one " R. Wever," whose body has now for many a century been slumbering on in its cocoon.

358. MILK-WHITE FINGERS, CHERRY NOSE.

This is the only poem I have ever seen in which the midmost feature of a pretty face is compared to a cherry. And yet a frosty morning must have given many a dainty nose that fair bright coral colour.

So too, Bob Cherry, in these lines *To His Lady* :

Black-heart were mine to love not thy
White-heart so sweet and tender ;
Be kind, my dear, for—Summer by—
What fruits hath cold December ?

ABOUT AND ROUNDABOUT

359. " OR THE BEES THEIR CAREFUL KING."

In old times the " Governor " of a Bee Hive was sometimes referred to as the King and sometimes as the Queen. The choice depended in part on which kind of monarch was on the throne. There is an entrancing story of the middle ages, told by Mr. Tickner Edwardes in his book on the Honey Bee.

" A certaine simple woman, on finding that her bees were storing little honey for her and were perishing of " the murraine," stole one of the holy wafers from the priest, and for miraculous remedy concealed it in one of her hives. " Whereupon the Murraine ceased and the Honie abounded. The Woman, therefore lifting up the hive at the due time to take out the Honie, saw there (most strange to be seene) a Chappell built by the Bees, with an altar to it, the wals adorned by marvellous skill of architecture, with windowes conveniently set in their places : also a doore and a steeple with bells. And the Host being laid upon the altar, the Bees making a sweet noise, flew around it." Apart from " the singing masons building roofs of gold," the gluttonous drones, the sentries, wax-makers, bread-kneaders, nurses, etc., there are the Queen's Ladies-in-waiting . " For difference from the rest they beare for their crest a tuft or tossell, in some coloured yellow, in some murrey, in manner of a plume ; whereof some turne downward like an Ostrich-feather, others stand upright like a Hern-top." But for truths even stranger than fantasy regarding bees and their kind, go to Henri Fabre.

360. " AND HERE, AND HERE."

As Flora slept and I lay waking,
I smiled to see a bird's mistaking,
For from a bough it down did skip
And for a cherry pecked her lip. . . .

362. " MY HEART IS GLADDER THAN ALL THESE."

How many times do I love thee, dear ?
Tell me how many thoughts there be
In the atmosphere
Of the new fall'n year,
Whose white and sable hours appear
The latest flake of eternity :
So many times do I love thee, dear !

ABOUT AND ROUNDABOUT

How many times do I love again ?
        Tell me how many beads there are
                In a silver chain
                Of evening rain
        Unravelled from the tumbling main,
        And threading the eye of a yellow star :
So many times do I love again !
                                THOMAS LOVELL BEDDOES

363.

The word screen (line 4) means, I think, " Hide and shelter those smiles away that in their beauty seem to burn in the air " : for all beauty resembles radiance in its influence on the mind. And this recalls to memory Southwell's poem, *The Burning Babe*, No. 256.

364. " A SONNET OF THE MOON."

The closer one looks at and examines a fine *sonnet*—its way of rhyming, its rise, poise, flight and fall, the ease and exactitude with which what is said in it fills its mould or form— the more, I was going to say, one should hesitate before attempting to write another. This particular sonnet (like No. 361), is of the English or Shakespearean kind, and is so lovely a thing that only a close attention would notice the carelessness of its rhymes. No. 342 is an example of the form which our sixteenth century poets borrowed from Italy. Comparison of them shows that, as with the old Chinese ginger jars, so in poetry : not only is the syrup delightful, but even the pot may be interesting.

Coleridge wrote few sonnets, and this is his explanation of the length one must be : " It is confined to fourteen lines, because as some particular number is necessary, and that particular number must be a small one, it may as well be fourteen as any other number. When no reason can be adduced against a thing, Custom is a sufficient reason for it."

When I read this last remark for the first time it was as if my mind had been startled into attention as one's body is when it collides with a stranger in the street. There is a wide wisdom in it. How many natural, human and delightful things there are in this world indeed for which Custom is a sufficient reason : Children, for instance, daisies in the grass, skylarks in the clouds, dreams in sleep, rhymes, gay clothes, friendship, laughter.

"THE PALE QUEEN."

There is the apparition of a lovely face in the Moon—proud and mute—to be discovered by careful eyes usually on the extreme right of the disc, her own eyes gazing towards the left.

368. "IT WAS IN AND ABOUT THE MARTINMAS TIME."

This old Scottish song was a favourite of Oliver Goldsmith's in his childhood. "The music of the finest singer," he said, "is dissonance to what I felt when our old dairy-maid sung me into tears with *Johnny Armstrong's Last Good-night*, or *The Cruelty of Barbara Allen.*

As with the Scottish ballads so with this last poem—it is the brevity and bareness with which the story is told and is *not* told that sets it apart. Without one express word to prove it so, we know that Sir John had always loved the proud Barbara even though he had spoken lightly of her, and that she too had always loved him, though she refuses the word that would have saved his life.

371. "I NEVER HAD BUT ONE TRUE LOVE, IN COLD GRAVE SHE WAS LAIN."

Yet another tragic and sorrowful poem of which, to some fancies, there may be too many in this book already. Well, here is the story of the beautiful Princess Uillanita: She cared only for flowers white and colourless as dew in the first light of day, or as laundered linen blanching on a hedge of thorn. And she came one still evening, when she was in search of what she could not find, to a valley wherein a forest gloomed above a deep but placid river. Within the forest, refreshed by the mists of the river, grew none but flowers blue and dark and purple, and such was the young Princess's hatred of them that she covered her eyes with her hands, fled on, and so lost her way.

In the middle of the night and long after she had wept herself to sleep, the wailing of a nocturnal bird pierced into her dreams, and she woke to find one solitary star of the colourlessness of Vega shining alone in radiance in the space of sky betwixt the branches above her head. Its thin ray silvered down—spearlike in its straightness—and of a beam easily sufficing to irradiate a tiny clustering flower which stood scarcely visible in the moss at her hand's side, and was drenching the air with its fragrance. It was a flower utterly strange to her, whiter than hoarfrost, fairer than foam.

The enravished Princess gazed spellbound. "Why," whispered she to herself, in the quiet of the dark gigantic forest ; "if I had not wept at the flowers of this sombre forest, if I had not lost my way, if I had not been moved in my sleep to awaken, I never should have seen this crystal thing ; that is lovelier than I deemed Paradise itself could bring to bloom." And she kissed the thin-spun petals, and happily fell again asleep.

372. "A Lament."

Only two stanzas out of six, and these, maybe, a little difficult in the old Scots :

> Depart, depart, depart !
> Alas ! I must depart
> From her that has my heart
> With heart full sore ;
> Against my will indeed
> And can find no remede—
> I wait the pains of death—
> Can do no more. . . .

> Adieu mine own sweet thing,
> My joy and comforting,
> My mirth and solacing
> Of earthly gloir :
> Farewell, my lady bright,
> And my remembrance right,
> Farewell, and have good night—
> I say no more.

380. To Helen.

Who " the wayworn wanderer " is, I am uncertain ; but apart from its rare music, how long a journey awaits the imagination in this poem, and how closely inwoven is its thought. Yet it is said to have been written when Poe was in his early 'teens.

ABOUT AND ROUNDABOUT

381. "THERE IS A LADY."

Mr. Nahum's picture for this poem was of a little winged boy at evening, his quiver of arrows on his back, his bow the perch of a nightingale, and himself lying fast asleep under a hawthorn bush in full flower—a narrow green sun-dappled river near-by, rosy clouds and birds in the air, and strange snow-peaked hills afar.

"TILL I DIE."

. . . Only our love hath no decay ;
This no to-morrow hath, nor yesterday ;
Running it never runs from us away,
But truly keeps his first, last, everlasting day.

JOHN DONNE

383. "IT IS NOT SO."

Silly boy 'tis ful Moon yet, thy night as day shines clearely.
Had thy youth but wit to feare, thou couldst not love so
dearely.
Shortly wilt thou mourne when all thy pleasures are bereavèd ;
Little knows he how to love that never was deceivèd. . . .

Yet be just and constant still ! Love may beget a wonder,
Not unlike a Summer's frost, or Winter's fatall thunder.
He that holds his Sweethart true, unto his day of dying,
Lives, of all that ever breathed, most worthy the envỳing.

THOMAS CAMPION

385.

In this poem, as in all Christina Rossetti's work, there is a rhythm and poise, a serpentining of music, so delicate that on clumsy lips it will vanish as rapidly as the bloom from a plum. Indeed, each stanza is like a branch (with its twigs) of a wild damson-tree, its wavering line broken and beautified with bud, flower and leaf. And certainly as fresh an air, and as clear a light, stirs and dwells in the poem as on the tree itself in April.

387.

This is from Part II., Act II., Scene i. of "Zapolya." Glycine sings unseen in a cavern—her voice comforting her lover wandering forlorn by night "in a savage wood."

ABOUT AND ROUNDABOUT

389.

For I'll cut my green coat a foot above my knee,
And I'll clip my yellow locks an inch below mine ee.
Hey, nonny, nonny, nonny.

I'll buy me a white cut, forth for to ride,
And I'll go seek him through the world that is so wide.
Hey, nonny, nonny, nonny.

391. "CHIMBORAZO, COTOPAXI."

In medieval days it seems that a traveller here and there, happily supposing the world to be a floating island of indiscoverable dimensions, hung in the wilds of space, and not knowing that it was merely an " oblate spheroid," would journey clean round it and so come back, to his amazement, to the place from which he started.   Here is such an experience from Sir John Mandeville, in his own words : " It was told that a certain worthy man departed some time from our Country for to go search the World. . . . He passed India and the Isles beyond it, where are more than 5000 Isles, and so long and for so many seasons he went by Sea and Land, and so environed the World, that he came at last to an Isle whereon he heard spoken his own language—a calling of oxen in the Plough—such Words in fact as men were wont to speak to Beasts in his own country. Whereof he greatly marvelled, knowing not how that might be." For there—as if it were a ghost or spectre—*there* was the chimney of his own house smoking up into the clear morning air !   And what did he do, maybe ?   He stared ; he sighed ; he grew pale ; he shuddered : and—he turned back !

392. " HALLO MY FANCY."

For the first sight of this poem I most gratefully thank my friend Mr. Ivor Gurney, though no doubt it was in Mr. Nahum's Book somewhere, and I was too indolent at the time to copy it out.   The poem was written by William Cleland while he was still at St. Andrews.   All else I know of him is that he was born about 1661, and fell at Dunkeld in 1689.   There is nothing in English to my knowledge that resembles it.   *Erra Pater* (stanza 4) was the name given to a busy astrologer and almanac-concocter, William Lilly, of the time.   King Phalaris's monstrous bull was of brass : he perished in it.

ABOUT AND ROUNDABOUT

By " the tapers " (stanza 2) is meant, I fancy, those phosphor-like fires that gather on the yard-arms of ships at sea when the air is electric with tempest. Sir Humphrey Gilbert's sailors were fearful at sight of this apparition, and of a monster, too, that appeared swimming in the waves beside their frigate, the *Squirrel*, a little before she and her riding lights disappeared for ever.

" . . . Men which all their life time had occupied the Sea, never saw more outragious Seas. We had also upon our maine yard, an apparition of a little fire by night, which seamen doe call Castor and Pollux. But we had onely one, which they take an evill signe of more tempest . . . The same Monday night, about twelve of the clocke . . . suddenly her lights were out . . . and withall our watch cryed, *the Generall was cast away*, which was too true. For in that moment, the Frigat was devoured and swallowed up of the Sea . . ."

As for Cupid (stanza 5), he is said to be the slyest archer that ever shot arrow—and a dangerous child either to entertain (as the poem proves that begins as follows) :

> Cupid abroade was 'lated in the night,
> His wings were wet with ranging in the raine ;
> Harbour he sought, to mee hee took his flight,
> To dry his plumes I heard the boy complaine.
> I opte the doore and graunted his desire,
> I rose my selfe, and made the wagge a fire . . . .

or—as yet another poem shows—to take as a scholar :

> I dreamt by me I saw fair Venus stand,
> Holding young Cupid in her lovely hand,
> And said, kind Shepherd, I a scholar bring
> My little son, to learn of you to sing. . . .

And last, the pelican (in stanza 7). She was supposed in old days to be " the lovingest bird that is," since at need she would pierce her breast with her bill to feed her young ones. The plaintive singing of the dying swan I have never heard, except in Tennyson's words :

> The plain was grassy, wild and bare,
> Wide, wild, and open to the air,
> Which had built up everywhere
> An under-roof of doleful gray.

630

ABOUT AND ROUNDABOUT

With an inner voice the river ran,
Adown it floated a dying swan,
   And loudly did lament.
  It was the middle of the day.
Ever the weary wind went on,
   And took the reed-tops as it went. . . .
Some blue peaks in the distance rose,
And white against the cold-white sky,
Shone out their crowning snows.

One willow over the river wept,
And shook the wave as the wind did sigh ;
Above in the wind was the swallow,
  Chasing itself at its own wild will,
  And far thro' the marish green and still
  The tangled water-courses slept,
Shot over with purple, and green, and yellow.

Hearke canst thou heare me ? I will play the Swan,
And dye in Musicke : Willough, Willough, Willough. . . .
                         Othello

393. "COLUMBUS'S DOOM-BURDENED CARAVELS." (line 13)

"... The next day, Thursday, October 11, 1492, was destined to be for ever memorable in the history of the world. . . . The people on the *Santa Maria* saw some petrels and a green branch in the water ; the *Pinta* saw a reed and two small sticks carved with iron, and one or two other pieces of reeds and grasses that had been grown on shore, as well as a small board. Most wonderful of all, the people of the *Nina* saw ' a little branch full of dog roses ' ; . . . The day drew to its close ; and after nightfall, according to their custom, the crews of the ships repeated the *Salve Regina*. Afterwards the Admiral addressed the people and sailors of his ship, ' very merry and pleasant,'. . . The moon was in its third quarter, and did not rise until eleven o'clock. The first part of the night was dark, and there was only a faint starlight into which the anxious eyes of the look-out men peered from the forecastles of the three ships. At ten o'clock Columbus was walking on the poop of his vessel, when he suddenly saw a light right ahead. The light seemed to rise and fall as though it

ABOUT AND ROUNDABOUT

were a candle or a lantern held in some one's hand and waved
up and down. The Admiral called Pedro Gutierrez to him
and asked him whether he saw anything ; and he also saw the
light. Then he sent for Rodrigo Sanchez and asked him if he
saw the light ; but he did not. . . . Dawn came at last,
flooding the sky with lemon and saffron and scarlet and orange,
until at last the pure gold of the sun glittered on the water.
And when it rose it showed the sea-weary mariners an island
lying in the blue sea ahead of them : the island of Guanahani ;
San Salvador. . . ."
                              Christopher Columbus, FILSON YOUNG

395.   " TO SEA, TO SEA."

. . . To the ocean now I fly,
And those happy climes that lie
Where day never shuts his eye.
Up in the broad fields of the sky ;
There I suck the liquid air
All amidst the gardens fair
Of Hesperus, and his daughters three
That sing about the golden tree :
Along the crispèd shades and bowers
Revels the spruce and jocund Spring ;
The Graces, and the rosy bosomed Hours,
Thither all their bounties bring ;
There eternal Summer dwells,
And west winds, with musky wing,
About the cedared alleys fling
Nard and Cassia's balmy smells. . . .
    But now my task is smoothly done,
I can fly, or I can run,
Quickly to the green earth's end,
Where the bowed welkin slow doth bend ;
And from thence can soar as soon
To the corners of the moon.
    Mortals, that would follow me,
Love Virtue ; she alone is free :
She can teach ye how to climb
Higher than the sphery chime ;
Or if Virtue feeble were,
Heaven itself would stoop to her.
                                        JOHN MILTON

ABOUT AND ROUNDABOUT

Master. Steersman, how stands the wind ?
Steersman. Full north-north-east.
Master. What course ?
Steersman. Full south-south-west.
Master. No worse, and blow so fair,
      Then sink despair,
         Come solace to the mind !
       Ere night, we shall the haven find.

JOHN DOWLAND

" CAVED TRITONS' AZURE DAY " (line 12)

—Dark-fated Clarence in *King Richard III.* dreamt of that
" azure day " :

         . . . As we paced along
Upon the giddy footing of the Hatches,
Me thought that Glouster stumbled, and in falling
Strooke me (that thought to stay him) over-board,
Into the tumbling billowes of the maine.
O Lord, methought what paine it was to drowne,
What dreadfull noise of water in mine eares,
What sightes of ugly death within mine eyes. . . .
Methought I saw a thousand fearfull wrackes :
A thousand men that Fishes gnawed upon :
Wedges of Gold, great Anchors, heapes of Pearle,
Inestimable Stones, unvalewed Jewels,
All scattered in the bottome of the Sea.
Some lay in dead-men's Sculles ; and in the holes
Where eyes did once inhabit, there were crept,
(As 'twere in scorne of eyes) reflecting Gemmes,
That wooed the slimy bottome of the deepe,
And mocked the dead bones that lay scattred by. . . .

396. " JEWELS MORE RICH THAN ORMUS SHOWS."
(line 20)

Mr. Nahum's picture to this was of a man clothed in rags
that must once have been rich and pompous. He sits, in the
picture, gnawing his nails upon a heap of what appears to be
precious stones and lumps of gold. All around him stretch
the sands of the seashore, and there is a little harbour with a
decayed quay, its river-mouth silted up with ooze and flotsam,
so that nothing but a row-boat could find entrance there. An

immense sun burns in the sky ; and, though a thread of fresh water flows nearby, the man among the jewels seems to be tormented with thirst. For Ormus, or Hormuz, on its narrow island of wild-coloured rocks, date-palms, parrots and many birds, was once the rich mart and treasure-house between Persia and India—spices, pearls, ivory, gold, precious stones, and, in particular, the diamond, being its merchandise. In 1507 the Portuguese Conqueror Alfonso Albuquerque stole it from its dark princes. In 1622 Shah Abbas the Great razed it to the ground. To-day it is but a waste, inhabited by a few fishermen and diggers, its only commodities—that once were gems—salt and sulphur ; while still in the height of its Summer blows Julot, Harmatan, Il Sirocco, the Flame-Wind, so deadly in its breath that the troops of an army of 1600 horsemen and 6000 foot, says Marco Polo, marching to punish the city for neglecting to pay tribute to the King of Kirman, and camping overnight without its walls, were baked next noon as dry as pumice, and not a voice among them to tell the tale, though their bodily shape and colour seemed to appearance unchanged. To protect themselves against this Julot, the citizens of Ormus would build huts of sheltering osier-work over the water, and in the heat of the morning would stand immersed in its coolness up to the chin.

" APPLES " (line 23)

—these are pineapples, the " price " of the next line meaning excellence. " Ambergris " (line 28), is a rare and costly stuff which, as its name tells, resembles grey amber. It has a wondrously sweet smell, was once used in cooking, and is disgorged by the whale that supplies the world with the comforting ointment of childhood called Spermaceti.

In Shakespeare's day, Marvell's " remote Bermudas " were known as the " Isle of Divels "—because of the nocturnal yellings, cries and yelpings that were reported to haunt them. English sailors, wrecked and cast away on Great Bermuda in 1709, however, brought home in their boats of cedar-wood the news that this wild music was caused (at least in part) by descendants of the hogs that had been left there by the long-gone Spaniard, Juan Bermudez and his men ! They told, too, that it was an island fair and commodious, of a gentle climate, and a sweet-smelling air ; and Shakespeare almost certainly had its enchantments in mind when he wrote of Ariel, Caliban and Miranda. Was not Ariel in Prospero's more solitary days called up at midnight "to fetch dewe from the still-vext Bermoothes"?

To the Puritan voyagers of Andrew Marvell's poem the Islands were as welcome and angelic as the Hesperides. And no poet could better tell of them than he. For in Marvell's verse dwells a curious happiness, like sunshine on a pool of water-lilies. Yet he, too, like other dreamers, was a man of affairs, and of endless industry and zeal. He was thrice Member of Parliament for his birthplace, Kingston-on-Hull, and, with Milton, was one of Oliver Cromwell's Latin Secretaries. John Aubrey describes him as " of a middling stature, pretty strong sett, roundish face, cherry-cheek't, hazell eie, brown hair. He was in his conversation very modest, and of very few words. And though he loved wine, he would never drink heartilie in company, and was wont to say, that, *he would not play the good fellow in any man's company in whose hands he would not trust his life.* . . . He lies interred under the pewes in the south side of St. Giles' church in-the-fields, under the window wherein is painted in glass a red lyon. . . ." And there George Chapman, William Shirley, and Lord Herbert of Cherbury share his rest.

397. " THAT TALKATIVE BALD-HEADED SEAMAN CAME."
(line 23)

" . . . And now my name ; which way shall lead to all
My miseries after, that their sounds may fall
Through your ears also, and shew (having fled
So much affliction) first, who rests his head
In your embraces, when. so far from home,
I knew not where t' obtain it resting room :
   I am Ulysses Laertiades,
The fear of all the world . . ."

The Odysseys, GEORGE CHAPMAN

398.

The prose " argument " to the " Ancient Mariner," which is almost as rare a piece of reading as the Rime itself, has been omitted. But here is a fragment of it relating to the passage on pages 390-4 : " . . . The Wedding-Guest feareth that a Spirit is talking to him ; but the ancient Mariner assureth him of his bodily life, and proceedeth to relate his horrible penance. He despiseth the creatures of the calm, and envieth that *they* should live, and so many lie dead. But the curse liveth for him in the eye of the dead men. In his loneliness and fixedness he yearneth towards the journeying Moon, and the stars that still sojourn, yet still move onward ; and every where the blue sky belongs to them, and is their appointed rest, and their native country and their own natural homes, which they enter unannounced, as lords that are certainly expected and yet there is a silent joy at their arrival.

" By the light of the Moon he beholdeth God's creatures of the great calm—their beauty and their happiness. He blesseth them in his heart. The spell begins to break. By grace of the holy Mother, the ancient Mariner is refreshed with rain. He heareth sounds and seeth strange sights and commotions in the sky and the element. The bodies of the ship's crew are inspired and inspirited, and the ship moves on ; but not by the souls of the men, nor by dæmons of earth or middle air, but by a blessed troop of angelic spirits, sent down by the invocation of the guardian saint. . . ."

" Daemons of earth or middle air " have been told of also by land travellers—by Friar Odoric, for example, in the account of his journey through Cathay during the years 1316-1330 :

" Another great and terrible thing I saw. For, as I went through a certain valley which lieth by the River of Delights, I saw therein many dead corpses lying. And I heard also therein sundry kinds of music, but chiefly nakers, which were marvellously played upon. And so great was the noise thereof that very great fear came upon me. Now, this valley is seven or eight miles long ; and if any unbeliever enter therein he quitteth it never again, but perisheth incontinently. Yet I hesitated not to go in that I might see once for all what the matter was. And when I had gone in I saw there, as I have said, such numbers of corpses as no one without seeing it could deem credible. And at one side of the valley, in the very rock, I beheld as it were the face of a man very great and terrible, so very terrible indeed that for my exceeding great fear my spirit seemed to die in me. Wherefore I made the sign of the cross, and began continually to repeat VERBUM CARO FACTUM, but I dared not at all to come nigh that face, but kept at seven

or eight paces from it. And so I came at length to the other
end of the valley, and there I ascended a hill of sand and looked
around me. But nothing could I descry, only I still heard
those nakers to play which were played so marvellously. And
when I got to the top of that hill I found there a great quantity
of silver heaped up as it had been fishes' scales, and some of this
I put into my bosom. But as I cared nought for it, and was
at the same time in fear lest it should be a snare to hinder my
escape, I cast it all down again to the ground. And so by
God's grace I came forth scathless. Then all the Saracens,
when they heard of this, showed me great worship, saying that
I was a baptised and holy man. But those who had perished
in that valley they said belonged to the devil."

As an Arab journeyeth
Through a sand of Ayaman,
Lean Thirst, lolling its cracked tongue,
Lagging by his side along ;
And a rusty wingèd Death
Grating its low flight before,
Casting ribbèd shadows o'er
The blank desert, blank and tan :
He lifts by hap to'rd where the morning's roots are
His weary stare,—
Sees, although they plashless mutes are,
Set in a silver air
Fountains of gelid shoots are,
Making the daylight fairest fair ;
Sees the palm and tamarind
Tangle the tresses of a phantom wind ;—
A sight like innocence when one has sinned
A green and maiden freshness smiling there,
While with unblinking glare
The tawny-hided desert crouches watching her. . . .
The Mirage, FRANCIS THOMPSON

Thou to me art such a spring
As the Arab seeks at eve,
Thirsty from the shining sands ;
There to bathe his face and hands,
While the sun is taking leave,
And dewy sleep is a delicious thing.

ABOUT AND ROUNDABOUT

Thou to me art such a dream
As he dreams upon the grass,
While the bubbling coolness near
Makes sweet music in his ear ;
And the stars that slowly pass
In solitary grandeur o'er him gleam.

Thou to me art such a dawn
As the dawn whose ruddy kiss
Wakes him to his darling steed ;
And again the desert speed,
And again the desert bliss,
Lightens thro' his veins, and he is gone !
GEORGE MEREDITH

399. "HE TOLD OF WAVES." (line 28)

So, too, does the Ship's Captain in yet such another ore-loaden poem of the marvellous, "The Sale of St. Thomas," by Lascelles Abercrombie, telling how the saint in terror of the unknown would turn back from his mission, is rebuked by his Master, and sold by him for twenty pieces of silver to the Captain of a slant-sailed vessel bound for the barbarous Indies. Here is but a fragment of the poem :

" . . . . *A Ship's Captain.* You are my man, my passenger ?
Thomas.   I am.
          I go to India with you.
Captain.   Well, I hope so.
          There's threatening in the weather. Have you a mind
          To hug your belly to the slanted deck,
          Like a louse on a whip-top, when the boat
          Spins on an axle in the hissing gales ?
Thomas. Fear not. 'Tis likely indeed that storms are now
          Plotting against our voyage ; ay, no doubt
          The very bottom of the sea prepares
          To stand up mountainous or reach a limb
          Out of his night of water and huge shingles,
          That he and the waves may break our keel. Fear not ;
          Like those who manage horses, I've a word
          Will fasten up within their evil natures
          The meanings of the winds and waves and reefs.

ABOUT AND ROUNDABOUT

Captain. You have a talisman ? I have one too ;
    I know not if the storms think much of it.
    I may be shark's meat yet. And would your spell
    Be daunting to a cuttle, think you now ?
    We had a bout with one on our way here ;
    It had green lidless eyes like lanterns, arms
    As many as the branches of a tree,
    But limber, and each one of them wise as a snake.
    It laid hold of our bulwarks, and with three
    Long knowing arms, slimy, and of a flesh
    So tough they'ld fool a hatchet, searcht the ship,
    And stole out of the midst of us all a man ;
    Yes, and he the proudest man upon the seas
    For the rare powerful talisman he'd got.
    And would yours have done better ?

Thomas.   I am one
    Not easily frightened. I'm for India. . . ."

.400. " PARROTS OF SHRILLY GREEN "

—this gaudy and longevous bird, that seems to contain all the
wisdom of Solomon and more than the craft of Cleopatra in
his eye, perched first upon England many centuries ago.
Skelton speaks of him :

    My name is parrot, a bird of Paradise . . .
    With my becke bent, my little wanton eye,
    My fethers fresh, as is the emrawde grene,
    About my neck a circulet, lyke the ryche rubye,
    My little legges, my fete both nete and cleane. . . .

And so, too, John Maplet, a " naturalist " who in 1567
wrote *A Greene Forest :*
  " The Parret hath all hir whole bodie greene, saving that
onely about hir necke she hath a Coller or Chaine naturally
wrought like to Sinople or Vermelon. Indie hath of this kinde
such as will counterfaite redily a mans speach : what wordes
they heare, those commonly they pronounce. There have
bene found of these that have saluted Emperours. . . ."
  But which Emperors, and when and to what end he does not
relate. A parrot of price indeed would be she that had held
converse with " Ozymandias, king of kings."

ABOUT AND ROUNDABOUT

402. " THE MARCH OF TIME." (line 2)

Say, is there aught that can convey
An image of its transient stay ?
'Tis an hand's breadth ; 'tis a tale ;
'Tis a vessel under sail :
'Tis a courser's straining steed ;
'Tis a shuttle in its speed ;
'Tis an eagle in its way,
Darting down upon its prey ;
'Tis an arrow in its flight,
Mocking the pursuing sight ;
'Tis a vapour in the air ;
'Tis a whirlwind rushing there ;
'Tis a short-lived fading flower ;
'Tis a rainbow on a shower ;
'Tis a momentary ray
Smiling in a winter's day ;
'Tis a torrent's rapid stream ;
'Tis a shadow ; 'tis a dream ;
'Tis the closing watch of night,
Dying at approaching light ;
'Tis a landscape vainly gay,
Painted upon crumbling clay ;
'Tis a lamp that wastes its fires,
'Tis a smoke that quick expires ;
'Tis a bubble, 'tis a sigh :
Be prepared, O Man ! to die.

They are like strings of precious stones, rosaries, these Tudor
laments, one image following another, and however sad in
colour, all making beauty :

As withereth the primrose by the river,
As fadeth summer's sun from gliding fountains,
As vanisheth the light-blown bubble ever,
As melteth snow upon the mossy mountains :
So melts, so vanisheth, so fades, so withers,
The rose, the shine, the bubble, and the snow,
Of praise, pomp, glory, joy, which short life gathers,
Fair praise, vain pomp, sweet glory, brittle joy.
The withered primrose by the mourning river,

ABOUT AND ROUNDABOUT

The faded summer's sun from weeping fountains,
The light-blown bubble vanishèd for ever,
The molten snow upon the naked mountains,
Are emblems that the treasures we uplay,
Soon wither, vanish, fade, and melt away. . . .

403. " THE WILD HYAENA." (line 11)

In old times it was believed that if a hungry hyaena or jaccatray—who cannot wry his neck " because his backbone stretches itself out to the head "—dreams, he dreams so vividly that he calls into his sleeping brain a vision of the beasts he covets for prey. And this vision is so lifelike that he howls out of his sleep in mockery of the beasts—and thus decoys them to his den ! He is a nocturnal scavenger, haunting graveyards, and " when " says Lyly, he " speaketh lyke a man," he " deviseth most mischief."

404. " IN XANADU DID KUBLA KHAN."

" Now, this lord (the Great Caan)," says Friar Odoric in his *Cathay*, " passeth the summer at a certain place which is called SANDU, situated towards the north, and the coolest habitation in the world. But in the winter season he abideth in Cambalech. And when he will ride from the one place to the other this is the order thereof. He hath four armies of horsemen, one of which goeth a day's march in front of him, one at each side, and one a day's march in rear, so that he goeth always as it were, in the middle of a cross. And marching thus, each army hath its route laid down for it day by day, and findeth at its halts all necessary provender. But his own immediate company hath its order of march thus. The king travelleth in a two-wheeled carriage, in which is formed a very goodly chamber, all of lign-aloes and gold, and covered over with great and fine skins, and set with many precious stones. And the carriage is drawn by four elephants, well broken in and harnessed, and also by four splendid horses, richly caparisoned. And alongside go four barons, who are called CUTHE, keeping watch and ward over the chariot that no hurt come to the king. Moreover, he carrieth with him in his chariot twelve gerfalcons ; so that even as he sits therein upon his chair of state or other seat, if he sees any birds pass he lets fly his hawks at them. And none may dare to approach within a stone's throw of the carriage, unless those whose duty brings them there. And thus it is that the king travelleth."

"A SUNLESS SEA."

Our English eyes, loving light, weary a little of the short cold days in our country, when the sun makes " winter arches." Sadder still would be our state in the regions told of by Marco Polo in the following passage :

" Beyond the most distant part of the territory of the Tartars, . . . there is another region [thick set with dark impenetrable woods] which extends to the utmost bounds of the north, and is called the Region of Darkness, because during most part of the winter months the sun is invisible, and the atmosphere is obscured to the same degree as that in which we find it just about the dawn of day, when we may be said to see and not to see. The men of this country are well made and tall, but of a very pallid complexion. They are not united under the government of a king or prince, and they live without any established laws or usages, in the manner of the brute creation. Their intellects also are dull, and they have an air of stupidity. The Tartars often proceed on plundering expeditions against these people, to rob them of their cattle and goods. For this purpose they avail themselves of those months in which the darkness prevails, in order that their approach may be unobserved ; but, being unable to ascertain the direction in which they should return homeward with their booty, they provide against the chance of going astray by riding mares that have young foals at the time, which latter they suffer to accompany the dams as far as the confines of their own territory, but leave them, under proper care, at the commencement of the gloomy region. When their works of darkness have been accomplished, and they are desirous of revisiting the region of light, they lay the bridles on the necks of their mares, and suffer them freely to take their own course. Guided by maternal instinct, they make their way directly to the spot where they had quitted their foals ; and by these means the riders are enabled to regain in safety the places of their residence."

ABOUT AND ROUNDABOUT

406. " ONE HELD A SHELL UNTO HIS SHELL-LIKE EAR."
(line 6)

. . . Gather a shell from the strown beach
And listen at its lips : they sigh
The same desire and mystery,
The echo of the whole sea's speech.
And all mankind is thus at heart
Not anything but what thou art :
And Earth, Sea, Man, are all in each.

DANTE GABRIEL ROSSETTI

407. " LIKE SOLEMN APPARITIONS LULLED SUBLIME TO
EVERLASTING REST." (line 11)

. . . In the caves of the deep—lost Youth ! lost Youth !—
O'er and o'er, fleeting billows ! fleeting billows !—
Rung to his restless everlasting sleep
By the heavy death-bells of the deep,
Under the slimy-drooping sea-green willows,
Poor Youth ! lost Youth !
Laying his dolorous head, forsooth,
On Carian reefs uncouth—
Poor Youth !
On the wild sand's ever-shifting pillows ! . . .

O could my Spirit wing
Hills over, where salt Ocean hath his fresh headspring
And snowy curls bedeck the Blue-haired King,
Up where sweet oral birds articulate sing
Within the desert ring—
Their mighty shadows o'er broad Earth the Lunar
Mountains fling,
Where the Sun's chariot bathes in Ocean's fresh head-
spring—
O could my Spirit wing ! . . .

GEORGE DARLEY

Full fathom five thy Father lies,
Of his bones are Corrall made :
Those are Pearles that were his eies,
Nothing of him that doth fade,

643

ABOUT AND ROUNDABOUT

But doth suffer a Sea-change
Into something rich, and strange :
Sea-Nimphs hourly ring his knell—
                                    Ding dong.
Harke now I heare them, *ding-dong bell.*

WILLIAM SHAKESPEARE

411. " THE GOLDEN VANITY."

This is a patchwork of stanzas from three versions of the
old ballad. In one version the " Golden Vanity " is said
to be the " Sweet Trinity," and to have been built by Sir
Walter Raleigh in the Netherlands. According to yet another,
the Cabin-boy, after threatening to sink the " Goulden Vanitie "
as he had " sunk the French gallee," is taken on board and the
Captain and merchant adventurers proved " far better than
their word." But if stanza 12 is any witness, this seems
unlikely. Can one not actually *see* the cold faces mocking
down upon the water ?

412.

To an eye and ear new to them, these old Scottish ballads
may seem a little difficult and forbidding. But read on, and
their enchantment has no match—the very strangeness of the
words, the rare music, the colour and light and clearness and
vehemence, and, besides these, a wildness and ancientness like
that of an old folk-tune which seems to carry with its burden
as many lost memories as an old churchyard has gravestones.
The stories they tell are world wide. How they came into that
world (for of some of them there are as many as twenty to
thirty different versions), how they have fared in their long
journey, and even when and by whom they were made, are
still questions on which even scholars are not yet agreed.

" Kevels " in line 5 of " Brown Robyn," means *lots,* and
recalls a far older story :

" Now the word of the Lord came unto Jonah the son of
Amittai, saying, Arise, go to Nineveh, that great city, and cry
against it ; for their wickedness is come up before me. But
Jonah rose up to flee unto Tarshish from the presence of the
Lord, and went down to Joppa ; and he found a ship going to
Tarshish, so he paid the fare thereof, and went down into it,
to go with them unto Tarshish from the presence of the Lord.

ABOUT AND ROUNDABOUT

But the Lord sent out a great wind into the sea, and there was a mighty tempest in the sea, so that the ship was like to be broken. Then the mariners were afraid, and cried every man unto his god, and cast forth the wares that were in the ship into the sea, to lighten it of them. But Jonah was gone down into the sides of the ship ; and he lay, and was fast asleep. . . . And they said every one to his fellow, Come, and let us cast lots, that we may know for whose cause this evil is upon us. So they cast lots, and the lot fell upon Jonah. . . . Then said they unto him, What shall we do unto thee, that the sea may be calm unto us ? for the sea wrought, and was tempestuous. And he said unto them, Take me up, and cast me forth into the sea ; so shall the sea be calm upon you : for I know that for my sake this great tempest is upon you. . . . So they took up Jonah, and cast him forth into the sea ; and the sea ceased from her raging."

415. "A SEAL MY FATHER WAS."

Notes of music for the enticement of seals, with other beautiful old Gaelic airs and poems and tales, will be found in Journals 23/5 of The Folk-Song Society, collected by Mr. Martin Freeman.

418. "SIR PATRICK SPENCE."

The longer version of the ballad into which the genius of Sir Walter Scott wove a few new stanzas is the better known. But this, I think, is the best. Indeed, the secret art of this naked and lovely poetry seems nowadays to be lost : its marvel is how much it tells by means of the little it says.

"LATE, LATE YESTREEN." (stanza 7)

With money in his pocket and bewaring of glass, the Man of Superstitions bows low and seven times to the new moon. If he sees a dim cindrous light filling in the circle of which this crescent is the edge, he " looks out for squalls "—the new moon has " the auld moone in hir arme." That light is the earth-shine. The sun illumines the earth ; the earth like a looking-glass reflects his radiance upon the moon ; and she thus melancholily returns it ; whereas the silver blaze on her eastern edge is light direct : eyes looking upward *thence* into her black skies are lit with her prodigious mornings.

ABOUT AND ROUNDABOUT

419. " ALLISON GROSS."

Here I have changed only two words of the original.

420. " SIR HUGH."

If this ballad tells of a fact, then the young Sir Hugh was beguiled out of his life by the dark beautiful Jewess in the year 1255. The story comes from a monastery, and it is historically certain that the wealthiest Jews of Lincoln were in this year crucified on this charge. True or false, what a clear, pellucid picture the ballad builds up in the imagination—the ancient town ; the boys at their game ; the narrow, gabled, cobbled streets ; the evening gold on roof and wall ; night ; lamentation ; and the clanging of the bells.

421. " EDWARD."

The spelling of this ballad usually begins " Why dois your brand sae dripp wie bluid," and so on. This spelling Professor Child thought " affectedly antique." But since, as he says, mere antiquated " spelling will not make an old ballad, so it will not *un*make one." And " Edward " in any guise is " one of the noblest " of the popular ballads. Here it is, then, in our own spelling for proof.

422. " I WILL SING."

The king in the third line is James the Sixth of Scotland and the First of England—the king, according to the old waggery, " who never said a foolish thing and never did a wise one." But see Green. The " wanton laird of young Logie " is John Wemyss who plotted against him with the Earl of Bothwell in 1592. His bold, crafty and merry young wife, May Margaret, says Mr. Sidgwick, had one of these four delectable maiden names—Vinstar, Weiksterne, Twynstoun, or Twinslace. It is dubious which.

All ladies in those old days carried knives at their girdles. The one in stanza 8 was clearly a wedding gift. And to judge from the ballads, doughty uses they sometimes put them to.

423. " FAIR ANNIE."

In the margins of Mr. Nahum's copy of this ballad, two exquisite damosels were painted in green, blue and amethyst

on gold (as in a monk's work), and between their fingers hung
a linen napkin seemingly broidered with pearls and in the
midst of it a sleeping dove. Whatever he may have meant by
this, I confess that at first reading I fell in love with both these
ladies. My feelings for the " noble knight " who ransomed
fair Annie, then wearied of her, were different. It was strange
to find a noble knight so hard a gentleman, not so much because
he wearied of her (since to weary of one so true, intelligent and
tender was even more of a punishment than a misfortune) but
most particularly, with regard to his craving for " gowd and
gear." He reminds me of a similar piece of humanity described in three short stanzas which were found by Mr. Macmath
written on the fly-leaf of a little volume printed at Edinburgh
about 1670, and which I found in Child's Ballads :

> " He steps full statly on the street,
> He hads the charters of him sell,
> In to his cloathing he is complete,
> In Craford's mure he bears the bell. . . .

> " I wish I had died my own fair death,
> In tender age, when I was young ;
> I would never [then] have broke my heart
> For the love of any churl's son.

> " Wo be to my parents all,
> That lives so farr beyond the sea !
> I might have lived a noble life,
> And wedded in my own countrée."

425. " BUT THINK NA' YE MY HEART WAS SAIR ?"
(line 21)

> Down in yon garden sweet and gay
> Where bonnie grows the lily,
> I heard a fair maid sighing say,
> " My wish be wi' sweet Willie ! "

> " Willie's rare, and Willie's fair,
> And Willie's wondrous bonny ;
> And Willie hecht to marry me
> Gin e'er he married ony.

ABOUT AND ROUNDABOUT

" O gentle wind, that bloweth south
　From where my Love repaireth,
Convey a kiss frae his dear mouth
　And tell me how he fareth !

" O tell sweet Willie to come doun
　And hear the mavis singing,
And see the birds on ilka bush
　And leaves around them hinging.

" The lav'rock there, wi' her white breast
　And gentle throat sae narrow ;
There's sport eneuch for gentlemen
　On Leader haughs and Yarrow.

" O Leader haughs are wide and braid
　And Yarrow haughs are bonny ;
There Willie hecht to marry me
　If e'er he married ony.

" But Willie's gone, whom I thought on,
　And does not hear the weeping
Draws many a tear frae's true love's e'e,
　When other maids are sleeping.

" Yestreen I made my bed fu' braid,
　The night I'll mak' it narrow,
For a' the lee-lang winter night
　I lie twined o' my marrow.

" O came ye by yon water-side ?
　Pu'd you the rose or lily ?
Or came you by yon meadow green,
　Or saw you my sweet Willie ?"

She sought him up, she sought him down,
　She sought him braid and narrow ;
Syne, in the cleaving of a crag,
　She found him drowned in Yarrow !

Hecht (line 6) means vowed ; *haughs* are water-meadows ;
and to be twined o' one's marrow, is to be separated from one's
loved one.

ABOUT AND ROUNDABOUT

427. THE TWA SISTERS.

Here is another ballad—" The Water o Wearie's Well,"—
of a similar pattern. But in this the drowner of the King's
daughters himself finds a " watery grave " :

There came a bird out o a bush,
  On water for to dine,
An sighing sair, says the king's daughter,
  " O wae's this heart o mine ! "

He's taen a harp into his hand,
  He's harped them all asleep,
Except it was the king's daughter,
  Who one wink couldna get.

He's luppen on his berry-brown steed,
  Taen 'er on behind himsell,
Then baith rede down to that water
  That they ca Wearie's Well.

" Wide in, wide in, my lady fair,
  No harm shall thee befall ;
Oft times I've watered my steed
  Wi the water o Wearie's Well."

The first step that she steppèd in,
  She stepped to the knee ;
And sighend says this lady fair,
  " This water's nae for me."

" Wide in, wide in, my lady fair,
  No harm shall thee befall ;
Oft times I've watered my steed
  Wi the water o Wearie's Well."

The next step that she stepped in,
  She stepped to the middle ;
" O," sighend says this lady fair,
  " I've wat my gowden girdle."

" Wide in, wide in, my lady fair,
  No harm shall thee befall ;
Oft times have I watered my steed
  Wi the water o Wearie's Well."

ABOUT AND ROUNDABOUT

The next step that she steppèd in,
  She stepped to the chin ;
" O," sighead says this lady fair,
  " They sud gar twa loves twin ! "

" Seven king's daughters I've drownd there,
  In the water o Wearie's Well,
And I'll make you the eight o them,
  And ring the common bell."

" Since I am standing here," she says,
  " This dowie death to die,
One kiss o your comely mouth
  I'm sure wad comfort me."

He louted him oer his saddle bow,
  To kiss her cheek and chin ;
She's taen him in her arms twa,
  And thrown him headlong in.

" Since seven king's daughters ye've drowned
      there,
  In the water o Wearie's Well,
I'll make you bridegroom to them a',
  An ring the bell mysell."

And aye she warsled, and aye she swam,
  And she swam to dry lan ;
She thankèd God most cheerfully
  The dangers she oercame.

428. " SWEET WILLIAM AND MAY MARGARET."

Hermione.   Come Sir, now I am for you againe :
        Pray you sit by us, and tell's a Tale.
Mamillius (her son).   Merry, or sad, shal't bee ?
Hermione.   As merry as you will.
Mamillius.   A sad Tale's best for Winter :
        I have one of Sprights, and Goblins.
Hermione.   Let's have that, good Sir.
        Come-on, sit downe, come-on, and doe your
          best
        To fright me with your Sprights : you're
          powrefull at it.

ABOUT AND ROUNDABOUT

Mamillius.   There was a man. . . .

Hermione   Nay, come sit downe : then on.

Mamillius.   Dwelt by a Churchyard :
I will tell it softly,
Yond Crickets shall not heare it.

Hermione.   Come on then, and giv't me in mine eare. . . .

The Winter's Tale

429.   "THAT BIRK GREW FAIR ENEUGH." (stanza 6)

The strangest feature of these ballads is that the stories they tell, the customs, beliefs, lore they refer to, may be found scattered up and down all over the world. In Russia, for one small instance, the birk or birch tree is honoured in this fashion : A little before Whitsuntide, says Sir James Fraser in *The Golden Bough*, the young women, with dancing and feasting, cut down a living birch-tree, deck it with bright clothes or hang it with ribbons ; then set it up as an honoured guest in one of the village houses. On Whit Sunday itself they fling it, finery and all, into a stream for a charm.

And now for England : "Thirty years ago," says Mrs. Wright, " it was still customary in some west-Midland districts to decorate village churches on Whit Sunday with sprigs of birch stuck in holes bored in the tops of the pews. I can remember this being done by an old village clerk in Herefordshire, but when he was gathered to his fathers in the same profession, the custom died with him." How happy must he have been then—as happy as for that one evening was the Wife of Usher's Well herself—to lift his eyes upon a silver birch brushing with its green tresses the very gates of Paradise !

433.   "A SPANGLE HERE."

Dew sate on Julia's haire,
And spangled too,
Like leaves that laden are
With trembling dew :
Or glittered to my sight,
As when the Beames
Have their reflected light,
Daunc't by the Streames.

ROBERT HERRICK

ABOUT AND ROUNDABOUT

If the daisies are not to shut their eyes until Julia shut hers, should they not most assuredly wait also until "dear love Isabella," shut *hers*? She was the bosom friend and aunt of Marjorie Fleming, Sir Walter Scott's little friend, who was born in 1803, and who, having written her few tim-tam-tot little rhymes, died in 1811. And here is Isabel :

> Here lies sweet Isabell in bed,
> With a night-cap on her head ;
> Her skin is soft, her face is fair,
> And she has very pretty hair ;
> She and I in bed lies nice,
> And undisturbed by rats or mice ;
> She is disgusted with Mr. Worgan,
> Though he plays upon the organ.
> Her nails are neat, her teeth are white,
> Her eyes are very, very bright ;
> In a conspicuous town she lives,
> And to the poor her money gives ;
> Here ends sweet Isabella's story,
> And may it be much to her glory.

434.

Bunyan's " Comparison " for this poem runs thus :

> Our Gospel has had here a Summers day ;
> But in its Sun-shine we, like Fools, did play,
> Or else fall out, and with each other wrangle,
> And did instead of work not much but jangle.
>   And if our Sun seems angry, hides his face,
> Shall it go down, shall Night possess this place ?
> Let not the voice of night-Birds us afflict,
> And of our mis-spent Summer us convict.

437.

From the " Songs of Innocence " ; and this is from the " Songs of Experience " :

> When the voices of children are heard on the green
> And whisp'rings are in the dale.
> The days of my youth rise fresh in my mind,
> My face turns green and pale.

ABOUT AND ROUNDABOUT

Then come home, my children, the sun is gone down,
And the dews of night arise ;
Your spring and your day are wasted in play,
And your winter and night in disguise.

For to grow old and look back on one's childhood, though
in much it is a happy thing, may be also a thing full of dread and
regret. The old poets never wearied of bidding youth gather
its roses, seize its fleeting moments. But not all roses are fresh
and fragrant in the keeping, and " lilies that fester smell far
worse than weeds."

440. " AFTERWARDS."

Every fine poem says much in little. It packs into the
fewest possible words—by means of their sound, their sense,
and their companionship—a wide or rare experience. So, in
particular, with such a poem as this. It tells of a man thinking
of the day when he shall have bidden goodbye to a world whose
every live and lovely thing—Spring, hawk, evening, wintry
skies—he has dearly loved. And if what it tells of is to be
seen as clearly and truly as if it were before one's very eyes,
it must be read intently—all one's imagination alert to gather
up the full virtue of the words, and to picture in the mind
each fleeting and living object in turn.

As I write these lines I cannot refrain from suggesting how
thankful we should be to be living in a day when three great
poets, who have been long in the world, are adding to the riches
of English poetry—Thomas Hardy, Charles Doughty, and the
Poet Laureate, Robert Bridges. It is but a little while, too,
since the death of that exquisite writer, and lover of all things
true and beautiful, Alice Meynell, and of W. H. Hudson,
who was no less a poet because he wrote not in verse but in
prose.

To compare the great things of one age with the great things
of another is an exceedingly difficult task (and to pit poet
against poet, or imagination against imagination, an exceedingly
stupid one). But that in Elizabeth's day England was indeed
a " nest of singing birds " may be realised by the fact that when
Shakespeare was finishing his last play, The Tempest, in the
Spring, apparently, of 1611—when, that is, he himself was
aged 47 (and his Queen had been eight years dead), Sir Walter

Raleigh was 50, Anthony Munday 58, Samuel Daniel 49, Michael Drayton 48, Thomas Campion 44, Thomas Dekker (?) 41, John Donne and Ben Jonson were 38, John Fletcher was 32, Francis Beaumont 27, William Drummond 26, John Ford 25, William Browne and Robert Herrick 20, Francis Quarles 19, George Herbert 18, Thomas Carew (?) 16, James Shirley 15, and John Milton (and Sir John Suckling) were 2. It was seven years before the birth of Richard Lovelace and Abraham Cowley, ten before Marvell's, and eleven before Vaughan's. Edmund Spenser had been twelve years dead, Sir Philip Sidney twenty-five and Chaucer 211.

Two hundred and fifty years afterwards—in 1861—another great queen was on the Throne, Victoria. It was the year in which the Prince Consort died, and Edward, Prince of Wales, came of age. Nor was England's garden silent then : for in that year William Barnes and Cardinal Newman were 60, Edward Fitzgerald and Tennyson were 52, Robert Browning 49, Charles Kingsley 42, Matthew Arnold 39, Coventry Patmore 38, William Allingham 37, Dante Gabriel Rossetti and George Meredith were 33, Christina Rossetti was 31, William Morris 27, Algernon Swinburne 24, Mr. Thomas Hardy was 21, Mr. Robert Bridges 17, Robert Louis Stevenson 11, and Francis Thompson was 2. Other great writers, in English, then alive were Carlyle, Thackeray, Dickens, Ruskin, Darwin and Huxley ; Emerson, Hawthorne, Longfellow and Walt Whitman. So the strange flame of genius fitfully burns in this world. And 1611 knew as little of 1861 as 1861 knew of 2111. (But would that 1923 could leave to the future one-tenth part of such a legacy as did 1611—the English Bible !)

But to return to Shakespeare. He was born in April 1564. About 1591 he wrote the first of his plays, *Love's Labour's Lost*. By 1611 he had finished the last of them ; 34 in all as they appear in the first Folio, 37 as they now appear in the Canon. And apart from these, his Poems. There followed a strange silence. On the 25th of March, 1616, " in perfect health and memory (God be praised !)," he made his will. On St. George's Day, 1616, he died. To reflect for a moment on that brief lifetime, on that twenty years' work which is now a perennial fountain of happiness, light and wisdom to the whole world, is to marvel indeed. The life-giving secret of this supreme genius none can tell. We know not even our own. But there

ABOUT AND ROUNDABOUT

is a story told by Thomas Campbell : " It was predicted of a young man lately belonging to one of our universities, that he would certainly become a prodigy because he read sixteen hours a day. ' Ah, but,' said somebody, ' how many hours a day does he *think* ? ' It might have been added, ' How many hours does he feel ? ' " So of Shakespeare. As, then, said his old friends and fellow-players, John Heminge and Henry Condell in their Preface to the Folio : " Reade him, therefore ; and againe, and againe : And if then you doe not like him, surely you are in some manifest danger. . . ."

441. " WITH SUCH A SKY."

It is a beauteous Evening, calm and free,
The holy time is quiet as a Nun
Breathless with adoration ; the broad sun
Is sinking down in its tranquillity ;
The gentleness of heaven broods o'er the Sea :
Listen ! the mighty Being is awake,
And doth with his eternal motion make
A sound like thunder—everlastingly. . . .
WILLIAM WORDSWORTH

442. " SHEPHERDS ALL, AND MAIDENS FAIR, FOLD YOUR FLOCKS."

The curfew tolls the knell of parting day,
The lowing herd winds slowly o'er the lea,
The ploughman homeward plods his weary way,
And leaves the world to darkness and to me.

Now fades the glimmering landscape on the sight,
And all the air a solemn stillness holds,
Save where the beetle wheels his droning flight,
And drowsy tinklings lull the distant folds : . . .

These lines and the stanzas that follow them in the *Elegy in a Country Churchyard* are as familiar as any in English, and may be found in almost every collection of poems. Here, " a figure on paper "—from a letter to a friend written by the author of them, Thomas Gray, on November 19, 1764, is a description—not of evening after the setting of the sun—

but of a sun-*rise* as vivid as if one's own naked eye had watched its " Levee " :

" I must not close my letter without giving you one principal event of my history ; which was, that (in the course of my late tour) I set out one morning before five o'clock, the moon shining through a dark and misty autumnal air, and got to the sea-coast time enough to be at the Sun's Levee. I saw the clouds and dark vapours open gradually to right and left, rolling over one another in great smoky wreathes, and the tide (as it flowed gently in upon the sands) first whitening, then slightly tinged with gold and blue ; and all at once a little line of unsufferable brightness that (before I can write these five words) was grown to half an orb, and now to a whole one, too glorious to be distinctly seen. It is very odd it makes no figure on paper ; yet I shall remember it, as long as the sun, or at least as long as I endure. I wonder whether anybody ever saw it before ? I hardly believe it."

So each day, one remembers, the sun rises, indeed is rising always above *some* watchful eye's horizon, and we come so to expect its rising, and so to be assured of it, as though it were no less certain than that twice two are four. But, in fact, it is only just certain enough to prevent night from being a dreadful apprehension, and life from becoming a mere routine. As Coleridge says in his *Table Talk :*

" Suppose Adam watching the sun sinking under the western horizon for the first time ; he is seized with gloom and terror, relieved by scarce a ray of hope that he shall ever see the glorious light again. The next evening, when it declines, his hopes are stronger, but still mixed with fear ; and even at the end of a thousand years, all that a man can feel is a hope and an expectation so strong as to preclude anxiety."

> . . . High among the lonely hills,
> While I lay beside my sheep,
> Rest came down and filled my soul,
> From the everlasting deep.
>
> Changeless march the stars above,
> Changeless morn succeeds to even ;
> Still the everlasting hills
> Changeless watch the changeless heaven. . . .

CHARLES KINGSLEY

ABOUT AND ROUNDABOUT

444. "THE CHILDREN ARE GOING TO BED."

Hush-a-ba, birdie, croon, croon,
    Hush-a-ba, birdie, croon.
The Sheep are gane to the siller wood,
    And the cows are gane to the broom, broom.

And it's braw milking the kye, kye,
    It's braw milking the kye,
The birds are singing, the bells are ringing,
    And the wild deer come galloping by, by.

And hush-a-ba, birdie, croon, croon,
    Hush-a-ba, birdie, croon.
The Gaits are gane to the mountain hie,
    And they'll no be hame till noon, noon.

This for the littlest ones, the cradle-creatures. But for the rest :

Boys and Girls, come out to play,
The Moon doth shine as bright as day ;
Come with a whoop, come with a call,
Come with a goodwill or don't come at all ;
Lose your supper and lose your sleep—
So come to your playmates in the street.

And if you should want actually to bring that Moon to earth, this is how Quince managed it in *A Midsummer Night's Dream :*

THE REHEARSAL.

Snout.	Doth the Moone shine that night wee play our play ?
Bottom.	A Calender, a Calender, looke in the Almanack, finde out Moone-shine, finde out Moone-shine.
Quince.	Yes, it doth shine that night.
Bottom.	Why then may you leave a casement of the great chamber window (where we play) open, and the Moone may shine in at the casement.
Quince.	Ay, or else one must come in with a bush of thorns and a lanthorne, and say he comes to disfigure, or to present the person of Moone-shine. . . .

ABOUT AND ROUNDABOUT

The Play.

Lysander.   Proceed, Moone.

Moone.   All that I have to say, is to tell you, that the
Lanthorne is the Moone ; I, the man in the
Moone ; this thorne bush, my thorne bush ;
and this dog, my dog. . . .

And here is a stanza from a very old poem about that same
" man in the Moone " :

> Mon, in the monĕ, stond ant streit,
>   On is bot-forke is burthen he bereth :
> Hit is muche wonder that he na down slyt,
>   For doute leste he valle he shoddreth ant shereth :
> When the frost freseth muche chele he byd,
>   The thornes beth kene is battren to-tereth ;
> Nis no wytht in the world that wot wen he syt,
>   Ne, bote hit bue the hegge, whet wedes he wereth.

which means, I gather, that

the Man in the Moon stands up there stark and still in her
silver, carrying his thornbush on his pitchfork.   It's a marvel
he doesn't slide down ; he's shuddering and shaking at the
thought of it.   When the frost sharpens, he'll be frozen to his
marrow.   The prickles stick out to tear his clothes ; but
nobody in the world has seen him sit down, or knows apart
from his thornbush what he has on.

> I see the Moon,
> The Moon sees me ;
> God bless the sailors,
> And bless me.

449.   " That busy Archer." (line 4)

> Though I am young and cannot tell
> Either what Love or Death is well,
> Yet I have heard they both bear darts
> And both do aim at human hearts. . . .
>
> Ben Jonson

ABOUT AND ROUNDABOUT

" Are Beauties there as proud as here they be."
(line 11)

. . . The palace of her father the King, was on that side the Moon no mortal sees, and of such an enchantment was her cold beauty that on earth none resembles it. Yet all her flattery and pride was but to win the idolatrous love of far-travelling Princes, or even of wanderers of common blood ; for the sake of that love and admiration only. And many perished in those rock-bound deserts and parched and icy lunar wildernesses on account of this proud damsel ; before a strange fate befell her. . . .

Here, too, is a fragment (from a thirteenth century MS.), to be found in *A Medieval Garner* :

" What shall we say of the ladies when they come to feasts ? Each marks well the other's head ; they wear bosses like horned beasts, and if any have no horns, she is a laughing stock for the rest. Their arms go merrily when they come into the room ; they display their kerchiefs of silk and cambric, set on their buttons of coral and amber, and cease not their babble so long as they are in the bower. . . . But however well their attire be fashioned, when the feast is come, it pleases them nought ; so great is their envy now and so high grows their pride, that the bailiff's daughter counterfeits the lady."

450. " She hath no Air." (line 5)

—and that being so :

" . . . . There will be no sounds on the moon. . . . Even a meteor shattering itself to a violent end against the surface of the moon would make no noise. Nor would it herald its coming by glowing into a ' shooting star,' as it would on entering the earth's atmosphere. There will be no floating dust, no scent, no twilight, no blue sky, no twinkling of the stars. The sky will be always black and the stars will be clearly visible by day as by night. The sun's wonderful corona, which no man on earth, even by seizing every oppor-tunity during eclipses, can hope to see for more than two hours in all, in a long lifetime, will be visible all day. So will the great red flames of the sun. . . . There will be no life (since) for fourteen days there is continuous night, when the temperature must sink away down towards the absolute cold of space. This will be followed without an instant of twilight by full daylight. For another fourteen days the sun's rays will bear straight down, with no diffusion or absorption of their heat, or light, on the way. . . ."

This is a matter-of-fact fragment out of " The Outline of Science," edited by Professor J. Arthur Thompson ; but it would not be easy to say exactly how in its magical *effect* on the mind it differs from poetry. Indeed, there can hardly be a quicker journey to the comprehension of scientific fact than by way of the imagination. Moonless mountainous Hesper, the Evening Star, is an even lovelier thing to watch shining in the fading rose and green of sunset when we realise that at her most radiant—a radiance that casts an earthly shadow even—it is but a slim crescent of the planet that we see, a planet, too, almost sister in magnitude to the earth, but whose briefer year is of an ardour that might be happiness to fiery sprite and salamander, but would be unendurable to watery creatures like ourselves. Nor could language be used more scientifically (concisely, pregnantly and exactly), than in the words *moving, human, mask*, in the following sonnet by John Keats—a sonnet written in mortal illness and in immortal sorrowfulness :

Bright star, would I were stedfast as thou art—
　　Not in lone splendour hung aloft the night
And watching, with eternal lids apart,
　　Like nature's patient, sleepless Eremite,
The moving waters at their priestlike task
　　Of pure ablution round earth's human shores,
Or gazing on the new soft-fallen mask
　　Of snow upon the mountains and the moors—

No—yet still stedfast, still unchangeable,
　　Pillowed upon my fair love's ripening breast,
To feel for ever its soft fall and swell,
　　Awake for ever in a sweet unrest,
Still, still to hear her tender-taken breath,
And so live ever—or else swoon to death.

　　　　　　　　　　　　　　　　JOHN KEATS

455. " RIGHT GOOD IS REST."

Come, Sleep, and with thy sweet deceiving
Lock me in delight awhile ;

ABOUT AND ROUNDABOUT

Let some pleasing dreams beguile
All my fancies : that from thence
I may feel an influence
All my powers of care bereaving !

Though but a shadow, but a sliding,
Let me know some little joy !
We that suffer long annoy
Are contented with a thought
Through an idle fancy wrought :
O let my joys have some abiding !

JOHN FLETCHER

457. BEFORE SLEEPING.

I have pieced this rhyme together from well-known versions
and fragments. But the Angels ?—

" And after that, I sawe iiij Angels stande on the iiij corners
of the erth holdynge the foure wyndes of the erth, that the
wyndes shuld not blowe on the erth, nether on the see, nether
on eny tree."

The Revelation of S. John the Divine (1539).

" And I beheld, and I heard the voice of many angels round
about the throne and the beasts and the elders : and the
number of them was ten thousand times ten thousand, and
thousands of thousands." The Same (1611).

Of these Angels, having their fitting place among the hier-
archies—Seraphim, Cherubim, Thrones ; Dominations, Virtues,
Powers ; Principalities, Archangels, Angels—no names are
given. But Michael and Gabriel are archangels named in the
Bible, and in the Apocrypha and elsewhere, Raphael, Zadkiel,
Uriel, Chamuel, Jophiel. These too ; steadfast or fallen :
Samael, Semalion, Abdiel and gigantic Sandalphon, Rahab,
Prince of the Sea ; Ridia, Prince of the Rain ; Yurkemi,
Prince of the Hail ; Af of Anger ; Abaddona of Destruction ;
Lailah of Night. And in *Paradise Lost* :

Now had night measured with her shadowy cone
Halfway up-hill this vast sublunar vault ;
And from their ivory port the Cherubim
Forth issuing, at the accustomed hour, stood armed. . . .

ABOUT AND ROUNDABOUT

Then speake together Gabriel, Uzziel, Ithuriel, Zephon. And last—not the most distant from mortal love—strangely-angelled Poe's shrill-tongued Israfel :

In Heaven a spirit doth dwell
  Whose heart-strings are a lute ;
None sing so wildly well
As the angel Israfel,
And the giddy stars (so legends tell),
Ceasing their hymns, attend the spell
  Of his voice, all mute. . . .

Yes, Heaven is thine ; but this
  Is a world of sweets and sours ;
  Our flowers are merely—flowers,
And the shadow of thy perfect bliss
  Is the sunshine of ours.

If I could dwell
  Where Israfel
Hath dwelt, and he where I,
He might not sing so wildly well
  A mortal melody,
While a bolder note than this might swell
  From my lyre within the sky.

Oh speake againe bright angell, for thou art
As glorious to this night being ore my head,
As is a wingèd messenger of heaven
Unto the white upturned wondring eyes
Of mortalls that fall backe to gaze on him.

Romeo and Juliet

In paint and wood and words and stone Man has for centuries made pictures and images for symbols of angelic might and beauty. But what does he know of these Beings in themselves ?—" That there are distinct orders of Angels, assuredly I believe, but what they are I cannot tell. . . . They are creatures that have not so much of a body as flesh is, as froth is, as a vapour is, as a sigh is ; and yet with a touch they shall moulder a rock into less atoms than the sand that it stands upon, and a millstone into smaller flour than it grinds. They are creatures made, and yet not a minute older than when they were first made, if they were made before all measures of time begun ; nor, if they were made in the beginning of time, and be now six thousand years old, have they one wrinkle of age in their face, one sob of weariness in their lungs. They are *primogeniti Dei*, God's eldest sons. . . ."

JOHN DONNE

459.

This is the Song sung by his guardian Angel to a young sleeping Prince who has been cheated of his inheritance. It was printed by Charles Lamb in his *English Dramatic Poets*, from a Tragedy entitled *The Conspiracy*, written by Henry Killigrew when he was seventeen.

460. THE LEGEND OF ST. MARK.

The relics of this Saint, who for his miracles was thought to be a sorcerer, and was murdered by a mob, were interred in Alexandria. Hundreds of years afterwards these relics were coveted by the Venetians by reason of the story that the Saint had once visited their city and had heard speak to him an angel : *Pax tibi, Marce. Hic requiescet corpus tuum.* At length two Venetian merchants, having persuaded the Alexandrians that the sacred bones lay in danger of the raiding Saracens, travelled back with them to their own city, where they were reinterred with solemn ceremony in St. Mark's. This church was afterwards burned to the ground, and the relics were lost. A century passed ; a wondrously beautiful church had arisen from the ashes of the old, and during the ceremony held in the faith that it would be revealed where they lay hid, suddenly a light shone forth from one of the great piers, there was a sound of falling masonry, and, lo, the body of the Saint, with arm outstretched, as if at finger's touch he had revealed his secret resting-place.

" DOVES OF SIAM, LIMA MICE,
AND LEGLESS BIRDS OF PARADISE." (p. 470.)

What particular kinds of doves and mice Keats had in mind here I cannot yet discover. But, according to Topsell, mice are of these kinds : the short, small, fearful, peaceable, ridiculous, rustik, or country mouse, the urbane or citty mouse, the greedy, wary, unhappy, harmefull, black, obscene, little, whiner, biter, and earthly mouse. Mice, too, he says, are

" sometimes blackish, sometimes white, sometimes yellow, sometimes broune and sometimes ashe colour. There are white mice amonge the people of Savoy, and Dolphin in France, called alaubroges, which the inhabitants of the country do beleev that they feede upon snow." Then, again, " the field mouse, the farie, with a long snout ; and the sleeper, that is of a dun colour and will run on the edge of a sword and sleep on the point."

What Topsell meant by " whiner " I am uncertain, but it may be he refers to the mouse that sings. That is a habit quite distinct from the common squeaking, shrilling and shrieking. It resembles the slow low trill of a very distant and sleepy canary, but sweeter and more domestic, and is as pleasant a thing to hear behind a wainscot, as it is to watch the creatures gambolling. Why women are apt to fear these tiny beasts is a mystery. But whatever mischief their ravagings may cause, may I never live under a roof wherein (Cat or no Cat) there is no inch of house-room for Mistress Mouse !

The fable that the Bird of Paradise is "legless" was set abroad by travellers who had seen in old days its exquisite dismembered carcase prepared for merchandise. It is hard to explain that Man, capable of imagining a bird " whose fixed abode is the region of the air," sustaining itself " solely on dew," can also slaughter it and tie it up in bundles for feminine finery. But so it is.

" AT VENICE. . . ." (p. 471)

So Keats left—unfinished—this, one of the happiest of his poems. There are others in this volume : but not the *Eve of St. Agnes*, or *Hyperion*, or the odes, *to a Nightingale, on a Grecian Urn*, or the strange *On Melancholy*. Nor are any of his Letters here—as full a revelation of the powers and understanding of that rare mind, as the poems are of his imagination.

466. " LOW IN THE SOUTH THE ' CROSS '."

We peoples of the Northern hemisphere, from the Chinese and Chaldaeans until this last flitting hour have the joy of so many brilliant and neighbouring stars in our night sky that for us it is now full of stories, and thronged with constellations of our own fantasy and naming. The Chair of Cassiopeia, for instance, is but a feigned passing picture. Nevertheless, how pleasant it is to recognise it set zigzag in the night. For this reason the peoples of the Southern hemisphere, with their Crown and Net, their Phoenix and Peacock, hold dear the Southern Cross. It marks their very home.

And, once more, let me repeat what Miss Taroone said to me : Learn the common names of every thing you see, Simon ; and especially of those that please you most to remember : then give them names also of your own making and choosing—if you can. Mr. Nahum has thousands upon thousands of words and names in his mind and yet he often fails to understand what I say to him. Nor does he always remember that though every snail is a snail and a Hoddydoddy, and every toad is a toad and a Joey, and every centipede is a centipede and a Maggie-monyfeet, each is just as much only its own self as you, Simon, are You.

469. " ONCE A DREAM DID WEAVE A SHADE."

Full in the passage of the vale, above,
A sable, silent, solemn, forest stood,
Where nought but shadowy forms was seen to move,
As idless fancy'd in her dreaming mood ;
And up the hills, on either side, a wood
Of blackening pines, ay waving to and fro,
Sent forth a sleepy horror thro' the blood ;
And where this valley winded out, below,
The murmuring main was heard, and scarcely heard, to
    flow.

A pleasing land of drowsy-head it was,
Of Dreams that wave before the half-shut eye,
And of gay Castles in the clouds that pass,
For ever flushing round a summer sky. . . .

JAMES THOMSON

470. " AWAKE, AWAKE ! "

" I thank God for my happy dreams," wrote Sir Thomas Browne in the *Religio Medici*, " as I do for my good rest. . . . And surely it is not a melancholy conceit [or fancy] to think we are all asleep in this world, and that the conceits of this life are as mere dreams to those of the next as the phantasms of the night to the conceits of the day. There is an equal

ABOUT AND ROUNDABOUT

delusion in both, and the one doth but seem to be the emblem
or picture of the other ; we are somewhat more than ourselves
in our sleeps, and the slumber of the body seems to be but the
waking of the soul. . . ."

> The Door of Death is made of gold,
> That Mortal Eyes cannot behold ;
> But, when the Mortal Eyes are closed,
> And cold and pale the Limbs reposed,
> The Soul awakes ; and, wondering sees
> In her mild Hand the golden Keys :
> The Grave is Heaven's golden Gate,
> And rich and poor around it wait ;
> O Shepherdess of England's Fold,
> Behold this Gate of Pearl and Gold ! . . .

> I give you the end of a golden string ;
>   Only wind it into a ball,
> It will lead you in at Heaven's gate,
>   Built in Jerusalem's wall.

WILLIAM BLAKE

473. " DOES THE ROAD WIND UP-HILL ALL THE WAY."

> " Gentle herdsman, tell to me,
>   Of courtesy I thee pray,
> Unto the town of Walsingham
>   Which is the right and ready way."

> " Unto the town of Walsingham
>   The way is hard for to be gone ;
> And very crooked are those paths,
>   For you to find out all alone. . . . '

Not so Babylon :

> How many Miles to Babylon ?
>   *Three score and ten.*
> Can I get there by candle-light ?
>   *Ay : and back again.*

477.

This poem for its full beauty must be read very slowly.
Eve in long memory is musing within herself, hardly able to

utter the words, because of her grief and sorrow, and of the
heavy sighs between them.

" Death is the Fruit."

I am Eve, great Adam's wife,
'Tis I that outraged Jesus of old ;
'Tis I that robbed my children of Heaven,
By rights 'tis I that should have gone upon the Cross. . . .

There would be no ice in any place,
There would be no glistening windy winter,
There would be no hell, there would be no sorrow,
There would be no fear, if it were not for me.

Tr. Kuno Meyer

" The kind Hart's Tears were falling." (stanza 7)

To day my Lord of Amiens, and my selfe,
Did steale behinde him as he lay along
Under an oake, whose anticke roote peepes out
Upon the brooke that brawles along this wood.
To the which place a poore sequestred Stag
That from the Hunter's aime had tane a hurt,
Did come to languish ; and indeed my Lord
The wretched annimall heaved forth such groanes
That their discharge did stretch his leatherne coat
Almost to bursting, and the big round teares
Coursed one another downe his innocent nose
In pitteous chase. . . .

As You Like It

483. " This is the Key."

And so—like the mediaeval traveller who had made a
complete circuit of the world without knowing it—we have
come back to the place which we started from.   " The
Elephant," says Topsell, in his *Historie of Foure-footed Beastes*,
" is delighted above measure with sweet savours, ointments,
and smelling flowers, for which cause their Keeper will in the
summer time lead them into the meadows of flowers, where
they of themselves will by the quickness of their smelling,
choose out and gather the sweetest flowers, and put them into
a basket if their Keeper have any. . . .

ABOUT AND ROUNDABOUT

(Having sought) out water (wherewith) to wash themselves, (they will) of their own accord return back again to the basket of flowers, which, if they find not, they will bray and call for them. Afterward, being led into their stable, they will not eat meat until they take off their flowers and dress the brims of their manger therewith, and likewise strew their room or standing place, pleasing themselves with their meat, because of the savour of the flowers stuck about their cratch." Mr. Nahum himself, it seems to me, might have written that. What was his *Other Worlde* but such " a Basket of Flowers": the forthshowing in formal beauty—in this world's soil, and beneath ministering rain, sunshine and dew—of the imaginations of men ? Even Miss Taroone could have uttered a secret word or two in the great ear of the Elephants at their cratch : and were there not in her garden at Thrae flowers beyond telling ? —William Blake's :

> First ere the morning breaks joy opens in the flowery bosoms,
> Joy even to tears. . . .   First the Wild Thyme
> And Meadow-sweet downy and soft waving among the reeds
> Light springing on the air lead the sweet Dance : they wake
> The Honeysuckle sleeping on the Oak : the flaunting beauty
> Revels along upon the wind : the White-thorn, lovely May,
> Opens her many lovely eyes : listening the Rose still sleeps :
> None dare to wake her : soon she bursts her crimson cur-
>   tained bed,
> And comes forth in the majesty of beauty : every Flower,
> The Pink, the Jessamine, the Wall-flower, the Carnation,
> The Jonquil, the mild Lilly opes her heavens : every Tree
> And Flower and Herb soon fill the air with an innumerable
>   Dance.
> Yet all in order sweet and lovely. . . .

And so, Farewell.

ACKNOWLEDGMENTS

FOR the use of copyright poems in this volume I have to thank
—and most gratefully I do so—the following authors and
publishers :—Mr. Martin Armstrong (and Mr. Martin Secker) ;
Mr. Lascelles Abercrombie (and Mr. John Lane) ; Mr. Edmund
Blunden (and Mr. Cobden Sanderson) ; Mr. H. H. Bashford
(Messrs. Harrap & Company and Messrs. Houghton, Mifflin,
& Company) ; Mrs. Bunston de Bary ; Mr. Laurence Binyon
(and Messrs. Elkin Matthews) ; Mr. Hilaire Belloc (and Messrs.
Duckworth & Company) ; Mr. Robert Bridges (and Mr. John
Murray) ; Mr. Gordon Bottomley ; Mr. Padraic Colum
(Messrs. Maunsell & Roberts Ltd., and Messrs. the Macmillan
Company) ; Mr. William H. Davies (Mr. Jonathan Cape
and Mr. Alfred A. Knopf) ; the executors of the late Lord
de Tabley ; Mr. C. M. Doughty ; Mr. Edward L. Davison
(and Messrs. G. Bell & Sons) ; Mr. Charles Dalmon (and
Messrs. Methuen & Company) ; Mr. John Drinkwater
(Messrs. Sidgwick & Jackson, and Messrs. Houghton, Mifflin
& Company) ; Mr. Vivian Locke Ellis ; Mr. Robert Frost (and
Messrs. Harcourt, Brace & Company) ; Mr. John Freeman ;
Miss Eleanor Farjeon (Messrs. Selwyn & Blount, Messrs.
J. M. Dent & Sons, and Messrs. E. P. Dutton & Company) ;
Mrs. Furse (and Messrs. Constable & Company) ; Mr. Robert
Graves ; the Viscountess Grey ; Mr. Edmund Gosse ; Mr.
Wilfrid Gibson (Messrs. Elkin Mathews, and Messrs. Macmillan
& Company) ; Mr. Crosbie Garstin (and Messrs. Sidgwick &
Jackson) ; Mr. Thomas Hardy (and Messrs. Macmillan & Com-
pany) ; Mr. Ralph Hodgson (and Messrs. Macmillan & Com-
pany); Miss Gwen John ; Mr. Rudyard Kipling (Messrs.
Macmillan & Company, and Messrs. Doubleday, Page &
Company) ; Mr. Sidney Royse Lysaght (and Messrs. Macmillan
& Company) ; Mr. Harold Monro ; Mr. John Masefield ; Mrs.
Manning-Sanders (and Messrs. the Hogarth Press) ; Mr.

ACKNOWLEDGMENTS

T. Sturge Moore (and Mr. Grant Richards) ; Miss Charlotte
Mew (Mr. Harold Monro and Messrs. the Macmillan Company) ;
Miss Viola Meynell ; Sir Henry Newbolt ; Mr. Alfred Noyes
(and Messrs. William Blackwood & Sons) ; Mr. Seumas
O'Sullivan (Messrs. Maunsell & Roberts) ; Mr. Conal O'Rior-
dan ; Mr. F. J. Patmore ; Miss Madeleine Caron Rock ; Miss
Lizette Woodworth Reese (and Mr. Thomas B. Mosher) ;
Mr. James Stephens (Messrs. Maunsell & Roberts and Messrs.
the Macmillan Company) ; Mr. Siegfried Sassoon ; Miss Edith
Sitwell (and Mr. B. H. Blackwell) ; Mr. Edward Shanks (and
Messrs. Collins, Sons & Company) ; Mr. J. C. Squire (and
Messrs. Hodder & Stoughton) ; Mrs. Katharine Tynan Hink-
son ; Mr. Herbert Trench ; Mr. Walter J. Turner (and Messrs.
Sidgwick & Jackson) ; Miss Elinor Wylie (and Messrs. Har-
court, Brace & Company) ; Mr. Francis Brett Young (and
Messrs. W. Collins, Sons & Company) ; Mr. W. B. Yeats
(Messrs. T. Fisher Unwin and Messrs. the Macmillan
Company).

It is, too, a happy privilege to have been permitted to include
poems by Mrs. Webb, Mr. Eric Batterham, Mr. Gilbert Sheldon,
Mr. Bernard Sleigh, Miss Elizabeth Ramal, and Mr. Colin
Francis which have not hitherto appeared in any other published collection.

My most grateful thanks are due also to Mr. Edward Marsh
(Messrs. Sidgwick & Jackson and Messrs. Dodd, Mead &
Company) for two poems by Rupert Brooke ; to Mr. Clement
Shorter for six poems by Emily Brontë, and a poem by Dora
Sigerson Shorter ; to Sir Henry Newbolt for seven poems by
Mary Coleridge ; to Mr. Cobden-Sanderson for three poems by
John Clare ; to Mr. John Murray and to the executors of
Canon Dixon for two poems ; to Mrs. Flecker (and Mr. Martin
Secker) for two poems by James Elroy Flecker ; to Lady
Gomme for rhymes from " Traditional Games " ; to the Vis-
countess Grey for poems from " The White Wallet " ; to Miss
Antonie Meyer (and Messrs. Constable & Company) for six
translations by Kuno Meyer ; to Mrs. Meynell herself and to
Mr. Wilfrid Meynell (and Messrs. Burns & Oates) for three
poems ; to Mr. William Meredith and to Messrs. Constable &
Company for two poems by George Meredith ; to Mrs. Sharp
for one poem by " Fiona Macleod " (William Sharp) ; to Miss
Morris, Mr. S. C. Cockerill (and Messrs. Longmans, Green &

ACKNOWLEDGMENTS

Company) for two poems by William Morris ; to Mrs. Owen
for a poem by Wilfred Owen ; to Mrs. C. Patmore (and Messrs.
G. Bell & Sons, Ltd.) for two poems by Coventry Patmore ;
to Messrs. Macmillan & Company for eight poems by Christina
Rossetti ; to Mr. Lloyd Osbourne (Messrs. Chatto & Windus
and Messrs. Charles Scribner's Sons) for four poems by Robert
Louis Stevenson ; to Mr. William Heinemann for a poem by
Algernon Charles Swinburne ; to Miss E. Margaret Courtney
Boyd for a poem by William Bell Scott ; to Mrs. Thomas
(and Messrs. Selwyn & Blount) for seven poems by Edward
Thomas ; to Mr. Wilfrid Meynell (and Messrs. Burns & Oates)
for three poems by Francis Thompson ; to Messrs. P. J.
and A. E. Dobell for quotations from the writings of Thomas
Traherne.

For permission to use prose extracts, etc., which for the
most part have already been referred to on pages 497-668. I
am gratefully indebted to Dr. Blackman for his translation on
page 593 ; to Mr. Basil Blackwell for first grateful sight of
Bunyan's " Book for Boys and Girls " ; to Mrs. Child Sargent,
Mr. George Lyman Kittredge and Messrs. George G. Harrap
& Company for selections from " English and Scottish Popular
Ballads " ; to Mr. G. G. Coulton ; to Dr. Courtenay Dunn
and to Messrs. Sampson Low, Marston & Company ; to Messrs.
J. M. Dent & Sons for a quotation from "A Hind in Richmond
Park " by W. H. Hudson ; to Mr. Tickner Edwardes (and
Messrs. Methuen & Company) ; to Lady Gomme ; to Messrs.
Longman for a quotation from " The Diary of Master William
Silence " ; to Miss Emma Phipson (and Messrs. Kegan Paul,
Trench, Trubner & Company) ; to Mr. H. M. Tomlinson ; to
Professor J. Arthur Thompson (and Messrs. George Newnes) ;
to Mrs. Wright ; to Mr. W. B. Yeats ; and to Mr. Filson Young.
Also to the Clarendon Press, and to the Hakluyt Society.

And I would ask forgiveness of any one whose rights I may
have inadvertently overlooked.

For generous help, counsel and kindness, in the preparation
of this book it is a happiness to express my gratitude to many
friends—to Miss Naomi Royde Smith, Mr. Martin Freeman,
Mr. J. W. Haines, Mr. Gilbert Sheldon, Mr. Frank Morley,
Mr. Forrest Reid, and to Mr. James MacLehose ; and, last,
to my niece, Miss Lucy Rowley, to whom it owes more than
words can say.

INDEXES

INDEX OF AUTHORS

[Poems by writers whose names are unknown will be found marked with an asterisk in the Index of Poems. In the following Index the names of writers still living are similarly denoted.]

INDEX OF AUTHORS

INDEX OF AUTHORS

INDEX OF POEMS

[*An asterisk denotes that the name of the author of the poem is
unknown.*]

INDEX OF POEMS

INDEX OF POEMS

INDEX OF POEMS

INDEX OF POEMS

INDEX OF POEMS

INDEX OF POEMS

2 X

INDEX OF POEMS

INDEX OF POEMS

2 x 2

INDEX OF POEMS

INDEX OF POEMS

INDEX OF POEMS

INDEX OF POEMS

INDEX OF POEMS

INDEX OF POEMS

INDEX OF POEMS

INDEX OF POEMS

PRINTED IN GREAT BRITAIN BY ROBERT MACLEHOSE AND CO. LTD.
THE UNIVERSITY PRESS, GLASGOW